M000251330

Sparse Matrix Technology

Sparse Matrix Technology

Sergio Pissanetzky

Centro Atómico Bariloche,
Bariloche, Argentina

1984

ACADEMIC PRESS
(*Harcourt Brace Jovanovich, Publishers*)

London Orlando San Diego San Francisco New York
Toronto Montreal Sydney Tokyo São Paulo

ACADEMIC PRESS INC. (LONDON) LTD.
24–28 Oval Road
London NW1 7DX

United States Edition Published by
ACADEMIC PRESS INC.
(Harcourt Brace Jovanovich, Inc.)
Orlando, Florida 32887

British Library Cataloguing in Publication Data
Pissanetzky, Sergio
Sparse matrix technology.
1. Sparse matrices—Data processing
I. Title
512.9′434 QA188

ISBN 0-12-557580-7

LCCCN 83-73144

Typeset by Eta Services (Typesetters) Ltd and printed in Great Britain
by Thomson Litho, East Kilbride.

Preface

As computers grow in power and speed, matrices grow in size. In 1968, practical production calculations with linear algebraic systems of order 5000 were commonplace, while a "large" system was one of order 10 000 or more.[1] In 1978, an overdetermined problem with 2.5 million equations in 400 000 unknowns was reported;[2] in 1981, the magnitude of the same problem had grown: it had 6000 000 equations, still in 400 000 unknowns.[3] The matrix of coefficients had 2.4×10^{12} entries, most of which were zero: it was a *sparse* matrix. A similar trend toward increasing size is observed in eigenvalue calculations, where a "large" matrix is one of order 4900 or 12 000.[4] Will matrix problems continue to grow even further? Will our ability to solve them increase at a sufficiently high rate?

But this is only one side of the question. The other side concerns the microcomputer explosion. Microcomputers now have about the same power as large computers had two decades ago. Are users constrained to solving matrix problems of the same size as those of twenty years ago?

The owner of a microcomputer may not care too much about the cost of computation; the main difficulty is storage. On a large machine, the cost of solving a matrix problem increases rapidly if the size of the problem does, because both storage and labour grow. The overall cost becomes a primary consideration. How can such cost be minimized for a given problem and installation?

Answers to these and other related questions are given in this book for the following classes of matrix problems: direct solution of sparse linear algebraic equations, solution of sparse standard and generalized eigenvalue problems, and sparse matrix algebra. Methods are described which range from very simple yet surprisingly effective ideas to highly sophisticated algorithms. Sparse matrix technology is now a well established discipline, which was defined as "the art of handling sparse matrices".[5] It is composed

[1] In the Preface, the pertinent references are given as footnotes, because this enhances clarity. The full list of references is given at the end of the book. Tinney, 1969, p. 28; Willoughby, 1971, p. 271.

[2] Kolata, 1978.

[3] Golub and Plemmons, 1981, p. 3.

[4] Cullum and Willoughby, 1981, p. 329; Parlett, 1980, p. XIII.

[5] Harary, 1971.

of a beautiful blend of theoretical developments, numerical experience and practical considerations. It is not only an important computational tool in a broad spectrum of application areas,[6] but also is in itself a valuable contribution to the general development of computer software. The new ideas developed during the last fifteen years were used to devise nearly optimum algorithms for a variety of matrix problems. Research in the field is currently very active and the spectrum of applications broadens continuously. Sparse matrix technology is here and will stay.

The concept expressing the nature of our concern is contained in the title of the book. Technology is applied science, the science or study of the practical or industrial arts.[7] The phrase "sparse matrix technology" was an everyday saying in the early nineteen seventies at the IBM T. J. Watson Research Centre.[8] Nowadays it seems to be in desuetude. The material for the book was selected from the several Symposia and Congresses on large matrix problems regularly held since 1968.[9] Major sources of inspiration were: an advanced course with four review articles,[10] excellent survey articles[11] and books,[12] a collection of papers,[13] and many publications which are cited where pertinent. Several basic ideas can be found in the literature published before 1973.[14] No attempt is made, however, to cover such an important amount of material. Rather, the fundamental methods and procedures are introduced and described in detail, the discussion reaching the point where the reader can understand the specialized literature on each subject. A unified treatment is provided whenever possible, although, like any field of human knowledge which grows fast, sparse matrix technology has grown unevenly. Some areas are well developed, while other areas lack further research. We have not included proofs of all the theorems, except when they are closely related to practical techniques which are used subsequently. The concepts and methods are introduced at an elementary level, in many cases with the help of simple examples. Many fundamental algorithms are described and carefully discussed. Ready-to-use yet very efficient and professional algorithms are given directly in Fortran. The reader is assumed to be familiar with this popular language. The algorithms, however, are explained so clearly that

[6] Rose and Willoughby, 1972.

[7] Webster's Dictionary, second edition, 1957.

[8] Willoughby, 1971; Rose and Willoughby, 1972, Preface; Willoughby, 1972; Hachtel, 1976, p. 349.

[9] Willoughby, 1969; Reid, 1971a; Rose and Willoughby, 1972; Bunch and Rose, 1976; Duff and Stewart, 1979; Duff, 1981b. The Proceedings of the Symposium held at Fairfield Glade, Tennessee, in 1982, will be published as a special issue of the SIAM Journal on Scientific and Statistical Computing, and possibly other SIAM journals, to appear in 1983. The Software Catalog prepared in conjunction with the Symposium is available (Heath, 1982).

[10] Barker, 1977.

[11] Duff, 1977, 1982.

[12] Wilkinson, 1965; Parlett, 1980; George and Liu, 1981.

[13] Björck *et al.*, 1981.

[14] Brayton *et al.*, 1970; Willoughby, 1972; Tewarson, 1973.

even a person with a limited knowledge of Fortran can understand them and eventually translate them into other languages. Linear algebra and graph theory are used extensively in the book. No particular acquaintance with these subjects is necessary because all definitions and properties are introduced from the beginning, although some preparation may be helpful. An extensive bibliography and a survey of the relevant literature are included in many sections. The book fills the gap between books on the design of computer algorithms and specialized literature on sparse matrix techniques, on the one side, and user needs and application oriented requirements on the other.

The purpose of the book is to bring sparse matrix technology within reach of engineers, programmers, analysts, teachers and students. This book will be found helpful by everyone who wishes to develop his own sparse matrix software, or who is using it and wishes to understand better how it operates, or who is planning to acquire a sparse matrix package and wishes to improve his understanding of the subject. Teachers who need an elementary presentation of sparse matrix methods and ideas and many examples of application at a professional level, will find such material in this book.

Chapter 1 covers all fundamental material such as storage schemes, basic definitions and computational techniques needed for sparse matrix technology. It is very convenient to read at least Sections 1 to 9 and Section 12 of Chapter 1 first. The first reading may, however, be superficial. The reader will feel motivated to examine this material in more detail while reading other chapters of the book, where numerous references to sections of Chapter 1 are found.

Chapters 2 to 5 deal with the solution of linear algebraic equations. They are not independent. The material in Chapter 2 is rather elementary, but its form of presentation serves as an introduction for Chapters 4 and 5, which contain the important material. Chapter 3 deals with numerical errors in the case where the linear system is sparse, and also serves as an introduction to Chapters 4 and 5. This material is not standard in the literature. Sparse matrix methods and algorithms for the direct solution of linear equations are presented in Chapters 4 and 5. Chapter 4 deals with symmetric matrices, and Chapter 5 with general matrices.

The calculation of eigenvalues and eigenvectors of a sparse matrix, or of a pair of sparse matrices in the case of a generalized eigenvalue problem, is discussed in Chapter 6. Chapter 6 can be read independently, except that some references are made to material in Chapters 1 and 7.

Chapters 7, 8 and 9 deal with sparse matrices stored in row-wise format. Algorithms for algebraic operations, triangular factorization and backsubstitution are explicitly given in Fortran and carefully discussed in Chapter 7. The material in Chapter 1 is a prerequisite, particularly Sections 8, 9, 10 and 12 to 17. In addition, Chapter 2 is a prerequisite for Sections 23 to 28 of

Chapter 7. Chapter 8 covers the sparse matrix techniques assoicated with mesh problems, in particular with the finite element method, and in Chapter 9 we present some general purpose Fortran algorithms.

Sparse matrix technology has been applied to almost every area where matrices are employed. Anyone interested in a particular application may find it helpful to read the literature where the application is described in detail, in addition to the relevant chapters of this book. A list of bibliographical references sorted by application was published[15] and many papers describing a variety of applications can be found in the Proceedings of the 1980 IMA Conference[16] and in other publications.[17]

Good, robust, sparse matrix software is now commercially available. The Sparse Matrix Software Catalog[18] lists more than 120 programs. Many subroutines are described in the Harwell Catalogue[19] and two surveys have also been published.[20] Producing a good piece of sparse matrix software is not an easy task. It requires expert programming skills. As in any field of engineering, the software designer must build a prototype, test it carefully[21] and improve it before the final product is obtained and mass production starts. In software engineering, mass production is equivalent to obtaining multiple copies of a program and implementing them in many different installations. This requires transportability. From the point of view of the user, the software engineer must assume responsibility for choosing the right program and file structures and installing them into the computer. For the user, the product is not the program but the result. The desirable attributes of a good program are not easily achieved.[22] In this book, the characteristics and availability of software for each particular application are discussed in the corresponding sections.

I would like to acknowledge the collaboration of Neil Callwood. He has read the manuscript several times, correcting many of my grammatical infelicities, and is responsible for the "British flavour" that the reader may find in some passages. I would also like to acknowledge the patience and dedication of Mrs Carlota R. Glücklich while typing the manuscript and coping with our revisions.

January 1984 *Sergio Pissanetzky*

[15] Duff, 1977, p. 501.
[16] Duff, 1981b.
[17] Bunch and Rose, 1976; Duff and Stewart, 1979.
[18] Heath, 1982.
[19] Hopper, 1980.
[20] Duff, 1982; Parlett, 1983.
[21] Duff, 1979; Eisenstat *et al.*, 1979; Duff *et al.*, 1982.
[22] Gentleman and George, 1976; Silvester, 1980.

Present address of author: Texas Accelerator Centre, 2319 Timberlock Place, The Woodlands, Texas 77380, USA.

Contents

CHAPTER 5 Ordering for Gauss Elimination: General Matrices

CHAPTER 6 Sparse Eigenanalysis

CHAPTER 7 Sparse Matrix Algebra

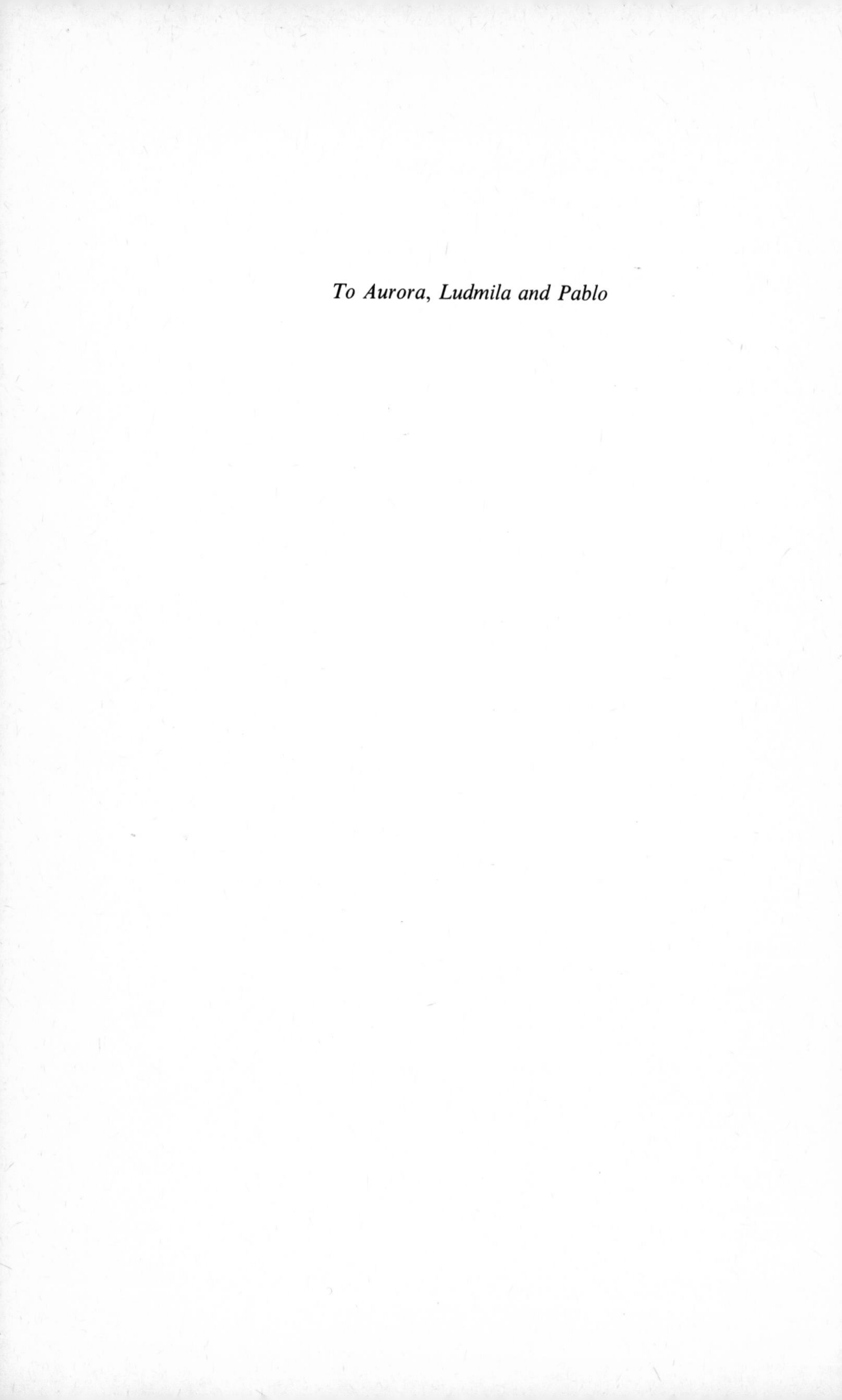

To Aurora, Ludmila and Pablo

Introduction

Information from many fields of human activity is frequently represented in the form of matrices. A matrix is a regular array of numbers. There are several definitions of *sparse matrix* in the specialized literature. All have in common the concept that a matrix is sparse when "many" of its elements are equal to zero. Some authors use the concept of limit: a matrix of order n is sparse when it has $O(n)$ nonzeros, which means that the number of elements different from zero is proportional to n for n sufficiently large. A given matrix, however, has a given n rather than a sufficiently large n. The definition is useful only for theoretical purposes, such as trying to assess the asymptotic behaviour of an algorithm. Brayton *et al.* (1970) suggest a constant number of nonzero entries per row, typically 2 to 10. An alternative was proposed by Alvarado (1979): for a matrix of order n to be sparse, the number of nonzeros must be $n^{1+\gamma}$, where $\gamma < 1$. Typical values of γ are 0.2 for electrical problems or 0.5 for a band matrix associated with a grid. A matrix of order 1000 with $\gamma = 0.9$ has 501 187 nonzeros, and one may wonder whether such a matrix should be considered as sparse or not.

A more practical approach to the definition of a sparse matrix relies on the interplay of the three fundamental ingredients: the matrix, the algorithm and the computer. The concept is heuristic in nature: a matrix is sparse when it is worthwhile to take explicit advantage of the existence of many zeros. Any sparse matrix can be processed as if it were dense, and, conversely, any dense or full matrix can be processed by the sparse matrix algorithms. The same numerical results would be obtained in both cases but at a higher computational cost. Attributing the property of sparseness to a matrix is equivalent to contending that an algorithm exists which takes advantage of sparsity and renders computation with the matrix cheaper than otherwise.

A sparse matrix can be seen as an array of numbers generally *not* regular, but we associate the numbers with the positions of a much larger *regular* array because we are used to thinking in terms of regular arrays and to employing regular arrays as a frame of reference for developing algorithms. Consider the following system of eight linear equations with eight unknowns:

$$x_3 = 3$$
$$x_1 + 2x_6 = 13$$
$$x_1 + x_2 = 3$$
$$x_2 - x_8 = -6$$
$$x_4 - 2x_5 + x_7 = 1$$
$$-x_3 + x_6 = 3$$
$$-x_5 + x_7 = 2$$
$$-2x_4 + x_8 = 0$$

The following matrix of coefficients is associated with the system:

	1	2	3	4	5	6	7	8
1	0	0	1	0	0	0	0	0
2	1	0	0	0	0	2	0	0
3	1	1	0	0	0	0	0	0
4	0	1	0	0	0	0	0	−1
5	0	0	0	1	−2	0	1	0
6	0	0	−1	0	0	1	0	0
7	0	0	0	0	−1	0	1	0
8	0	0	0	−2	0	0	0	1

The system has only 16 coefficients, but we are using 64 entries! From this viewpoint, it even seems quite unnatural to fill the irrelevant positions with zeros and then try to take advantage of the existence of so many zeros. Rigorously speaking, a sparse matrix should not be thought of as a matrix at all, but rather as a graph, where each equation–unknown pair is associated with a vertex and each coefficient with an edge. This is why graph theory plays such an important role in Sparse Matrix Technology. It is also why Sparse Matrix Technology itself has originated. A sparse matrix, being a set of numbers lacking regularity, cannot be represented in the memory of a computer in the same simple way as full matrices are. If we store the numerical values of the coefficients of our system of equations, we must also store the number of the equation and the number of the unknown corresponding to each coefficient, along with the value of the coefficient. In sparse matrix jargon, we say that we store the values of the nonzeros plus indexing information telling where each nonzero belongs in the *regular* array. This additional information constitutes an overhead and is the price paid for avoiding storing the zeros.

Matrix algorithms must be devised in such a way that only nonzeros are processed, and that irrelevant operations like addition with or multiplication by zero are avoided by taking advantage of the previous knowledge of the positions of the nonzeros. The number of operations performed by the computer during execution of the algorithm is thus proportional to the number of nonzeros, rather than to the number of elements of the matrix. Notice that it would not be correct to store all the elements including zeros and then to skip operations involving zeros by means of an IF statement. The IF statement would be unnecessarily executed n^2 times or more, making the algorithm quadratic in the order n of the matrix. A good sparse matrix algorithm uses the knowledge it has of the positions of the nonzeros for performing only the necessary operations. The order of a good algorithm is in many cases as low as n when the sparse matrix has a constant number of nonzeros per row.

A sparse matrix which represents given information has a certain given sparsity. However, when the sparse matrix is generated by an algorithm as an intermediate result during a more extensive reckoning, we may ask whether ways exist for improving sparsity by generating fewer nonzeros. The most important case where the answer is yes, is Gauss elimination. Gauss elimination impairs the sparsity of the original matrix by introducing new nonzeros. The resulting matrix is less sparse than the original one, but the fill-in depends drastically on the order in which the pivots are chosen. A good sparse matrix algorithm tries to preserve sparsity by keeping the fill-in as low as possible.

We have thus stated the three leading concepts which have guided the development of most of Sparse Matrix Technology: to store only the nonzeros, to operate only on the nonzeros, and to preserve sparsity. Of course not every sparse matrix algorithm achieves these ends. Only the more sophisticated ones do. Many storage schemes admit a certain proportion of zeros in storage, and the algorithms process them as if they were nonzeros. An algorithm which stores and processes fewer zeros is more complicated and difficult to program, and is convenient only when the matrix is sufficiently large. There exists a whole range of algorithms, from full matrix to strictly sparse matrix algorithms, thus providing the various degrees of sophistication, simplicity and efficiency necessary in practice.

CHAPTER 1

Fundamentals

1.1. Introduction

In this chapter we discuss certain computational techniques of sufficiently general use to be considered as Fundamentals of Sparse Matrix Technology. The chapter begins with a description of structures and internal representations used for storing lists of numbers, graphs, and various types of sparse matrices and sparse block-partitioned matrices. The aim is to introduce precisely those ideas which are relevant to the subject and to illustrate them with simple examples. Symbolic and numerical processing of sparse matrices and dynamic storage allocation are examined. Finally, the computational algebra of sparse vectors is discussed, since a row of a sparse matrix is a sparse vector and most of sparse matrix algebra requires that operations be performed with sparse vectors.

1.2. Storage of arrays, lists, stacks and queues

Sparse matrix technology frequently requires the storage and manipulation of lists of items, where "item" may be an integer number, a real or complex number, or an entity having a more complicated structure such as a matrix, an array or a vertex of a graph together with the corresponding edges or branching information. Examples of operations commonly performed with lists are: adding an item at the end of the list, deleting an item from the end of the list, inserting or deleting an item in the middle or at the beginning of the list, finding the position of a certain item or of the "next" item to a certain item, sorting, ordering, etc. The selection of a storage scheme depends on the operations to be performed, since the effectiveness of a certain operation may vary widely from one storage scheme to another.

The simplest data structure is the *array*, with which we shall assume the reader to be sufficiently familiar. Examples are A(I), B(I, J), etc. Numbers can be directly stored in an array. Alternatively, an array may contain pointers to items of a more complex nature which are actually stored elsewhere. All elements of an array are directly accessible in a time which is independent of the size of the array. However, it must be borne in mind that the computer memory is one-dimensional, and therefore the use of double or multiple indices must be paid for. It should also be noted that, in virtual memory machines, an array may be stored in peripheral storage and may not be readily accessible.

A linear *linked list* is a set of *cells* linked together in some order. Each cell contains an item of the list and a pointer which indicates where the next cell is located. As an example, consider that we wish to store the numbers a, b, c and d, in that order, in an array A(I). The storage could look as follows, where x indicates irrelevant values:

$$
\begin{array}{rcccccccc}
\text{position} = & 1 & 2 & 3 & 4 & 5 & 6 & 7 & 8 \\
\text{A(I)} = & x & b & x & d & a & x & c & x \\
\text{NEXT(I)} = & x & 7 & x & 0 & 2 & x & 4 & x \\
\text{IP} = & 5 \\
\text{terminator} = & 0
\end{array}
$$

The array A(I) contains the actual items, while NEXT(I) indicates the position of the next item. A list head IP which points to the position of the first item is also necessary. In this case the head is 5. At position 5 we find the first item A(5) = a, and NEXT(5) = 2 indicates that the next item is to be found at position 2. In this way the list can be followed. A *terminator* has to be stored in the last cell to indicate where the list terminates; in the example above 0 is used as the terminator. Alternatively, we may keep in storage the total number of items in the list, and use this number to find out when the list is exhausted. An empty list can be conveniently indicated by a list head which points to no position in the arrays, for example a nonpositive number.

Items can be inserted or deleted at any point in a simple manner. For example, let us assume that the number e has to be inserted between b and c. Let us also assume that we know that cell 3 is empty and that b is at position 2. The following procedure will do the job:

$$\mathrm{A}(3) \leftarrow e$$
$$\mathrm{NEXT}(3) \leftarrow \mathrm{NEXT}(2)$$
$$\mathrm{NEXT}(2) \leftarrow 3$$

The procedure to delete an element, say c from position 7 of the original linked list, is even simpler:

$$\mathrm{NEXT}(2) \leftarrow \mathrm{NEXT}(7)$$

Of course, what we really need to know is that the item preceding c is at position 2, so that this procedure actually deletes "the item which is after b" rather than c. If an item must be inserted before the first item, or the first item must be deleted, the head has to be redefined. Inserting or deleting items does not modify the order in which the remaining items are stored.

When lists are stored in arrays, it is important to keep track of the positions of the array which are empty. A common practice is just to link them together forming another list, which in turn requires another list head. The two lists are certainly disjoint, and can thus be stored in the same arrays. The following data structure results when the empty positions of our example are linked and IE is the head of the new list:

position =	1	2	3	4	5	6	7	8
A(I) =	x	b	x	d	a	x	c	x
NEXT(I) =	3	7	6	0	2	8	4	0

IP = 5

IE = 1

terminator = 0

The procedures for inserting or deleting an item now become slightly more complicated and are left to the reader as an exercise.

The linked list becomes a *circular linked list* when in the last position we store the pointer to the initial position instead of the terminator. A circular list does not have a beginning or an end, but it still requires a list head separately stored, which may now point to any of the occupied positions. In our example, we would have NEXT(4) = 5, so *a* comes after *d*, and the head could be 7, in which case the list would be *c*, *d*, *a*, *b*. Circular lists do not require a terminator, the "end" of the list being recognized by the fact that 7, the value of the head, is found in NEXT(2). Elements can be deleted or added, order being preserved, and empty positions can be linked together for a circular list in the same way as for a linear list.

A *bidirectional linked list*, either linear or circular, is obtained by adding another array which contains, for each cell, the location of the preceding cell. A bidirectional list can be traversed in both directions, and has the advantage that an item can be inserted or deleted without knowledge of the location of the preceding item. A bidirectional list requires two list heads if it is linear, one pointing to its beginning and the other to its end. When the bidirectional list is circular, a single list head is sufficient. Empty locations in a bidirectional list can be linked together, although it will seldom be necessary to use a bidirectional list for this purpose.

A *stack* is a list stored and manipulated in a simplified manner (Aho *et al.*, 1976). In a stack items are stored in consecutive locations, no linkage thus being necessary. A pointer is used to point to the location of the last item, the *top* of the stack. Stacks are used in situations where items should be added or deleted only at the top of the stack. To add or *push* a new item onto the stack, increase the pointer in one unit, check whether sufficient storage is available, and then store the item in the location to which the pointer points. To delete or *pop* the last item from the top of the stack, just decrease the pointer by one unit. An empty stack is recognized by the fact that the pointer contains 0. Stacks are used in several sparse matrix algorithms, examples being the tree partitioning algorithm of George to be discussed in Section 4.9, and Tarjan's algorithm for block triangularization of a matrix, discussed in Chapter 5.

A *queue* is a list of items stored in consecutive locations, in which items are added only at one end, the *front*, and deleted from the other end, the *rear* (Aho *et al.*, 1976). Two pointers are used to indicate the locations of the front and rear of the queue. An empty queue is recognized by the fact that the rear pointer points to a location which is immediately after the location indicated by the front pointer. When a queue has a single item, both pointers indicate the same location. When the available storage length is exhausted, new items can be stored at the beginning of the storage, treating it as circular, provided the front does not overlap with the rear.

All the storage schemes just discussed are based on the *array data structure*, the only one supported by Fortran. The elegant properties of linked lists can also be implemented in an efficient way using the *record data structure* supported, for example, by Pascal and Algolw. This scheme does not need indirect addressing and can allocate storage dynamically, at the price of some extra system storage. Some aspects of using the record data structure for sparse matrices have been outlined by N. Houbak (1981), and will be further examined in Section 1.12.

1.3. Storage of lists of integers

Lists of integers deserve special consideration because of their importance in sparse matrix technology. A list of integers is a subset of $(1, 2, \ldots, n)$, in which some integers may be repeated, although the case with all integers different will be of particular interest to us. Let m be the number of elements in the list; n is called the *range* of the list. We say that the list is *sparse* when $m \ll n$. A list of integers such as 3, 11, 7, 4 can be stored in *compact* form, in an array, say JA, of dimension at least equal to m:

position =	1	2	3	4	5	6
JA =	3	11	7	4		
M =	4					

In addition to the array, it is also necessary to store in M the number m of elements, 4 in this example. An empty list is recognized because M = 0. A new element is added to the list simply by incrementing M by one unit and then storing the new element in position M. In order to delete an element from position i, we simply store the last element in position i and decrease M by one unit. Of course, if some order of the integers should be preserved, inserting or deleting an element at some position would require moving all the elements which lie to the right of that position.

Lists of integers, with or without repeated entries, can be stored as linked lists, either linear or circular, in an array JA of dimension at least m and using an additional array NEXT as discussed in Section 1.2. This type of storage is also compact and is thus very convenient for sparse lists.

An important alternative exists for lists of integers in which all entries are different. Such lists can be stored in a single array of dimension n or more, say JA, in the form of a linked list either linear or circular. For our example, using a circular linked list and "x" to represent irrelevant values:

position =	1	2	3	4	5	6	7	8	9	10	11	12
JA =	x	x	11	3	x	x	4	x	x	x	7	x
IP =	3											

The value stored at each position in JA gives both the value of one of the integers of the list and the location of the next integer, the additional array NEXT being thus unnecessary. A list head IP which points to the first integer of the list is also necessary to enter the chain. This storage is said to be *expanded*, rather than compact, because an array of dimension at least n is necessary. Elements can be inserted or deleted at any point in the list in a simple way, without affecting the order in which the remaining elements are stored. For example, let us assume that i, k are two successive elements of the list stored in the array JA, so we have $\mathrm{JA}(i) = k$. Now we want to insert j between i and k. We simply let:

$$\mathrm{JA}(j) \leftarrow \mathrm{JA}(i)$$

$$\mathrm{JA}(i) \leftarrow j$$

Conversely, if we want to delete k, we let:

$$\mathrm{JA}(i) \leftarrow \mathrm{JA}(k)$$

Of course, if an element must be added before the first element, or if the first element must be deleted, we must redefine the list head. A list with only one element, say 5, stored in expanded storage would look as follows:

position =	1	2	3	4	5	6	7	8	9
JA =	x	x	x	x	5	x	x	x	x
IP =	5								

An empty list may be recognized by storing 0 or a negative number as the list head.

One of the main applications of expanded storage is to store *multiple disjoint lists*, that is to say, a set of lists which have no common integers. In most applications all lists have the same range, but in order to make our argument more general we will consider n to be the maximum range of all the lists. All lists can be stored in the same array, say JA, of dimension n or more. An array of heads, say IP, is also necessary. An example is all we need to illustrate the point. Consider the three disjoint lists of integers:

list 1: 2, 8, 6, 3

list 2: 5, 4, 9

list 3: 7, 1, 10

They are stored as linked circular lists in a single array of dimension 10 as follows:

position =	1	2	3	4	5	6	7	8	9	10
JA =	10	8	2	9	4	3	1	6	5	7
IP =	2	5	7							

Operations such as splitting a list into two lists, or concatenating two lists to form a single one, can easily be performed when this type of storage is used. The reader may write the corresponding procedures as an exercise.

1.4. Representation and storage of graphs

Figure 1.1(a) represents a graph. It consists of a set of *vertices*, five in this case, and a set of *edges*, seven in this example. More precisely, a graph $G = (U, E)$ consists of a set U of vertices together with a set E of edges, where an edge is a pair (u, v) of distinct vertices of U. For example, in Fig. 1.1(a), 3 is a vertex, and (3, 5) is an edge, represented by a line joining vertices 3 and 5. Graphs are very important in sparse matrix technology because a correspondence exists between matrices and graphs and certain invariant properties are preserved. Graphs, however, have many other useful applications. Graphs will be considered in much more detail in Chapters 4 and 5.

When no distinction is established between the pair (u, v) and the pair (v, u), we say that the edges are represented by unordered pairs and that the graph is *undirected*. If, however, the pairs which represent edges are ordered, the graph is a *directed* graph or a *digraph*. In a digraph, if (u, v) is an edge of E, we say that v is *adjacent* to u. In an undirected graph, if (u, v) is an edge, we say that v is adjacent to u and that u is adjacent to v. An undirected graph may be regarded as a digraph for which, if (u, v) is an edge, then also (v, u) is an edge. In order to represent a graph with n vertices, it is convenient to *label* the graph by establishing a correspondence between the vertices and the integers $1, 2, \ldots, n$. Figure 1.1 shows examples of an undirected graph and of a digraph, labelled in both cases.

A graph can be represented in the computer memory by storing, for each vertex, the list of vertices which are adjacent to it. Such a set of lists is called the *adjacency structure* of the graph (Tarjan, 1972). If the lists are stored in

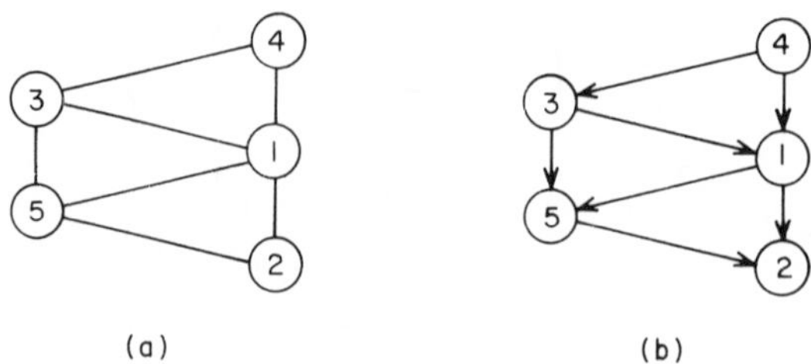

Figure 1.1 Representation of an undirected graph (a) and a directed graph or digraph (b). Both are labelled.

compact form, say in an array LIST, an array of pointers, say IP, is also required to indicate the location where each list begins. The adjacency structure for the digraph (b) of Fig. 1.1. is:

position =	1	2	3	4	5	6	7	8
LIST =	2	5	1	5	1	3	2	
IP =	1	3	3	5	7	8		

The adjacency list for vertex 4, for example, begins at position 5 of LIST, as indicated by the pointer IP(4) = 5, and ends at position 6 because the next list, that for vertex 5, begins at position IP(5) = 7. Thus, vertices 1 and 3 are adjacent to vertex 4. Note that the list for vertex 2 is empty, as indicated by the pointers IP(2) and IP(3), which are equal (their value being 3 in this case). An extra pointer has been included at the end of the array IP, pointing to the first empty place in the array LIST. This is done for programming convenience.

The following adjacency structure represents the undirected graph of Fig. 1.1(a):

position =	1	2	3	4	5	6	7	8	9	10	11	12	13	14	15
LIST =	2	3	4	5	1	5	1	4	5	1	3	1	2	3	
IP =	1	5	7	10	12	15									

Note that each edge is represented twice. The compact storage of adjacency lists is identical to the row-wise storage of the structure of the sparse matrix associated with the graph, to be discussed in Section 1.8.

When this type of storage is used it may be convenient to correlate both copies of an edge, using an additional array, say LINK. Thus, if the same edge is stored at positions i and j of LIST, then LINK(i) $= j$ and LINK(j) $= i$.

A disadvantage of the compact storage of an adjacency structure is that edges cannot easily be added or deleted. This difficulty is overcome by storing the structure as a set of linked lists, either linear or circular, with an array of pointers IP indicating how to enter each list (Rheinboldt and Mesztenyi, 1973). The lists are usually not disjoint, so that the storage technique discussed in Section 1.3 cannot be applied, and an additional array NEXT is required. The digraph of Fig. 1.1(b) could be represent as follows, using circular lists and indicating irrelevant numbers by "x":

position =	1	2	3	4	5	6	7	8	9
LIST =	3	5	1	2	x	5	1	x	2
NEXT =	3	7	1	6	x	4	2	x	9
IP =	4	0	7	3	9				

The linked representation of the undirected graph of Fig. 1.1(a) could be:

position =	1	2	3	4	5	6	7	8	9	10	11	12	13	14	15	16	17
LIST =	5	x	5	1	4	x	3	5	2	2	1	1	4	3	1	3	x
NEXT =	4	x	13	1	14	x	11	5	12	8	7	16	15	10	3	9	x
IP =	8	4	13	11	9												

Note that each edge is again stored twice. For example, edge (1, 5) is stored at positions 8 and 12, first as (1, 5) and then as (5, 1). An array LINK can be used to correlate both copies of each edge, as mentioned above. When edges are to be deleted from an undirected graph, it may be convenient to use bidirectional lists, discussed in Section 1.2. In all cases, empty positions may be linked together for using again.

Another common storage scheme is the *connection table* (George, 1977, p. 64). If the graph has n vertices and m is the maximum number of adjacent vertices that any vertex has (its *degree*), then the table is an array with n rows and m columns with the adjacent list of vertex i stored in row i. For the graph of Fig. 1.1(b), the connection table has 5 rows and 2 columns:

	1	2
1	2	5
2	0	0
3	1	5
4	1	3
5	2	0

Finally, an *adjacency* or *connectivity matrix* can be used to represent a graph (Aho *et al*., 1976, p. 50). For a graph with n vertices, the matrix is square of order n, and is defined as follows: $A_{ij} = 1$ if and only if (i, j) is an edge, otherwise $A_{ij} = 0$. For the graph of Fig. 1.1(b), the connectivity matrix is:

	1	2	3	4	5
1	0	1	0	0	1
2	0	0	0	0	0
3	1	0	0	0	1
4	1	0	1	0	0
5	0	1	0	0	0

The connectivity matrix of an undirected graph is symmetric. This type of storage is usually quite wasteful if the complete matrix is stored in memory, but it may still be convenient for algorithms which frequently require knowledge of whether certain edges are present or not. The connectivity matrix can also be stored as a sparse matrix, say by rows, without storing the numerical values of its elements (Section 1.8). In this case, what is obtained is precisely the compact storage of the adjacency structure discussed at the beginning of this section.

A graph is a *clique* when every pair of vertices is joined by an edge. Clearly, to describe a clique it is sufficient to store the list of the reference numbers of its vertices, and it is not necessary to store any information concerning edges. This property has found an important application in Gauss elimination and will be discussed further in Chapter 4.

1.5. Diagonal storage of band matrices

Band matrices represent the simplest and more widely used strategy for exploiting the zeros of a matrix. A matrix **A** is said to be banded when all its nonzero elements are confined within a band formed by diagonals parallel to the main diagonal. Thus $A_{ij} = 0$ when $|i - j| > \beta$, and $A_{k,k-\beta} \neq 0$ or $A_{k,k+\beta} \neq 0$ for at least one value of k, where β is the *half-bandwidth* and $2\beta + 1$ is the *bandwidth*. The *band* of the matrix is the set of elements for which $|i - j| \leqslant \beta$. In other words, for a certain row i, all elements having column indices in the range $i - \beta$ to $i + \beta$, a total of $2\beta + 1$ elements per row, belong to the band. This can be much smaller than the order of the matrix.

When the matrix is symmetric, only a *semiband* needs to be represented. The upper semiband consists of all the elements in the upper portion of the band, i.e. $0 < j - i \leqslant \beta$; the lower semiband consists of all the elements in the lower portion of the band, i.e. $0 < i - j \leqslant \beta$, in both cases a total of β elements per row. Some authors call band what we have called semiband and define the bandwidth as equal to β (Cuthill, 1972, p. 160; George, 1977, p. 67) or to $\beta + 1$ (EISPACK guide, Smith *et al.*, 1976). We will use throughout the definitions of band, semiband, bandwidth and half-bandwidth given above.

The *diagonal storage* of a symmetric band matrix **A** in an array AN(I, J) is illustrated by means of an example in Fig. 1.2. If the matrix is of order n and half-bandwidth β, the dimensions of the array are n by $\beta + 1$. The main diagonal is stored in the last column and the lower codiagonals are stored down-justified in the remaining columns. In the example $n = 7, \beta = 2$ and the array requires 21 memory locations. For an unsymmetric matrix **A** an array of n by $2\beta + 1$ is required; the lower semiband and main diagonal are stored as before, and the upper codiagonals are stored up-justified in the right-hand portion of the array. Diagonal storage is convenient when $\beta \ll n$; it provides direct access, in the sense that there is a one–one simple correspondence

A =

	1	2	3	4	5	6	7
1	1.						
2		2.	8.	9.			
3		8.	3.				
4		9.		4.	10.		
5				10.	5.	11.	12.
6					11.	6.	
7					12.		7.

(a)

AN(I,J) =

		1.
	0.	2.
0.	8.	3.
9.	0.	4.
0.	10.	5.
0.	11.	6.
12.	0.	7.

(b)

Figure 1.2 A symmetric 7 × 7 band matrix (a) with bandwidth equal to 5, and its 7 × 3 diagonal storage (b) in the rectangular array AN(I, J).

between the position of an element in the matrix **A** and its position in the array: A_{ij} is stored in AN($i, j - i + \beta + 1$).

Band matrices have the important property that the bandwidth depends on the order in which the rows and columns are arranged. One may thus seek a permutation of the rows and a permutation of the columns to make the resulting bandwidth small. A small bandwidth means fewer storage requirements; also, it usually requires less labour when the matrix is used for computation. For a symmetric matrix, the valuable property of symmetry will be preserved if identical permutations are used for both the rows and the columns. Algorithms for bandwidth reduction are discussed in Chapter 4.

When a system of linear equations has a banded matrix of coefficients and the system is solved by Gauss elimination, with pivots taken from the diagonal, all arithmetic is confined to the band and no new nonzero elements are generated outside the band. Gauss elimination can be carried out in place, since a memory location was already reserved for any new nonzeros that might be introduced.

The eigenvalues and eigenvectors of a band matrix, and even those of a generalized eigenproblem with two band matrices of the same bandwidth, can be computed without using extra storage. This point will be examined in Chapter 6.

1.6. Envelope storage of symmetric matrices

A band matrix of high order may have a wide band and a large quantity of zeros inside it. The diagonal storage of such a matrix may be quite wasteful. Jennings (1966) proposed a more efficient scheme for symmetric matrices, which has become very popular due to its simplicity. It is known as the *envelope* or *variable band* scheme. For each row i of a symmetric matrix $\mathbf{A}$ define:

$$\beta_i = i - j_{\min}(i),$$

where $j_{\min}(i)$ is the minimum column index in row i for which $A_{ij} \neq 0$. Thus, the first nonzero of row i lies β_i positions to the left of the diagonal, and the half-bandwidth β defined in Section 1.5 is simply:

$$\beta = \max_i (\beta_i).$$

The *envelope* of $\mathbf{A}$ is the set of elements A_{ij} such that $0 < i - j \leqslant \beta_i$. For a certain row i, all elements with column indices in the range $j_{\min}(i)$ to $i - 1$ belong to the envelope, a total of β_i elements. Diagonal elements do not belong to the envelope. The *profile* of $\mathbf{A}$ is the number of elements in the envelope:

$$\text{profile}\ (\mathbf{A}) = \sum_i \beta_i.$$

When Jennings' storage scheme is used, all elements which belong to the envelope are stored, orderly and row by row, including zeros, in a one-dimensional array, say AN. Diagonal elements are stored at the end of each row. The length of AN is equal to the profile plus the order of $\mathbf{A}$. An array of pointers, say IA, is also necessary; the entries are pointers to the locations of the diagonal elements in AN. Thus, the elements of row i, when $i > 1$, are in positions IA$(i - 1) + 1$ to IA(i). The only element of row 1 is A_{11}, stored in AN(1). The elements have consecutive, easily calculable column indices. For example, the matrix of Fig. 1.2(a) has a profile equal to 7, and its envelope storage is:

position =	1	2	3	4	5	6	7	8	9	10	11	12	13	14
AN =	1.	2.	8.	3.	9.	0.	4.	10.	5.	11.	6.	12.	0.	7.
IA =	1	2	4	7	9	11	14							

A variant of Jennings' scheme is obtained when the transpose of the lower envelope is stored. In this case elements are stored column-wise, and since the columns of the matrix retain their lengths, the scheme is often termed *skyline storage*. Another useful concept used in the design of storage schemes for symmetric matrices is the following. Consider a certain row i of $\mathbf{A}$. We say that a column $j, j > i$, is *active* in that row if it contains a nonzero on or above row i. Let ω_i be the number of columns active in row i. Then $\max_i \omega_i$ is termed the *wavefront* or *frontwidth* of $\mathbf{A}$ (see, e.g., Cuthill, 1972). In the example of Fig. 1.2(a), column 4 is active in row 3, and the frontwidth of $\mathbf{A}$ is 2.

As with band matrices, the profile of a matrix will usually change if the rows and the columns are permuted. A smaller profile means less storage and fewer operations when computations are performed on the matrix, so that profile minimization algorithms play a role in sparse matrix technology. They are discussed in Section 4.6.

Observing the pattern of elements contained in the envelope, it is seen that the value of β_i for each row is not affected by Gauss elimination with diagonal pivoting. New nonzero elements can never be generated at positions outside the envelope. New nonzeros can appear inside the envelope, where memory locations have already been prepared to store them, with the result that elimination can be performed statically. This desirable property was the original motivation for Jennings' scheme, but the same scheme can also be used advantageously for other applications. For example, it is very well suited for iterative algorithms which require efficiency in forming products of **A** by certain vectors but do not modify **A**. The conjugate gradient and the Lanczos algorithm fall in this category. In this last context, the envelope concept can immediately be extended to unsymmetric matrices.

The variable band storage scheme is row-oriented, in the sense that a row of the matrix can be scanned efficiently, but any attempt to scan a column would result in computational inefficiency. The scheme is also static, since, unless records of variable length are used, incorporating a new element outside the envelope requires changing the entire structure.

1.7. Linked sparse storage schemes

The storage schemes for matrices described in Sections 1.5 and 1.6 produce excellent results for an important range of practical applications. A sparse matrix **A** which can be conveniently rearranged so that it has a narrow band or a small envelope, requires much fewer storage locations than if it were stored in a two-dimensional array as a dense matrix. Although many zeros which lie inside the band or the envelope will still be stored and operated upon, or at least skipped when found, the inherent simplicity of the schemes and the associated programming may largely outweigh this inconvenience. A comparison between the two methods shows that fewer zeros are stored when envelope storage is used, and that the price paid for the reduction is that of having to store an array IA which only contains ancillary information, and consequently having to use a more complicated program. The additional storage is termed *overhead* storage.

Both programming difficulties and overhead storage increase when the sophistication of the storage scheme increases. Highly sophisticated schemes require really expert programming to avoid losing the potential advantages.

From this point of view a simple scheme may be the most convenient for a small or medium-size problem. On the other hand, the possibility of using a highly sophisticated scheme may determine whether a large problem is tractable at all with a given computer.

In this and the following sections, storage schemes will be examined for which either no zeros at all are stored, or "some" zeros may be stored. Consider a sparse matrix **A** and, to fix ideas and without loss of generality, imagine that **A** is very large. Its nonzero elements, in minimum proportion when compared with the number of zeros, are scattered throughout the entire matrix, giving rise to what is called the *structure* of the matrix or the *zero–nonzero pattern*. We describe first the sparse storage scheme proposed by Knuth (1968, pp. 299–302). The nonzero elements are stored in the computer memory, in any order and in compact form, in a one-dimensional array, say AN. Information regarding where each nonzero belongs can be stored in two additional parallel one-dimensional arrays, say I and J, which contain the row and column indices of each corresponding nonzero. Thus, for each $A_{ij} \neq 0$, the *triple* (A_{ij}, i, j) is kept in memory. Furthermore, in order to be able to find easily the elements in a certain row or column of the matrix, it becomes necessary to store a pair of pointers together with each triple and *row* and *column heads*, which tell where to enter each row or column list. Let NR ("next nonzero element in the same row") be the array which keeps the row pointers, and NC ("next nonzero element in the same column") be the array with the column pointers. The five arrays AN, I, J, NR and NC are of the same length, with their positions in correspondence. Let JR and JC be the arrays which contain the row and column heads, respectively, in correspondence with the rows and columns of the matrix. Figure 1.3(b) shows an example of a matrix **A** stored according to Knuth's scheme. If we want, for example, the elements of column 2, we notice that JC(2) = 1 and start at position 1 of the arrays AN, I and NC. We find AN(1) = 6. and I(1) = 1, so the element 6. is in column 2, row 1. Since NC(1) = 3, we next look at position 3 and find element 4. in row 2. Since NC(3) = 6 we look at position 6 and find element 2. in row 4. There are no more elements in column 2 because NC(6) = 0. Note that JC(3) = 0, which means that column 3 is empty. Using this scheme, an element A_{ij} can only be found by entering the list of row i and scanning it until column index j is found, or *vice versa*. The reverse problem has the obvious solution: given any location k, the row and column indices of AN(k) are I(k) and J(k).

Knuth's scheme requires five memory locations for each nonzero of **A**, plus the row and column heads. Such a scheme is quite wasteful due to the large overhead. The advantages are that elements can be added or deleted at any position and that both rows and columns can be efficiently scanned. The linked list processing techniques described in Section 1.2 are used for this

(a)

A =	1	2	3	4
1		6.		
2	9.	4.		7.
3	5.			
4		2.		8.

KNUTH STORAGE

(b)

Position:	1	2	3	4	5	6	7
AN =	6.	9.	4.	7.	5.	2.	8.
I =	1	2	2	2	3	4	4
J =	2	1	2	4	1	2	4
NR =	0	3	4	0	0	7	0
NC =	3	5	6	7	0	0	0
JR =	1	2	5	6			
JC =	2	1	0	4			

KRM CIRCULAR STORAGE

(c)

Position:	1	2	3	4	5	6	7
AN =	6.	9.	4.	7.	5.	2.	8.
NR =	1	3	4	2	5	7	6
NC =	3	5	6	7	2	1	4
JR =	1	2	5	6			
JC =	2	1	0	4			

MODIFIED KRM CIRCULAR STORAGE

(d)

Position:	1	2	3	4	5	6	7
AN =	6.	9.	4.	7.	5.	2.	8.
NR =	-1	3	4	-2	-3	7	-4
NC =	3	5	6	7	-1	-2	-4
JR =	1	2	5	6			
JC =	2	1	0	4			

Figure 1.3 Three storage schemes for sparse matrices, in the form of linked lists for both rows and columns.

purpose. Records, which are of fixed length, can be stored anywhere in the physical memory and then linked, free records being also linked together for using again. The scheme is ideally suited for cases where **A** is to be constructed by some algorithm but no forecast can be made of the final number and positions of the nonzeros, the most important example being Gauss elimination on indefinite matrices.

A modification of Knuth's scheme with the same valuable properties but much less storage overhead was proposed by Rheinboldt and Mesztenyi (1973). We call it Knuth–Rheinboldt–Mesztenyi or *KRM circular scheme*. The linked lists of both the rows and the columns are made circular and the row and column indices are included in the list heads. The set of lists associated with the rows (columns) is necessarily disjoint, and so all lists can be stored in the single array NR (NC for the columns), as discussed in Section 1.3. An example is provided in Fig. 1.3(c). This scheme is more dense than Knuth's scheme, but it must be made clear that if an algorithm should scan the elements of a certain row (column), then it will have no knowledge of the column (row) indices of those elements. Let us examine how an element A_{ij} can be found. First, row i is scanned and the set S_i is determined. S_i is a set of integers, which are the positions in AN of all the elements of row i, i.e.:

$$S_i = \{p|\text{AN}(p) \text{ is an element of row } i\}$$

It is understood that repeated entries are absent, i.e., to each pair p, q of row/column indices there corresponds at most one position of the arrays AN, NR and NC. Next, the set S_j is determined by scanning column j list. S_j consists of all pointers to the positions in AN where elements of column j are stored. Finally, form $S_{ij} = S_i \cap S_j$ (the symbol $\cap$ means "intersection"; an element belongs to S_{ij} if and only if it belongs to both S_i and S_j). S_{ij} may be either empty, or contain one element. If S_{ij} is empty, then $A_{ij} = 0$. If S_{ij} contains one integer, say k, then $A_{ij} = \text{AN}(k)$. The reverse problem, i.e. given a position k of AN find the corresponding row and column indices i and j, has no solution except that of inspecting the entire matrix.

A variant of KRM scheme (Duff, 1977, p. 517) which provides a procedure for finding the necessary indices is shown in Fig. 1.3(d). Row and column heads are actually *included* in the circular lists associated with the rows and the columns. There are several ways of doing this, and the one illustrated in Fig. 1.3(d) utilizes negative numbers to point to row or column heads. In this scheme it suffices to scan a line (a line of the matrix is either a row or a column) until a negative pointer is found. The magnitude of the pointer is the line index and it points to the corresponding line head, so that scanning of the line can continue if necessary. For example, suppose that we wish to find the row index of element AN(3). Since NR(3) = 4, and NR(4) = −2, the desired index is 2. Besides, JR(2) = 2, so that AN(2) contains the next element in row 2. To find the location in AN for an element A_{ij}, the same procedure described above can be used. Alternatively, it is also possible to scan row i and find the column index of each element by following the corresponding column list, until j is encountered. Subroutine MA18A in the Harwell library (Curtis and Reid, 1971a) incorporates most of these ideas.

Another variant of Knuth's scheme was used by Larcombe (1971) for

$$\begin{vmatrix} A_{11} & & A_{13} & A_{14} & \\ & A_{22} & & & A_{25} \\ & & A_{33} & & A_{35} \\ \text{SYMMETRIC} & & & A_{44} & \\ & & & & A_{55} \end{vmatrix}$$

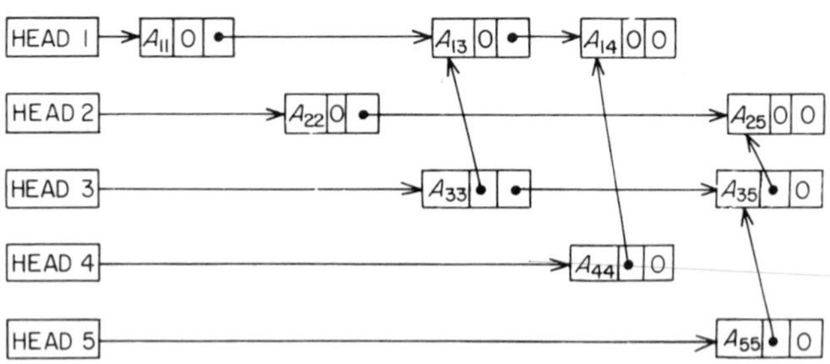

Figure 1.4 Larcombe's version of Knuth's storage scheme for symmetric matrices with no zero elements on the diagonal.

symmetric positive definite matrices with elements which are either numbers or submatrices. It is called the *forward row–backward column* scheme. Only the diagonal and upper triangle of the matrix are stored and only one array of line heads is necessary. The heads point to the diagonal elements. From each diagonal element two lists start: one describing the corresponding row to the right of the diagonal in the forward direction, the other describing the corresponding column above the diagonal in the reverse direction, i.e. upwards. This explains the name. An example is shown in Fig. 1.4. The idea can easily be extended to general matrices. If a diagonal of nonzeros exists (a transversal, see Section 5.7), then four lists can start at each diagonal element. Alternatively, two unordered lists would suffice: as discussed in Section 1.9, ordered representations are not always desirable when working with sparse matrices.

1.8. The sparse row-wise format

The *sparse row-wise format* (Chang, 1969; Curtis and Reid, 1971b; Gustavson, 1972) to be described here is one of the most commonly used storage schemes for sparse matrices. The scheme has minimal storage requirements and at the same time it has proved to be very convenient for several important operations such as addition, multiplication, permutation and transposition of sparse matrices, the solution of linear equations with a sparse matrix of coefficients by either direct or iterative methods, etc. In this scheme, the values of the nonzero elements of the matrix are stored by rows, along with their corresponding column indices, in two arrays, say AN and JA, respectively. An array of pointers, say IA, is also provided to indicate the locations in AN and JA where the description of each row begins. An extra entry in IA contains a pointer to the first empty position in JA and AN. An example is convenient at this point. Consider the matrix:

$$\mathbf{A} = \begin{array}{c} \\ 1 \\ 2 \\ 3 \end{array} \begin{array}{cccccccccc} 1 & 2 & 3 & 4 & 5 & 6 & 7 & 8 & 9 & 10 \\ \hline 0 & 0 & 1. & 3. & 0 & 0 & 0 & 5. & 0 & 0 \\ 0 & 0 & 0 & 0 & 0 & 0 & 0 & 0 & 0 & 0 \\ 0 & 0 & 0 & 0 & 0 & 7. & 0 & 1. & 0 & 0 \end{array}$$

A is represented as follows:

position =	1	2	3	4	5	6	
IA =	1	4	4	6			
JA =	3	4	8	6	8		RR(C)O
AN =	1.	3.	5.	7.	1.		

The description of row 1 of **A** begins at the position IA(1) = 1 of AN and JA. Since the description of row 2 begins at IA(2) = 4, this means that row 1 of **A** is described in the positions 1, 2 and 3 of AN and JA. In the example:

IA(1) = 1 first row begins at JA(1) and AN(1).
IA(2) = 4 second row begins at JA(4) and AN(4).
IA(3) = 4 third row begins at JA(4) and AN(4). Since this is the same position at which row 2 begins, this means that row 2 is empty.
IA(4) = 6 this is the first empty location in JA and AN. The description of row 3 thus ends at position 6 − 1 = 5 of JA and AN.

In general, row r of **A** is described in positions IA(r) to IA($r + 1$) − 1 of JA and AN, except when IA($r + 1$) = IA(r) in which case row r is empty. If matrix **A** has m rows, then IA has $m + 1$ positions.

This representation is said to be *complete* because the entire matrix **A** is represented, and *ordered* because the elements of each row are stored in the ascending order of their column indices. It is thus a *R*ow-wise *R*epresentation *C*omplete and *O*rdered, or RR(C)O.

The arrays IA and JA represent the structure of **A**, given as the set of the adjacency lists of the graph associated with **A**. If an algorithm is divided into a symbolic section and a numerical section (Section 1.12), the arrays IA and JA are computed by the symbolic section, and the array AN by the numerical section.

Gustavson (1972) also proposed a variant of row-wise storage, suitable for applications requiring both row and column operations. **A** is stored row-wise as described, and in addition the structure of $\mathbf{A}^T$ is computed and also stored row-wise. A row-wise representation of the structure of $\mathbf{A}^T$ is identical to a column-wise representation of the structure of **A**. It can be obtained by transposition of the row-wise structure of **A** (Chapter 7). This scheme has been used, for example, for linear programming applications (Reid, 1976).

A much simpler row-oriented scheme was proposed by Key (1973) for unsymmetric matrices. The nonzeros are held in a two-dimensional array of size n by m, where n is the order of the matrix and m is the maximum number of nonzeros in a row. This scheme is easy to manipulate but has the disadvantage that m may not be predictable and may turn out to be large.

1.9. Ordered and unordered representations

Sparse matrix representations do not necessarily have to be ordered, in the sense that the elements of each row can be stored in any order while still preserving the order of the rows. The matrix **A** of our example can equally well be given in a *R*ow-wise *R*epresentation, *C*omplete but *U*nordered, e.g.:

position =	1	2	3	4	5	
IA =	1	4	4	6		
JA =	8	3	4	8	6	RR(C)U
AN =	5.	1.	3.	1.	7.	

Unordered representations may be very convenient. The results of most matrix operations are obtained in unordered representations, and it would be computationally very costly to order them. On the other hand, with few exceptions, sparse matrix algorithms do not require the representations to be ordered.

Column-wise representations are also used, but they can be considered as row-wise representations of the transposed matrices. For our example, matrix **A** can be represented *C*olumn-wise as follows:

position =	1	2	3	4	5	6	7	8	9	10	11	
IAT =	1	1	1	2	3	3	4	4	6	6	6	
JAT =	1	1	3	1	3							CR(C)O
ANT =	1	3	7	5	1							

which can also be considered as a RR(C)O of $\mathbf{A}^T$. Note that, since **A** has 10 columns, IAT has 11 positions.

When the given matrix is symmetric, it is sufficient to represent only its diagonal and upper triangle. Consider the following example:

$$\mathbf{B} = \begin{array}{c} \\ 1 \\ 2 \\ 3 \\ 4 \end{array} \begin{array}{c} \begin{array}{cccc} 1 & 2 & 3 & 4 \end{array} \\ \left|\begin{array}{cccc} 2. & 0 & 0 & 1. \\ 0 & 1. & 0 & 1. \\ 0 & 0 & 3. & 0 \\ 1. & 1. & 0 & 3. \end{array}\right| \end{array}$$

The *R*ow-wise *R*epresentation, *D*iagonal and *U*pper, *O*rdered, of **B**, is:

position =	1	2	3	4	5	6	7	
IB =	1	3	5	6	7			
JB =	1	4	2	4	3	4		RR(DU)O
BN =	2.	1.	1.	1.	3.	3.		

If, in addition, most of the diagonal elements of the given symmetric matrix are different from zero (as in the case of symmetric positive-definite matrices), then they can be stored in a separate array BD, and only the upper triangle of **B** is represented in sparse format:

position =	1	2	3	4	5	
IB =	1	2	3	3	3	RR(U)O
JB =	4	4				
BN =	1.	1.				
BD =	2.	1.	3.	3.		

This is a very dense and convenient representation.

1.10. Sherman's compression

In this section we will discuss a compressed storage scheme proposed by Sherman (1975), which is a variant of the sparse format discussed in Section 1.8. Sherman's scheme is used to store triangular sparse matrices obtained by Gauss factorization. In order to explain Sherman's scheme, we must first define a *lower triangular matrix* as a matrix with nonzeros only in its lower triangle and main diagonal, and an *upper triangular matrix* as a matrix with nonzeros only in its upper triangle and main diagonal, i.e.:

$$\text{lower triangular matrix } A_{ij} = 0 \quad \text{if} \quad j > i$$

$$\text{upper triangular matrix } A_{ij} = 0 \quad \text{if} \quad j < i$$

Triangular matrices will be discussed in more detail in Chapter 9. The most important application of triangular matrices is the *triangular factorization* of a matrix **A**:

$$\mathbf{A} = \mathbf{LDU},$$

where **L** is lower triangular, **U** is upper triangular and **D** is diagonal. Triangular factorization will be discussed in Chapter 2. If **A** is sparse, then **L** and **U** are likely to be sparse.

L, **D** and **U** are obtained from **A** by means of some elimination process, e.g. Gauss elimination, and it often happens that sets of rows of **U**, or of **L**, have a similar structure. In particular, it will frequently be the case that rows i and j of **U**, $i < j$, have identical structure to the right of position j. In order to avoid storing the same strings of colum indices several times, Sherman has proposed a compressed storage of column indices, which requires an additional array of pointers. The following example illustrates the idea. Consider the upper triangular matrix:

U =

	1	2	3	4	5	6	7	8	9	10
1	1.		11.				12.			13.
2		2.				14.			15.	
3			3.				16.			17.
4				4.					18.	
5					5.		19.			20.
6						6.		21.	22.	23.
7							7.	24.	25.	
8								8.	26.	
9									9.	27.
10										10.

This matrix is stored as follows:

position =	1	2	3	4	5	6	7	8	9	10	11	12	13	14	15	16	17	18
UD =	1.	2.	3.	4.	5.	6.	7.	8.	9.	10.								
UN =	11.	12.	13.	14.	15.	16.	17.	18.	19.	20.	21.	22.	23.	24.	25.	26.	27.	
IU =	1	4	6	8	9	11	15	16	17	18	18							
JU =	3	7	10	6	9	8	9	10	8	9	10							
IJ =	1	4	2	5	2	6	9	10	11									

The diagonal elements of **U** are stored in the array UD, and the off-diagonal elements in UN, by rows. The array IU contains pointers to UN, defined in the usual way. An extra entry in IU(11) points to the first empty position in UN, position 18. The column indices which correspond to the nonzeros stored in UN, are stored in JU in compressed form. Now there is no longer a correspondence between UN and JU. The column indices can be retrieved from JU using the additional array of pointers IJ. Several rows are described in JU by the same set of column indices. Rows 1, 3 and 5, for example, have the same structure beyond column 5, and the indices 3, 7 and 10 in JU serve for row 1, while 7 and 10 serve also for rows 3 and 5. Thus IJ(1) = 1, IJ(3) = IJ(5) = 2. If we want to retrieve a complete row, say row 1, from the representation, we proceed in the usual way. The numerical values are found in UN, in the locations between IU(1) = 1 and IU(2) − 1 = 3. The column indices are found in JU starting at location IJ(1) = 1, and since we know that we need 3 column indices, we can retrieve them sequentially from JU.

The storage could have been compressed even more if we had realized by examination that row 7 has the column indices 8 and 9, which are also the leading indices for row 6. Such examination is not usually done because only low storage savings could be achieved at a high computational cost. The elimination algorithm systematically produces sets of rows having the same structure beyond a certain column, thus directly furnishing the information needed to construct the compressed storage. Compressing the storage even more would require an expensive search. Comparisons between compressed and uncompressed storage have been provided by George and Liu (1981, p. 142 and Ch. 9), and a systematic procedure for finding isostructural rows will be discussed in Section 4.8.

1.11. Storage of block-partitioned matrices

The idea of dividing a large matrix into submatrices or blocks arises naturally. The blocks can be treated as if they were the elements of the matrix and the partitioned matrix becomes a matrix of matrices. Partitioning plays an important role in sparse matrix technology because many algorithms designed primarily for matrices of numbers can be generalized to operate on matrices of matrices. The greater flexibility of the concept of partitioning then brings useful computational advantages. Alternatively, partitioning can be considered simply as a data management tool, which helps to organize the transfer of information between main memory and auxiliary devices. The partitionings of rows and columns need not be the same; if they are, as often happens, the diagonal blocks are square. Storing a partitioned matrix implies storing a set of submatrices. We describe first the *implicit storage* scheme (George, 1977), designed primarily for symmetric matrices with square diagonal blocks. The diagonal blocks are treated as if they were a single matrix and stored according to Jennings' envelope scheme of Section 1.6. The values of the elements are stored row-wise in the array AN and pointers to the diagonal element of each row are stored in the integer array IA. The lower off-diagonal blocks, again considered to form a single matrix, are stored according to the sparse row-wise format of Section 1.8. The nonzeros are stored by rows in the real array AP, along with their corresponding column indices in the parallel integer array JA. Pointers to AP and JA by row are kept in IP, where an additional pointer to the first empty location in AP and JA is included for programming convenience. The partitioning itself is defined by pointers to the first row of each block, stored in LP, together with the usual additional entry. LP can be used in conjunction with either IA or IP. This hybrid storage scheme has been used with success for Gauss elimination in combination with the ordering methods of tree partitioning and dissection to be discussed in Sections 4.9 and 4.10, respectively.

An example of a symmetric block-partitioned matrix **A** is shown in Fig. 1.5(a). The rows and columns of **A** have been grouped into the subsets (1, 2, 3, 4), (5, 6, 7) and (8, 9, 10), and as a result **A** is divided into 9 blocks. Diagonal blocks are square because rows and columns have been partitioned in the same manner. Figure 1.5(b) shows **A** as a 3 by 3 matrix of matrices, and Fig. 1.5(c) displays the corresponding implicit storage.

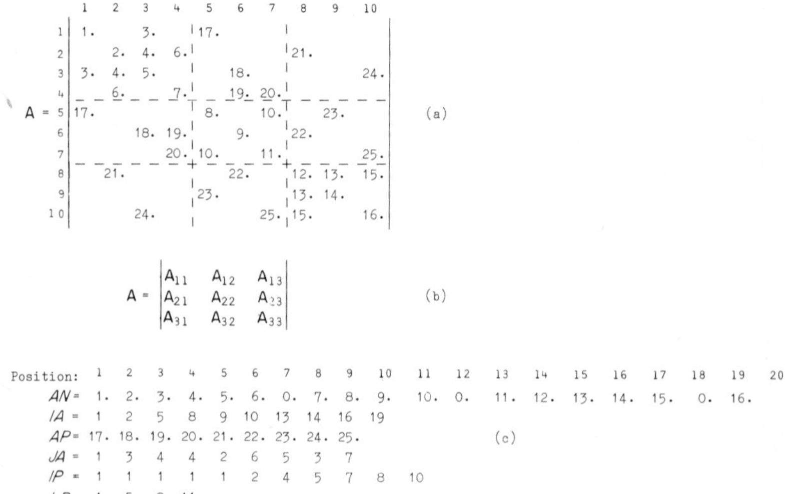

Figure 1.5 Block-partitioned matrix and its implicit storage.

Another scheme, called the *block-within-block-column* scheme, was suggested by George (1977) and is particularly convenient for use with the dissection methods of Chapter 4. Diagonal blocks are stored as before, but lower off-diagonal blocks are treated as block columns. Dissection causes nonzeros in each block column to cluster into blocks. These blocks are stored successively in a real array, together with information indicating where each block begins, which is the row index of the first row of each block, and to which block column each block belongs.

The *hypermatrix scheme* is obtained when **A** is stored as a matrix of which the elements are matrices (Argyris, 1960, 1964; Von Fuchs *et al.*, 1972), and it has long been realized how useful this scheme is when many of the blocks are empty (Swift, 1960). Any of the methods discussed in this chapter can be used to store **A**, except that information regarding the location and size of each submatrix has to be stored in place of the numerical values. The submatrices themselves, of which the elements are numbers, are stored according to some standard format. Of particular interest is the case where **A**, the matrix of submatrices, is sparse. Then **A** can be stored in a sparse representation, which is kept in main memory, while the submatrices, also stored in some sparse representation, are kept in peripheral storage and brought to the main memory when required by the execution of the algorithm. This variant is the *supersparse scheme* (Pissanetzky, 1979). All hypermatrix schemes allow the handling of very large problems with modest memory requirements, and their main advantage is the ease with which the user can trade off storage for time by specifying finer or coarser partitions according to the available memory. The technique has been used successfully for Gauss elimination and eigenvalue calculations. It requires an efficient implementation of matrix operations like addition, multiplication and permutation for rectangular, square and triangular sparse matrices and vectors, and factorization of the square diagonal blocks. These operations are discussed at length in Chapters 7 and 9.

1.12. Symbolic processing and dynamic storage schemes

A sparse matrix algorithm may produce new nonzeros and modify the values of the nonzeros of an already existing matrix; or it may just use a given matrix without ever modifying it, as in the case of iterative algorithms which only need products of the matrix with certain vectors. The set of new nonzero elements added to an already existing sparse matrix is the *fill*. The algorithm may also construct an entirely new matrix, but this is conceptually equivalent to generating new nonzeros for an initially empty matrix. The discussion in this section concerns algorithms which generate new nonzeros and how the new nonzeros can be stored.

Before execution of such an algorithm starts, memory locations for the new elements must be available. Storage management rules must also be enforced, which define the internal representation of data or *data structure*, telling where and how to store each new number. For the data structure there is a choice: either it may be prepared before numerical execution starts, or it may be developed during execution keeping pace with the stream of computed numbers.

A data structure which is ready before initiation of numerical execution is termed a *static* structure. Preparing it requires knowledge of the number of nonzero elements and of their positions in the matrix before they are actually calculated. A number of matrix algorithms allow prediction of the necessary information. Matrix addition and multiplication fall into this category. Gauss elimination also does when the sequence of pivots is known *a priori*, as happens with symmetric positive definite matrices. Any such algorithm splits naturally into two parts: the *symbolic section* which does the *symbolic processing*, or *storage allocation*, or *data structure set-up*, and the *numerical section* which performs the actual numerical calculations or *numerical processing*. The result of the symbolic step is the static data structure, the result of the numerical step are the values of the nonzeros, stored in the memory locations previously set aside by the symbolic step.

Some static schemes, when used for certain specific applications, may not require an explicit symbolic step. Band and envelope schemes have been designed in such a way that Gauss elimination with diagonal pivots can only produce nonzeros inside the band or the envelope, which is therefore the required static structure. The same holds when a band matrix is reduced to tridiagonal form for eigenvalue calculations (Section 6.6), but not in the case of envelope storage. Clearly, adding two matrices with the same band or envelope preserves the band or the envelope, but multiplication of two band matrices enlarges the band. Also, if Gauss elimination is performed on a band matrix choosing the pivots by means of row permutations, the lower semiband remains the same and the upper semiband can at worst double (Martin and Wilkinson, 1967). Tewarson (1971) has proposed a number of static schemes, generally known as *desirable forms*, for use with Gauss elimination on symmetric or unsymmetric matrices.

On the other hand, techniques such as band or profile minimization must be viewed as true symbolic steps since they only allocate memory with the purpose of reducing storage and labour but do not compute any numerical results. In the same category fall several other techniques such as dissection, tree partitioning and block triangularization, to be discussed in Chapters 4 and 5. When a matrix is stored in sparse row-wise format (Section 1.8), a necessary symbolic step is the computation of IA, JA, the structure of the matrix; it will be discussed in connection with specific algorithms: multiplication, transposition, triangular factorization, etc.

Static schemes promote modularity, because the symbolic and numerical steps are executed separately and consequently can be independently optimized. Furthermore, in the case of direct solution of linear equations, modern and powerful procedures exist which allow the symbolic step to be performed much faster than the numerical one, and using fixed storage only slightly larger than that required for the matrix, while still providing essential information for the user: the amount of storage and labour required for the numerical step. Another important advantage arises in the case of applications which require the repeated use of the same algorithm with different numerical values. Examples are iterative methods needing the solution of many linear systems with the same matrix and different right-hand sides, or with matrices having the same structure but different numerical values. In such cases the symbolic step may be performed once only and the same static structure used for the entire calculation.

Unfortunately, static data structures cannot be employed in all cases, the most notable exception being Gauss elimination with pivot selection on an indefinite matrix, to be discussed in Section 3.4. In order to keep errors low, pivots are selected on numerical grounds while elimination proceeds, using techniques such as complete pivoting, partial pivoting, or threshold pivoting. Selecting pivots amounts to permuting rows and columns, which in turn affects the location of the resulting fill. The consequence is that the structure of the final matrix cannot be foreseen, and decisions as to where and how to store each new nonzero element must be made when that element has already been computed and is ready for storage. This procedure is called *dynamic storage allocation* and a *dynamic* structure results.

It has already been mentioned that Gauss elimination can be performed on an indefinite band matrix provided the pivots are chosen by means of row permutations alone, with the result that the upper semiband doubles while the lower remains unchanged. Strictly speaking, this scheme is static because it can be organized beforehand. It also has the disadvantage inherent in every static scheme: that storage savings cannot be made during execution and many zeros may have to be stored and operated upon, or at least by-passed. True dynamic structures require a scheme which is independent of the essentially static character of computer memory. This demanding requirement is usually achieved by means of an effective system of links and pointers. Knuth's scheme and KRM scheme are ideally suited for the purpose (Section 1.7). Each nonzero element of the matrix is internally represented by a record of fixed length, which is stored anywhere in the computer memory and then linked with the corresponding row and column lists. Elements can be inserted or deleted at any position in the matrix without moving any other data, and both rows and columns can be scanned as the algorithm requires.

The use of *records of variable length* for dynamic storage of sparse matrices has been suggested by Houbak (1981). A record is a special type of two-dimensional array to which rows can be added dynamically and of which the columns may be simple variables of different types. Unused rows are automatically detected and the storage compressed when necessary. No pointers or links need to be stored and no indirect addressing is necessary. Linked lists are formed by letting a reference variable stored in a row hold the address of the next row. The price paid in terms of extra storage is equivalent to an INTEGER variable per row. This scheme is supported by modern versions of compilers for languages such as Pascal and Algolw, but not by standard Fortran, and its use is equivalent to letting the compiler manage the links and pointers. A code based on this data structure compares favourably, at least for matrices of small or moderate size, with two other codes which use an ordered list storage scheme, in Algolw and Fortran, respectively (Barker *et al.*, 1976; Thomsen and Zlatev, 1978).

1.13. Merging sparse lists of integers

Now that the fundamental storage schemes employed in sparse matrix technology have been examined, we initiate the analysis of some of the fundamental procedures employed for processing lists of integers or real numbers. These procedures are very frequently used as part of matrix algorithms, particularly when the matrices are represented in a sparse format. We use Fortran symbols directly in the text in order to avoid unnecessary introduction of algebraic symbols. The usual conventions of INTEGER and REAL types apply. The first procedure to be examined is used to merge sparse lists of integers.

Merging is an inclusive OR operation. By merging two or more sparse lists, a new sparse list is obtained. An integer belongs to the resulting list if and only if it belongs to any of the given lists, and no repeated integers are allowed. The operation of merging lists of integers is very important in sparse matrix technology because it is commonly used to form the list of the column indices associated with each of the rows of a new matrix, obtained by performing algebraic operations on another matrix or matrices particularly when sparse formats are used. Examples are addition, multiplication and triangular factorization of sparse matrices. The following example illustrates the concept of merging. Given the three lists:

list A: 2, 7, 3, 5
list B: 3, 11, 5
list C: 7, 2

the resulting list, say M, is:

merged list M: 2, 7, 3, 5, 11

The resulting list M is obtained by inscribing each integer from each of the given lists, provided the integer was not previously inscribed. In order to determine efficiently whether an integer was previously inscribed or not, we use an expanded array or *switch array*, say IX, where a conventional number, the *switch*, is stored at position I immediately after the integer I has been added to the list M under construction. Conversely, before adding an integer K to the list M, we check whether the value stored in IX(K) is equal to the switch or not, and we add K only if it is not. The first given list can be entirely inscribed in M, turning the corresponding switches "ON", but without checking whether they are ON or not before adding the integers. This is so because we have assumed that no repeated integers exist in the lists. The inspection of the switch array for switches ON should start at the time the second list given is examined. Turning back to our example, after the first list has been inscribed, and if the switch array was initialized to 0 and 1 is used as the switch, we would have the following situation:

merged list M: 2, 7, 3, 5

position in IX:	1	2	3	4	5	6	7	8	9	10	11	12	...
value in IX:	0	1	1	0	1	0	1	0	0	0	0	0	...

Now, in the second list, the value 3 is found. Since IX(3) = 1, the switch, we know that 3 has already been included in M and should not be included again. Note that if this information were not directly available, we would have to examine all the elements in M, an inefficient operation. Next, 11 is found. Since IX(11) $\neq$ 1, 11 is added to the array M, and IX(11) is set to the value of 1. None of the remaining integers, 5, 7, 2, are added to M. The merged list is always unordered, even if the given lists were ordered.

When the lists are disjoint merging is a simple concatenation. Two or more disjoint lists stored in the linked mode can be concatenated by simply resetting the appropriate pointers and deleting the unnecessary list heads. In a more general context, Tarjan (1975) has considered the efficiency of instructions which manipulate a family of disjoint sets to compute their union or to find to which set a given element belongs.

1.14. The multiple switch technique

Each time a merging operation starts, the switch array IX just discussed should not contain the switch value in any of its positions. This can be achieved by setting IX(I) = 0 for $I = 1, \ldots, N$ at the beginning, and then using a positive integer as the switch. However, the sentence $IX(I) = 0$ is executed N times and the advantage of using sparse techniques is lost if the merging operation is going to be performed only once.

However, in sparse matrix technology, merging operations are used to construct the lists of column indices for, say, the N rows of a $N \times N$ matrix. N different merging operations are required for this purpose, all of them to be performed using the same array IX of length N as the switch array. In this case, we set to 0 the N positions of IX only once, and then we perform the N merging operations using each time a *different* value for the switch parameter (Gustavson, 1976b). The rule of thumb is to use 1 as the switch for the first merging operation, 2 for the second, and so on. In this way, when the first merging operation is starting, all positions of IX contain 0. When the second one is starting, all positions of IX contain either 0 or 1, which does not conflict with the use of 2 as the switch, and so on. Now, N executions of the sentence $IX(I) = 0$ are required for N merging operations. There is an average of only one execution of $IX(I) = 0$ per each merging operation. This is acceptable when the number of nonzeros of the $N \times N$ matrix is at least of order N, as usually happens in practice.

An alternative to the multiple switch technique is to reset IX to 0 each time. When a merging operation has been concluded, the integers stored in the merged list point to the positions in IX where nonzeros have been stored. If the merged list contains $M \ll N$ integers, only M operations are required to reset IX. This technique may be convenient in some cases, for example when an array of bits is used as the switch array in order to save memory. The multiple switch technique cannot be used with an array of bits, because the only numbers which can be stored in such an array are 0 or 1.

The multiple switch technique is also known as the *phase counter* technique (Gustavson, 1976c).

1.15. Addition of sparse vectors with the help of an expanded real accumulator

A vector of order N is said to be sparse when only a few of its N elements are different from zero. A sparse vector is a sparse matrix with only one row (a row vector) or one column (a column vector). In either case, the numerical values of the nonzeros are stored in the computer memory in a real array, say AN, and their corresponding position indices in an integer array, say JA. Both arrays are of the same length, which is much smaller than N, and as a consequence this storage is said to be *compact* or *packed*. It is also necessary to store information describing the number of nonzeros in the vector. This number can be stored directly in an integer variable and used as a pointer to the end of JA and AN, or a 0 can be stored as a terminator in JA immediately after the last occupied position to indicate the end of the list of integers.

The numerical values of the nonzeros of the sparse vector can also be stored in *expanded* form in a real array of length N, say X, as if it were a full vector. The position indices, however, are stored in the array JA as before. This type of storage is used only temporarily, usually during the execution of a program and when certain algebraic operations are to be performed on the vector. The existence of the array JA allows the algorithm to operate directly on the nonzeros and to keep the operation count much smaller than N. Note that, if the vector were full, JA could be omitted, but the algorithm would have to deal with each of the N elements of X, at least to determine whether its value is 0 or not, and then the operation count would be proportional to N.

The operation of adding two or more sparse vectors is best illustrated with the help of an example. Consider two sparse vectors, **a** and **b**, of order N. a is stored in compact unordered format in the arrays JA, AN and b in the arrays JB, BN. We wish to calculate:

$$\mathbf{c} = \mathbf{a} + \mathbf{b},$$

with **c** to be stored in JC, CN. Let:

JA =	10	3	7	4
AN =	0.2	0.3	0.4	−0.7
JB =	5	4	10	
BN =	0.6	0.7	0.5	

If we start trying to calculate $c_1 = a_1 + b_1$, we will soon realize that this can be achieved only by inspection of JA and JB, followed by convenient operations on the real numbers stored in AN and BN. In fact, to determine a_1 we inspect JA and find that, since none of the numbers stored in JA is 1, then $a_1 = 0$. In the same way, by inspection of JB we find $b_1 = 0.$, and so $c_1 = a_1 + b_1 = 0.$. The same conclusion is reached for c_2, while for c_3 we find that $a_3 = 0.3$ and $b_3 = 0.$, so $c_3 = 0.3$, and so on. For *each* element in **c** we have to inspect *all* of JA and *all* of JB. This procedure is very inefficient because it requires a number of elementary computations roughly proportional to the *square* of the number of nonzeros in **a** and **b**.

An efficient procedure is obtained when the algorithm is split into a symbolic section and a numerical section. A fixed, small number of inspections of JA and JB is required, no matter how many nonzeros are present. This means that the total number of elementary operations will be a *linear* function of the number of nonzeros.

The symbolic section consists of the determination of the positions of the nonzeros of **c**, by merging the lists JA and JB with the help of an expanded switch array IX of dimension N, as explained in Section 1.13. The switch array has to be previously initialized to 0. The result is:

$$\text{JC} = 10 \quad 3 \quad 7 \quad 4 \quad 5$$

Now that we know the positions of the nonzeros or structure of **c**, we use the numerical section of the algorithm to determine their numerical values. Again, this is not straightforward. We cannot calculate C_{10}, the first nonzero in **c** as indicated by JC, trying to find the index 10 in JA and JB. Instead, we use an expanded storage of the vectors in an expanded array of dimension N, say X, called an *expanded real accumulator*. First, we store 0. in all useful positions of X, which are those indicated by JC. The result is:

position:	1	2	3	4	5	6	7	8	9	10	11	12	...
value X:	x	x	0.	0.	0.	x	0.	x	x	0.	x	x	...

where x indicates irrelevant numbers. Next, we *load* AN into X. The result is

position:	1	2	3	4	5	6	7	8	9	10	11	...
value X:	x	x	0.3	−0.7	0.	x	0.4	x	x	0.2	x	...

Now, we *add* BN to X:

position:	1	2	3	4	5	6	7	8	9	10	11	...
value X:	x	x	0.3	0.	0.6	x	0.4	x	x	0.7	x	...

Finally, we *retrieve* the useful numbers from X to form CN. We use JC to find where the useful numbers are in X; e.g., for JC(1) = 10, we find X(10) = 0.7, so we set CN(1) = X(10). The final result is:

$$\begin{aligned} \text{JC} &= 10 \quad\; 3 \quad\;\; 7 \quad\;\; 4 \quad 5 \\ \text{CN} &= \;0.7 \quad 0.3 \quad 0.4 \quad 0. \quad 0.6, \end{aligned}$$

and it was obtained with a number of computations which is proportional to the number of nonzeros in **a** and **b**, *except* that N computations were required to initialize the switch array IX with zeros before merging JA and JB. At this point, we restrict our attention to the case of interest: sparse matrix algebra. Most matrix operations require not one but O(N) additions of sparse vectors, where O(N) means "a number of order N", since each row of a matrix is a sparse vector. Using the multiple switch technique of Section 1.14, IX is reset to 0 only once, with a total of N computations for O(N) additions, which is totally acceptable.

The numerical example was chosen purposely to obtain $c_4 = 0.$.

Cancellation between real numbers is rare and is usually disregarded. This means that a few of the "nonzeros" of a sparse matrix may in fact be zeros, and the algorithms should be prepared to accept this circumstance. In some cases, however, cancellation may be frequent, e.g. for matrices composed entirely of 1. and −1.. In such cases it may be convenient to devise an algorithm for preventing the appearance of zeros in the result.

Any number of sparse vectors can be added using one symbolic and one numerical step. Subtraction of sparse vectors, or addition of sparse vectors multiplied by constants, is also straightforward. The results will be unordered even if the given vectors are ordered. However, the numerical algorithm preserves the order because the nonzeros are retrieved from X and stored in CN in the same order that their corresponding indices are stored in JC. Thus, if the results should be ordered, it suffices to order JC alone before performing the numerical algorithm.

1.16. Addition of sparse vectors with the help of an expanded integer array of pointers

There is an alternative algorithm for the numerical section of sparse vector addition, in which the resulting vector is used directly as the accumulator. We refer again to the example of Section 1.15, and assume that JC has already been obtained by the symbolic section, and that we want to compute the numerical values in CN, the resulting vector. Since CN is going to be used as the accumulator, we initialize it to 0., so we have:

$$\begin{aligned} \text{JC} &= 10 \quad 3 \quad 7 \quad 4 \quad 5 \\ \text{CN} &= \;\;0. \quad 0. \quad 0. \quad 0. \quad 0. \end{aligned}$$

Now, we define the *expanded array of pointers* IP, initialized to 0. We run over JC and set pointers in IP to the positions in CN where the nonzeros will be stored. For example, in the first position of JC we find 10, which tells us that the nonzero c_{10} is stored in the position 1 of CN. Therefore we set IP(10) = 1. Similarly, we set IP(3) = 2, and so on. After JC is exhausted we have:

position:	1	2	3	4	5	6	7	8	9	10	11	...
value IP:	0	0	2	4	5	0	3	0	0	1	0	...

Next, we run over JA and AN, and use IP to find the position of CN where each nonzero should be accumulated. For example, at position 1 of JA we find 10 and 0.2, respectively; at position 10 of IP we find 1; therefore we accumulate 0.2 in position 1 of CN. This procedure is repeated with all the elements in JA, AN and JB, BN and finally IP is reset to zero with the help of

JC in order to be ready for the next usage. Any number of sparse vectors can be added efficiently and with a minimum of data movement using this algorithm. Order is preserved by the numerical section since JC is not affected.

We note that the correct result would have been obtained if CN were first initialized to 0 and then the elements from AN were directly loaded into CN without any reference to IP. This is so because, when two lists of integers such as JA and JB are merged, the resultant list JC contains exactly the *first* of the given lists, JA in this case. This procedure is more efficient than the one we have just described and can be used for the first of two or more addends. But care must be exercised to ensure that the vectors are specified in the same order to both the symbolic and the numerical algorithms.

1.17. Scalar product of two sparse vectors with the help of an array of pointers

In this Section we consider the following problem: two sparse vectors **a** and **b**, both of order N, are stored in the arrays JA, AN and JB, BN. Both representations are compact and unordered, and we wish to compute the scalar product of the two vectors:

$$h = \sum_{i=1}^{N} a_i b_i$$

Let us consider again the example of Section 1.15. An attempt to compute the scalar product directly would lead us to perform numerous inspections of JB. In fact, let us start with the first nonzero stored in JA, AN, which is $a_{10} = 0.2$. This value must be multiplied by b_{10}. In order to find b_{10} we must inspect all of JB and discover that b_{10} is stored as BN(3) = 0.5. The product $a_{10}b_{10}$ is now computed and stored. The next nonzero is $a_3 = 0.3$, and we inspect JB again just to find that $b_3 = 0.$. For each element in **a** we have to inspect JB. This procedure is very inefficient because the number of inspections performed is proportional to the product of the number of nonzeros in **a** and the number of nonzeros in **b**.

The following algorithm requires only one inspection of **a** and **b** plus a fixed, small number of elementary operations for each nonzero of the vectors. Since the final result is a single real number, h, the algorithm does not have a symbolic section. An expanded integer array IP is used to store pointers to the positions of the nonzeros in AN. This array, which must be initialized to zero, is constructed by means of a single run over JA. For the example of Section 1.15 the result is:

position:	1	2	3	4	5	6	7	8	9	10	11	...
value IP:	0	0	2	4	0	0	3	0	0	1	0	...

This array tells us that a_3 is stored in position 2 of AN, a_4 in position 4, etc. It also tells us that $a_1 = 0.$, $a_2 = 0.$, etc.

Next, we run over the nonzeros of **b**, use IP to find the corresponding nonzeros of **a**, perform the products when required and accumulate the results in the variable h. For example, in the first position of JB, BN we find that $b_5 = 0.6$. However, since $\mathrm{IP}(5) = 0$, we know that $a_5 = 0.$ and the product $a_5 b_5$ must be skipped. Then, we find $b_4 = 0.7$, and since $\mathrm{IP}(4) = 4$, we find the value of a_4 stored in position 4 of AN and we compute the product $a_4 b_4$. This procedure is continued until JB is exhausted.

A particularly interesting application of this algorithm arises when a vector **a** must be multiplied by several vectors. In this case, IP is constructed just once and then used to compute all the required scalar products. This case arises when a sparse vector and a sparse matrix must be multiplied, and will be discussed further in Chapter 7.

CHAPTER 2

Linear Algebraic Equations

2.1. Introduction

In this and the following chapters we will discuss algorithms which find the solution $\mathbf{x}$ of the system

$$\mathbf{A}\mathbf{x} = \mathbf{b} \tag{2.1}$$

where $\mathbf{A}$ is a nonsingular square n by n real sparse matrix and $\mathbf{b}$ a full vector. The algorithms may be grouped into two categories: direct methods and iterative methods. Direct methods are based on Gauss elimination: the equations or the unknowns of the system are modified in successive steps until the solution is found. In the iterative methods, an initial guess is usually made for $\mathbf{x}$, and this guess is then improved until sufficient accuracy is obtained. Both methods have advantages and disadvantages in each particular case and it is difficult to state general rules as to which is the most convenient.

Our attention is restricted to direct methods for solving Equation (2.1) with $\mathbf{A}$ a real nonsingular square matrix of order n. A complex system of linear equations can be transformed into a real one of twice the order, as shown at the end of Section 2.2. The solution of Equation (2.1) can be written $\mathbf{x} = \mathbf{A}^{-1}\mathbf{b}$, but explicit use of this form is made only in the case of small n (say $n \sim 100$ or less). $\mathbf{A}^{-1}$ is a dense matrix even if $\mathbf{A}$ is sparse, and its computation implies losing the advantages of sparsity. For a large system advantage is taken of the fact that $\mathbf{A}^{-1}$ is not needed explicitly: $\mathbf{A}^{-1}$ can be expressed in the form of a product of matrices such that the action on $\mathbf{b}$ is easy to compute. Of course such a procedure is convenient because the factor matrices are sparse and can all be stored in much less space than would be required for $\mathbf{A}^{-1}$ alone, and also because the product of the factor matrices and $\mathbf{b}$ requires fewer operations than the product $\mathbf{A}^{-1}\mathbf{b}$ alone would require. The usual way for solving Equation (2.1) by a direct method is to compute the *triangular factorization* of $\mathbf{A}$:

$$\mathbf{A} = \mathbf{LU} \tag{2.2}$$

where $\mathbf{U}$ is an upper triangular matrix (its lower triangle contains only zeros) with a diagonal of ones, and $\mathbf{L}$ is lower triangular (its upper triangle contains only zeros). Then $\mathbf{A}^{-1} = \mathbf{U}^{-1}\mathbf{L}^{-1}$ and $\mathbf{x} = \mathbf{U}^{-1}\mathbf{w}$ where $\mathbf{w} = \mathbf{L}^{-1}\mathbf{b}$. Thus, the solution of Equation (2.1) is found by solving the linear systems:

$$\mathbf{Lw} = \mathbf{b} \tag{2.3}$$

for $\mathbf{w}$, and

$$\mathbf{Ux} = \mathbf{w} \tag{2.4}$$

for $\mathbf{x}$. If $\mathbf{A}$ is sparse, both $\mathbf{L}$ and $\mathbf{U}$ are sparse, although usually less sparse than $\mathbf{A}$. Systems like (2.3) and (2.4), which are very simple to solve, are examined in Section 2.13.

Decomposition (2.2) is unique if $\mathbf{A}$ is representable as such a product and is nonsingular (Wilkinson, 1965, p. 201). Frequently a diagonal matrix $\mathbf{D}$ is factored out from $\mathbf{L}$ in such a way that $\mathbf{L} = \mathbf{L}'\mathbf{D}$ where $\mathbf{L}'$ is lower triangular with unit diagonal. Equation (2.2) becomes:

$$\mathbf{A} = \mathbf{L}'\mathbf{DU} \tag{2.5}$$

If $\mathbf{A}$ is symmetric, then $\mathbf{L}' = \mathbf{U}^{\mathrm{T}}$. Other decompositions of $\mathbf{A}$ are possible. It is important to examine the various possibilities because they provide flexibility in the design of algorithms and storage schemes. This task is undertaken in the present chapter.

Computers introduce round-off errors when performing arithmetic operations. Large scale computations like the solution of a system (2.1) of high order require a careful error analysis and the use of special techniques to guarantee a meaningful final result with a specified accuracy. In Gauss elimination, excessive error accumulation is usually prevented by scaling the original matrix, selecting suitable pivots in the course of elimination, and monitoring element growth in the successive reduced matrices. These matters are examined in Chapter 3.

The zero–nonzero structure of **A** depends on the source from which the system (2.1) was obtained; for example, the matrix associated with a finite element problem and that associated with an electrical network have completely different structures (see for example Duff, 1981a, p. 17). A consequence of this is the existence of two categories of algorithms: those which take advantage of the particular properties of **A** and are thus devised for specific applications, and those which work equally well with any general sparse matrix. Usually, when more restrictions are placed, more efficient algorithms result. There is great interest in developing algorithms for specific applications and research in this field is currently very active.

The structure of the matrix of a system of linear equations can be modified if the unknowns are renumbered and the equations permuted. While this does very little to the efficiency of most iterative algorithms, important effects are obtained when a direct method is used. This is so because in the course of elimination new nonzero coefficients are generated and the matrix of the system becomes less sparse: it suffers *fill*. It is a well established fact that the amount of fill depends drastically on the way in which the unknowns and the equations are ordered. Since the storage and processing required to solve the system, and the accuracy of the final result depend in turn on the amount of fill, it is important to consider orderings which reduce the fill as much as possible. Research in this field has led to important improvements in direct solution algorithms, which are examined in Chapters 4 and 5.

An alternative direct method for solving linear equations is *orthogonal factorization*. We discuss orthogonalization techniques in Chapter 6, in connection with eigenvalue calculations. Orthogonalization gives better numerical stability than Gauss elimination, but the fill-in is much higher. Methods based on orthogonalization are not recommended for general sparse systems (Duff, 1974b; Duff and Reid, 1975). However, they can be beneficial in some cases, for example in linear least-squares and linear programming (Gill and Murray, 1976), and in the AQ algorithm (Borland, 1981) for cases where the matrix of coefficients can be permuted near to lower Hessenberg form.

Elimination and factorization methods can be applied not only to matrices of numbers but also to matrices of submatrices, giving rise to *block methods*. These are algebraically similar to ordinary elimination, except that operations such as addition, multiplication and inversion must be replaced by matrix addition, matrix multiplication and matrix inversion. However, block methods are different from the point of view of sparsity and stability, aspects which we examine in Chapters 3, 4 and 5.

2.2. Some definitions and properties

The matrix $\mathbf{A}$ is *symmetric* when $\mathbf{A}^T = \mathbf{A}$, where T means transpose, i.e. when $A_{ij} = A_{ji}$ for all i, j. Otherwise $\mathbf{A}$ is *unsymmetric*. A symmetric matrix $\mathbf{A}$ is said to be *positive definite* when

$$\mathbf{y}^T\mathbf{A}\mathbf{y} > 0 \tag{2.6}$$

for any vector $\mathbf{y}$ having at least one nonvanishing component. If two vectors $\mathbf{y}$ and $\mathbf{z}$ can be found for which:

$$\mathbf{y}^T\mathbf{A}\mathbf{y} > 0, \qquad \mathbf{z}^T\mathbf{A}\mathbf{z} < 0 \tag{2.7}$$

then $\mathbf{A}$ is said to be *indefinite* or nondefinite. Symmetry and positive definiteness are important in computation. It is worth examining these properties in slightly more detail. A summary of properties follows.

(1) If $\mathbf{A}$ and $\mathbf{B}$ are symmetric positive definite, $\mathbf{A} + \mathbf{B}$ is also symmetric positive definite. This is a useful property because frequently a large matrix is obtained as the sum of smaller ones, which are known to be positive definite. Besides, it is difficult to check positive definiteness for a large matrix, but usually not for the small ones. See Chapter 8 for an important example.

(2) A symmetric positive definite matrix has n eigenvalues which are all real positive numbers.

(3) The determinant of a symmetric positive definite matrix is positive.

(4) A *minor* of $\mathbf{A}$ is a submatrix obtained by deleting some rows and some columns. A *principal minor* is obtained when identical sets of rows and columns are deleted. If $\mathbf{A}$ is symmetric positive definite, any principal minor is also symmetric positive definite and has therefore a positive determinant. In particular the diagonal elements of $\mathbf{A}$ are all positive:

$$A_{ii} > 0 \qquad \text{for all } i$$

(5) Let $\mathbf{A}$ be symmetric positive definite, and consider the determinant of any 2×2 principal minor, which by Property 4 must be positive:

$$\text{Det} \begin{vmatrix} A_{ii} & A_{ij} \\ A_{ij} & A_{jj} \end{vmatrix} = A_{ii}A_{jj} - A_{ij}^2 > 0.$$

Thus

$$|A_{ij}| < (A_{ii}A_{jj})^{1/2} \leqslant \max(A_{ii}, A_{jj}).$$

In particular, if a is the value of the largest diagonal element of **A**, no element of **A** may exceed a in absolute value:

$$|A_{ij}| \leqslant a \qquad \text{for all } i, j.$$

(6) A necessary and sufficient condition for a symmetric matrix **A** to be positive definite is that the determinants of the n leading principal minors of **A** be positive (Wilkinson, 1965).

(7) If **A** is symmetric positive definite, a unique *Cholesky factorization*

$$\mathbf{A} = \mathbf{U}^{\mathrm{T}}\mathbf{U}$$

exists, where **U** is upper triangular with positive diagonal elements (Stewart, 1973). Besides, **U** can be written $\mathbf{U} = \mathbf{D}'\mathbf{U}'$, where $\mathbf{D}'$ is diagonal with positive diagonal elements and $\mathbf{U}'$ is upper triangular with unit diagonal. Thus:

$$\mathbf{A} = \mathbf{U}'^{\mathrm{T}}\mathbf{D}\mathbf{U}',$$

where $\mathbf{D} = \mathbf{D}'^2$, is also a unique triangular factorization of **A** (Martin and Wilkinson, 1965).

(8) A nonsingular square matrix **R** such that $\mathbf{R}^{\mathrm{T}} = \mathbf{R}^{-1}$ is said to be *orthogonal*. If **A** is symmetric positive definite and **R** is orthogonal, then $\mathbf{B} = \mathbf{R}^{\mathrm{T}}\mathbf{A}\mathbf{R}$ is also symmetric positive definite.

(9) If **C** is any matrix, either square or rectangular, then $\mathbf{A} = \mathbf{C}^{\mathrm{T}}\mathbf{C}$ is symmetric non-negative definite. **A** is clearly symmetric. To show that **A** is non-negative definite, consider any non-null vector **x** of the appropriate length. Then $\mathbf{x}^{\mathrm{T}}\mathbf{A}\mathbf{x} = \mathbf{x}^{\mathrm{T}}\mathbf{C}^{\mathrm{T}}\mathbf{C}\mathbf{x} = (\mathbf{C}\mathbf{x})^{\mathrm{T}}(\mathbf{C}\mathbf{x}) \geqslant 0$. Besides, if the columns of **C** are linearly independent, $\mathbf{C}\mathbf{x} \neq \mathbf{0}$ and **A** is positive definite.

(10) When **A** is indefinite, the triangular factorization may not exist, and a singular **A** may have an infinite number of factorizations (Wilkinson, 1965, p. 224).

(11) The problem of determining whether a given **A** is positive definite seldom arises in practice. We usually know that **A** is symmetric positive definite by construction, frequently by Properties 1, 8 or 9. Then we take advantage of that fact using Property 2 or Property 7. The remaining properties have a great theoretical value but limited practical application.

The *rank* r of any matrix **A** is the order of the largest submatrix which has a nonvanishing determinant. A matrix of order n is *singular* when $r < n$. The quantity $n - r$ is the *nullity* or *rank deficiency* of the matrix. A symmetric positive definite matrix has rank $r = n$. A *matrix of rank one* has necessarily the form $\mathbf{x}\mathbf{y}^{\mathrm{T}}$, with **x**, **y** any non-null column vectors, because then every row is a multiple of $\mathbf{y}^{\mathrm{T}}$ and every column is a multiple of **x**.

The matrix $\mathbf{A}$ is *diagonally dominant* when

$$|A_{ii}| \geqslant \sum_{j \neq i} |A_{ij}| \tag{2.8}$$

for all i, with inequality for at least one i. $\mathbf{A}$ is *properly diagonally dominant* when

$$|A_{ii}| > \sum_{j \neq i} |A_{ij}| \tag{2.9}$$

for all i. It is possible to show that if $\mathbf{A}$ is properly diagonally dominant and all its diagonal elements are positive, i.e., if

$$A_{ii} > \sum_{j \neq i} |A_{ij}| \tag{2.10}$$

for all i, then all the eigenvalues of $\mathbf{A}$ are positive and $\mathbf{A}$ is positive definite. The simple proof is based on a theorem due to Gerschgorin (1931) and discussed in Section 6.3 (see also Wilkinson (1965, p. 71)).

We will be interested only in linear systems (2.1) with real $\mathbf{A}$ and $\mathbf{b}$; as a consequence $\mathbf{x}$ will also be real. A complex system such as

$$(\mathbf{A} + \mathrm{i}\mathbf{B})(\mathbf{x} + \mathrm{i}\mathbf{y}) = \mathbf{b} + \mathrm{i}\mathbf{c} \tag{2.11}$$

where $\mathbf{A}$, $\mathbf{B}$, $\mathbf{x}$, $\mathbf{y}$, $\mathbf{b}$ and $\mathbf{c}$ are all real, is equivalent to the following real system of twice the order:

$$\begin{vmatrix} \mathbf{A} & -\mathbf{B} \\ \mathbf{B} & \mathbf{A} \end{vmatrix} \begin{vmatrix} \mathbf{x} \\ \mathbf{y} \end{vmatrix} = \begin{vmatrix} \mathbf{b} \\ \mathbf{c} \end{vmatrix} \tag{2.12}$$

A complex matrix $\mathbf{M}$ is *hermitian* when $\mathbf{M} = \mathbf{M}^{\mathrm{CT}}$, where CT means "conjugate transpose". The conjugate transpose of $\mathbf{A} + \mathrm{i}\mathbf{B}$ is $\mathbf{A}^{\mathrm{T}} - \mathrm{i}\mathbf{B}^{\mathrm{T}}$ thus $\mathbf{A} + \mathrm{i}\mathbf{B}$ is hermitian if $\mathbf{A}^{\mathrm{T}} = \mathbf{A}$ and $\mathbf{B}^{\mathrm{T}} = -\mathbf{B}$; in case $\mathbf{A} + \mathrm{i}\mathbf{B}$ is hermitian, system (2.12) is symmetric. Solving (2.12) in place of (2.11) we remain in the real field, which is computationally convenient in case complex arithmetic is not efficiently implemented on the computer.

2.3. Elementary matrices and triangular matrices

A number of results will be required repeatedly in this and other chapters and we assemble them here for convenience. An *elementary matrix* $\mathbf{E}$ is of the form $\mathbf{E} = \mathbf{I} + \mathbf{B}$, where $\mathbf{I}$ is the identity matrix and $\mathbf{B}$ is a rank one matrix. Since any rank one matrix has the form $\mathbf{B} = \mathbf{x}\mathbf{y}^{\mathrm{T}}$, where $\mathbf{x}$ and $\mathbf{y}$ are two arbitrary non-null column vectors (Section 2.2), the most general form of an elementary matrix is

$$\mathbf{E} = \mathbf{I} + \mathbf{x}\mathbf{y}^{\mathrm{T}}. \tag{2.13}$$

(a) A square matrix **L** is *lower triangular* when it has nonzero elements only on or below the diagonal: $L_{ij} = 0$ if $i < j$ and some $L_{ij} \neq 0$ for $i \geqslant j$, with at least one $L_{ij} \neq 0$ for $i > j$. A lower triangular matrix is said to be *unit diagonal* if its diagonal elements are all equal to 1: $L_{ii} = 1$ for all i.

(b) A square matrix **U** is *upper triangular* when it has nonzero elements only on or above the diagonal: $U_{ij} = 0$ if $i > j$ and some $U_{ij} \neq 0$ for $i \leqslant j$, with at least one $U_{ij} \neq 0$ for $i < j$. An upper triangular matrix is said to be *unit diagonal* if its diagonal elements are all equal to 1: $U_{ii} = 1$ for all i.

(c) Examples and definitions of some square elementary matrices which we shall need are given below. "x" indicates an element which is allowed to be different from zero, and positions corresponding to zeros have been left blank.

$$\begin{vmatrix} 1 & & & & \\ & 1 & & & \\ & & x & & \\ & & & 1 & \\ & & & & 1 \end{vmatrix}$$

Diagonal elementary matrix $\mathbf{D}_k$.
A diagonal matrix with $(D_k)_{i\,i} = 1$ for all $i \neq k$, $(D_k)_{k\,k} \neq 0$.

$$\begin{vmatrix} 1 & & & & \\ & 1 & & & \\ & & 1 & & \\ & & x & 1 & \\ & & x & & 1 \end{vmatrix}$$

Lower column elementary matrix $\mathbf{L}_k^{\mathrm{C}}$.
Off-diagonal nonzeros exist only on column k below the diagonal.

$$\begin{vmatrix} 1 & & & & \\ & 1 & & & \\ x & x & 1 & & \\ & & & 1 & \\ & & & & 1 \end{vmatrix}$$

Left row elementary matrix $\mathbf{L}_k^{\mathrm{R}}$.
Off-diagonal nonzeros exist only on row k to the left of the diagonal.

$$\begin{vmatrix} 1 & & x & & \\ & 1 & x & & \\ & & 1 & & \\ & & & 1 & \\ & & & & 1 \end{vmatrix}$$

Upper column elementary matrix $\mathbf{U}_k^{\mathrm{C}}$.
Off-diagonal nonzeros exist only on column k above the diagonal.

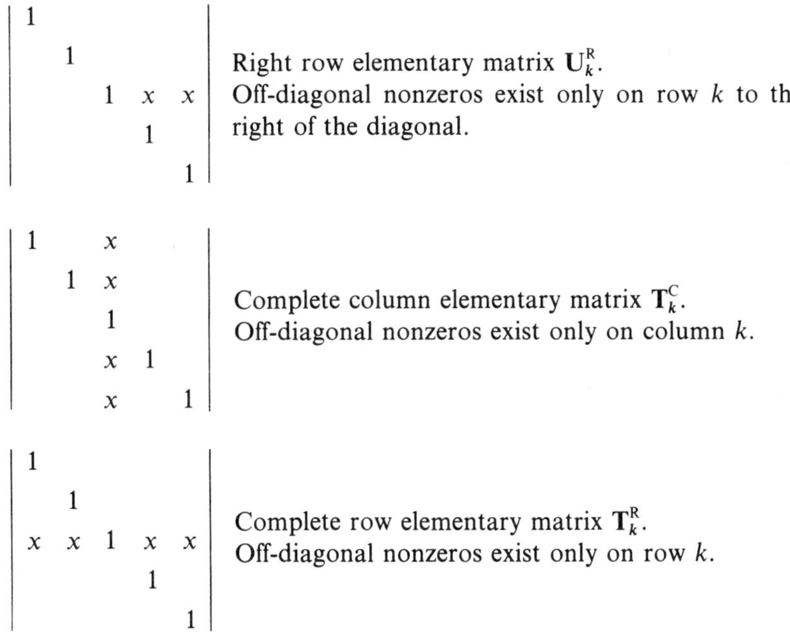

Right row elementary matrix $\mathbf{U}_k^R$. Off-diagonal nonzeros exist only on row k to the right of the diagonal.

Complete column elementary matrix $\mathbf{T}_k^C$. Off-diagonal nonzeros exist only on column k.

Complete row elementary matrix $\mathbf{T}_k^R$. Off-diagonal nonzeros exist only on row k.

Confusion should not arise between the names of these matrices and terms like "column matrix" (a $n \times 1$ matrix), which is usually called a "column vector". Of course, any of our elementary matrices can be represented in the computer memory by storing just its useful row or column.

2.4. Some properties of elementary matrices

(a) The elementary matrices commute with diagonal elementary matrices in some cases:

$$\mathbf{L}_i^C\mathbf{D}_j = \mathbf{D}_j\mathbf{L}_i^C \quad \text{if} \quad i > j \qquad \mathbf{U}_i^C\mathbf{D}_j = \mathbf{D}_j\mathbf{U}_i^C \quad \text{if} \quad i < j$$

$$\mathbf{L}_i^R\mathbf{D}_j = \mathbf{D}_j\mathbf{L}_i^R \quad \text{if} \quad i < j \qquad \mathbf{U}_i^R\mathbf{D}_j = \mathbf{D}_j\mathbf{U}_i^R \quad \text{if} \quad i > j.$$

(b) Lower and upper column matrices commute in certain cases:

$$\mathbf{L}_i^C\mathbf{U}_j^C = \mathbf{U}_j^C\mathbf{L}_i^C \quad \text{if} \quad i \geqslant j$$

$$\mathbf{L}_i^R\mathbf{U}_j^R = \mathbf{U}_j^R\mathbf{L}_i^R \quad \text{if} \quad i \leqslant j.$$

These products are obtained by superposition of the off-diagonal elements.

(c) Complete column or row matrices are obtained as products between incomplete column or row matrices:

$$\mathbf{L}_k^C \mathbf{U}_k^C = \mathbf{U}_k^C \mathbf{L}_k^C = \mathbf{T}_k^C$$

$$\mathbf{L}_k^R \mathbf{U}_k^R = \mathbf{U}_k^R \mathbf{L}_k^R = \mathbf{T}_k^R,$$

where the products are obtained by superposition of the off-diagonal elements.

(d) The inverse of any of the elementary matrices, except $\mathbf{D}_k$, is obtained by reversing the algebraic signs of the off-diagonal elements. The inverse of $\mathbf{D}_k$ involves only the reciprocal of $(D_k)_{kk}$.

(e) Products of the following forms are calculated by simple superposition of the off-diagonal elements.

$$\mathbf{L}_i^C \mathbf{L}_j^C \quad \text{if} \quad i < j$$

$$\mathbf{L}_i^R \mathbf{L}_j^R \quad \text{if} \quad i < j$$

$$\mathbf{U}_i^C \mathbf{U}_j^C \quad \text{if} \quad i > j$$

$$\mathbf{U}_i^R \mathbf{U}_j^R \quad \text{if} \quad i > j$$

2.5. Some properties of triangular matrices

(a) The product of two lower triangular matrices is a lower triangular matrix. As a consequence, the product of any number of lower triangular matrices is a lower triangular matrix. If all the factor matrices are unit diagonal, then the resulting matrix is also unit diagonal. A similar property holds for upper triangular matrices.

(b) By Property 2.4(e), any lower triangular unit diagonal matrix $\mathbf{L}$ can be written as the product of $n - 1$ elementary matrices of either the lower column or the left row type:

$$\mathbf{L} = \mathbf{L}_1^C \mathbf{L}_2^C \ldots \mathbf{L}_{n-1}^C$$

$$\mathbf{L} = \mathbf{L}_2^R \mathbf{L}_3^R \ldots \mathbf{L}_n^R,$$

where the off-diagonal elements of $\mathbf{L}_i^C$ are those of column i of $\mathbf{L}$, and the off-diagonal elements of $\mathbf{L}_i^R$ are those of row i of $\mathbf{L}$. The following examples illustrate this point for the case $n = 4$:

$$\mathbf{L} = \begin{vmatrix} 1 & & & \\ a & 1 & & \\ b & c & 1 & \\ d & e & f & 1 \end{vmatrix} = \begin{vmatrix} 1 & & & \\ a & 1 & & \\ b & & 1 & \\ d & & & 1 \end{vmatrix} \begin{vmatrix} 1 & & & \\ & 1 & & \\ & c & 1 & \\ & e & & 1 \end{vmatrix} \begin{vmatrix} 1 & & & \\ & 1 & & \\ & & 1 & \\ & & f & 1 \end{vmatrix}$$

$$\mathbf{L} = \begin{vmatrix} 1 & & & \\ a & 1 & & \\ b & c & 1 & \\ d & e & f & 1 \end{vmatrix} = \begin{vmatrix} 1 & & & \\ a & 1 & & \\ & & 1 & \\ & & & 1 \end{vmatrix} \begin{vmatrix} 1 & & & \\ & 1 & & \\ b & c & 1 & \\ & & & 1 \end{vmatrix} \begin{vmatrix} 1 & & & \\ & 1 & & \\ & & 1 & \\ d & e & f & 1 \end{vmatrix}$$

As a result we can consider that **L** is a *table of factors* (Tinney and Walker, 1967) representing either the set of matrices $\mathbf{L}_i^C$ or the set of matrices $\mathbf{L}_i^R$ stored in compact form. Note that these factors do not commute.

(c) The inverse of a lower triangular unit diagonal matrix **L** is trivial to obtain. By Property 2.5(b) we have, either

$$\mathbf{L}^{-1} = (\mathbf{L}_{n-1}^C)^{-1} \ldots (\mathbf{L}_2^C)^{-1}(\mathbf{L}_1^C)^{-1}$$

or

$$\mathbf{L}^{-1} = (\mathbf{L}_n^R)^{-1} \ldots (\mathbf{L}_3^R)^{-1}(\mathbf{L}_2^R)^{-1}$$

Now, by Property 2.4(d), the inverses $(\mathbf{L}_i^C)^{-1}$ or $(\mathbf{L}_i^R)^{-1}$ are identical to $\mathbf{L}_i^C$ or $\mathbf{L}_i^R$, respectively, with the algebraic signs of the off-diagonal elements reversed. The computation of $\mathbf{L}^{-1}$ is thus straightforward using any of the two expressions, and involves only multiplications and additions. As a consequence of this property and Property 2.5(a), we know that $\mathbf{L}^{-1}$ is also a lower triangular unit diagonal matrix.

(d) The product of $\mathbf{L}^{-1}$ with another matrix (or vector) can be calculated if **L** is available, without ever calculating $\mathbf{L}^{-1}$ explicitly. For this purpose, the given matrix (or vector) is multiplied by the factors $(\mathbf{L}_i^C)^{-1}$ or $(\mathbf{L}_i^R)^{-1}$ into which $\mathbf{L}^{-1}$ has been decomposed, in the convenient order. These factors, by Property 2.4(d), are obtained directly from the columns or rows of **L** by reversing the signs of the off-diagonal elements. As an example of this property, we show two ways of pre-multiplying a column vector by the inverse of the matrix **L** given in 2.5(b):

$$\begin{vmatrix} 1 & & & \\ a & 1 & & \\ b & c & 1 & \\ d & e & f & 1 \end{vmatrix}^{-1} \begin{vmatrix} p \\ q \\ r \\ s \end{vmatrix} =$$

$$\begin{vmatrix} 1 & & & \\ & 1 & & \\ & & 1 & \\ & & -f & 1 \end{vmatrix} \begin{vmatrix} 1 & & & \\ & 1 & & \\ & -c & 1 & \\ & -e & & 1 \end{vmatrix} \begin{vmatrix} 1 & & & \\ -a & 1 & & \\ -b & & 1 & \\ -d & & & 1 \end{vmatrix} \begin{vmatrix} p \\ q \\ r \\ s \end{vmatrix}$$

$$\begin{vmatrix} 1 & & & \\ a & 1 & & \\ b & c & 1 & \\ d & e & f & 1 \end{vmatrix}^{-1} \begin{vmatrix} p \\ q \\ r \\ s \end{vmatrix} =$$

$$\begin{vmatrix} 1 & & & \\ & 1 & & \\ & & 1 & \\ -d & -e & -f & 1 \end{vmatrix} \begin{vmatrix} 1 & & & \\ & 1 & & \\ -b & -c & 1 & \\ & & & 1 \end{vmatrix} \begin{vmatrix} 1 & & & \\ -a & 1 & & \\ & & 1 & \\ & & & 1 \end{vmatrix} \begin{vmatrix} p \\ q \\ r \\ s \end{vmatrix}$$

One important consequence of this property is that additional storage for $\mathbf{L}^{-1}$ is not required in the computer memory. It is sufficient to store **L**.

(e) An upper triangular unit diagonal matrix **U** can be written as a product of $n - 1$ elementary matrices of either the upper column or right row type:

$$\mathbf{U} = \mathbf{U}_n^C \mathbf{U}_{n-1}^C \ldots \mathbf{U}_2^C$$

$$\mathbf{U} = \mathbf{U}_{n-1}^R \mathbf{U}_{n-2}^R \ldots \mathbf{U}_1^R$$

where the off-diagonal elements of $\mathbf{U}_i^C$ are those of column i of **U**, and the off-diagonal elements of $\mathbf{U}_i^R$ are those of row i of **U**. As in 2.5(b), **U** can be considered as a table of factors.

(f) The inverse $\mathbf{U}^{-1}$ of an upper triangular unit diagonal matrix can be calculated in either of the following ways:

$$\mathbf{U}^{-1} = (\mathbf{U}_2^C)^{-1} \ldots (\mathbf{U}_{n-1}^C)^{-1} (\mathbf{U}_n^C)^{-1}$$

$$\mathbf{U}^{-1} = (\mathbf{U}_1^R)^{-1} \ldots (\mathbf{U}_{n-2}^R)^{-1} (\mathbf{U}_{n-1}^R)^{-1}$$

$\mathbf{U}^{-1}$ is also upper triangular unit diagonal and its computation involves the same table of factors used to represent **U**, with the signs of the off-diagonal elements reversed, as was explained in 2.5(c) for **L** matrices.

(g) The product of $\mathbf{U}^{-1}$ with another matrix or vector can be obtained if **U** is available using a procedure similar to that explained in 2.5(d) for **L** matrices. The same important consequence as in 2.5(d) holds in this case: additional storage is not required for $\mathbf{U}^{-1}$.

2.6. Permutation matrices

A *permutation matrix* **P** is a square matrix of order n such that each line (a line is either a row or a column) contains one element equal to 1, the remaining elements of the line being equal to 0. The simplest permutation matrix is **I**, the identity matrix. It is very easy to verify that the product of any permutation matrix **P** and its transpose $\mathbf{P}^T$ is equal to **I**. Thus:

$$\mathbf{P}^{-1} = \mathbf{P}^T$$

and **P** is an orthogonal matrix. If a matrix with n rows is pre-multiplied by **P**, its rows are permuted. Similarly, the n columns of a matrix are permuted by post-multiplication with a permutation matrix.

P can be stored in the computer memory as a vector of integers: the integer at position i is the column index of the unit element of row i of **P**.

2.7. Gauss elimination by columns

Gauss elimination is a well known procedure for solving linear equations. The elimination by columns is the most popular version of the algorithm and will be described first. On the other hand, for a sparse matrix stored in row-wise format, elimination by rows is more efficient. This version will be described in the following section.

For simplicity we will assume that **A**, the matrix of the linear system (2.1), is already prepared for elimination, in the sense that the diagonal elements can be used directly as pivots in the same order in which they are given. In general, pivots are selected among the nonzero elements of **A** and brought to the main diagonal by means of row and column permutations, the selection being done in such a way that sparsity is preserved and numerical stability is ensured. The question of pivot selection or *ordering* is examined in Chapters 4 and 5, but assumed inexistent in the present chapter.

Consider the system (2.1). Gauss elimination by columns consists of n steps. The purpose of the kth step is to eliminate all the nonzero elements of the matrix which lie on column k below the diagonal. At the first step, the nonzeros of column 1 of $\mathbf{A} \equiv \mathbf{A}^{(1)}$ are eliminated by subtracting convenient multiples of row 1, element by element, from each of the remaining rows with a nonzero in column 1. The element A_{11}, belonging to the row that is going to be subtracted from other rows (row 1 in this case) and to the column that will be eliminated (column 1 in this case), is called the *pivot* and assumed to be nonzero. Previous to the elimination, row 1 is normalized by dividing all its nonzero elements by the pivot. A matrix $\mathbf{A}^{(2)}$ is obtained, with $A_{i1}^{(2)} = 0$ for $i > 1$ and $A_{11}^{(2)} = 1$.

At the second step, $A_{22}^{(2)}$ is selected to be the pivot. Again we assume $A_{22}^{(2)} \neq 0$. Row 2 is normalized and all nonzeros of the second column below the diagonal are eliminated by subtraction of convenient multiples of the normalized second row from the corresponding rows. Note that, since $A_{21}^{(2)} = 0$, the elements of column 1 will not be affected. A matrix $\mathbf{A}^{(3)}$ is obtained with $A_{i1}^{(3)} = 0$ for $i > 1$, $A_{i2}^{(3)} = 0$ for $i > 2$, and $A_{11}^{(3)} = A_{22}^{(3)} = 1$. In other words, $\mathbf{A}^{(3)}$ is upper triangular unit diagonal in its first two columns.

At the beginning of the kth step we have a matrix $\mathbf{A}^{(k)}$ with zeros on its first $k - 1$ columns below the diagonal and ones on the $k - 1$ initial positions of the diagonal. The following example shows $\mathbf{A}^{(k)}$ for the case $n = 6$, $k = 3$:

$$\mathbf{A}^{(3)} = \begin{array}{c|cccccc|} & 1 & 2 & 3 & 4 & 5 & 6 \\ 1 & 1 & x & x & x & x & x \\ 2 & & 1 & x & x & x & x \\ 3 & & & x & x & x & x \\ 4 & & & x & x & x & x \\ 5 & & & x & x & x & x \\ 6 & & & x & x & x & x \end{array} \tag{2.14}$$

At the kth step, $A_{kk}^{(k)}$ is selected to be the pivot. Row k is normalized and the elements on column k below the diagonal of $\mathbf{A}^{(k)}$ are eliminated by subtraction of convenient multiples of the normalized row k from all those rows which have a nonzero in column k below the diagonal. The matrix $\mathbf{A}^{(k+1)}$ is obtained with zeros on its first k columns below the diagonal and ones on the first k positions of the diagonal.

This process is continued until, at the end of step n the matrix $\mathbf{A}^{(n+1)}$ is obtained, which has only zeros below the diagonal and ones on the diagonal, and is thus upper triangular unit diagonal.

A convenient notation for the algorithm is obtained by using the elementary matrices $\mathbf{D}_k$ and $\mathbf{L}_k^{\mathrm{C}}$ of Section 2.3. The kth step of Gauss elimination by columns is equivalent to pre-multiplication of $\mathbf{A}^{(k)}$ by $(\mathbf{L}_k^{\mathrm{C}})^{-1}\mathbf{D}_k^{-1}$:

$$\mathbf{A}^{(k+1)} = (\mathbf{L}_k^{\mathrm{C}})^{-1}\mathbf{D}_k^{-1}\mathbf{A}^{(k)} \tag{2.15}$$

where

$$\begin{aligned} (D_k)_{kk} &= A_{kk}^{(k)} \\ (L_k^{\mathrm{C}})_{ik} &= A_{ik}^{(k)} \quad \text{for } i > k \end{aligned} \tag{2.16}$$

and $\mathbf{A}^{(1)} = \mathbf{A}$. Note that by property 2.4(d) the off-diagonal elements of $(\mathbf{L}_k^{\mathrm{C}})^{-1}$ are those of $\mathbf{L}_k^{\mathrm{C}}$ with their signs reversed, i.e. $-A_{ik}^{(k)}$.

Therefore, if for the sake of completeness we add a trivial pre-multiplication of $\mathbf{D}_n^{-1}\mathbf{A}^{(n)}$ by $(\mathbf{L}_n^{\mathrm{C}})^{-1} \equiv \mathbf{I}$ (the identity matrix) to obtain $\mathbf{A}^{(n+1)}$, we have:

$$(\mathbf{L}_n^{\mathrm{C}})^{-1}\mathbf{D}_n^{-1} \ldots (\mathbf{L}_2^{\mathrm{C}})^{-1}\mathbf{D}_2^{-1}(\mathbf{L}_1^{\mathrm{C}})^{-1}\mathbf{D}_1^{-1}\mathbf{A} = \mathbf{U}, \tag{2.17}$$

where $\mathbf{U} \equiv \mathbf{A}^{(n+1)}$ is upper triangular unit diagonal, with

$$U_{kj} = (D_k)_{kk}^{-1} A_{kj}^{(k)} \equiv A_{kj}^{(k+1)} \qquad \text{for } j > k. \tag{2.18}$$

From this expression the factorized form of $\mathbf{A}$ is obtained:

$$\mathbf{A} = \mathbf{LU} \tag{2.19}$$

where

$$\mathbf{L} = \mathbf{D}_1 \mathbf{L}_1^{\mathrm{C}} \mathbf{D}_2 \mathbf{L}_2^{\mathrm{C}} \ldots \mathbf{D}_n \mathbf{L}_n^{\mathrm{C}} \tag{2.20}$$

is a lower triangular matrix (by Property 2.5(a)) with nonzero diagonal elements. Since the products in Equation (2.20) are calculated by superposition, the elements of $\mathbf{L}$ can easily be obtained from Equation (2.16):

$$L_{ik} = A_{ik}^{(k)} \qquad \text{for } i \geqslant k \tag{2.21}$$

Using Equations (2.18) and (2.21), the operations performed on $\mathbf{A}^{(k)}$ to obtain $\mathbf{A}^{(k+1)}$ can be indicated

$$A_{ij}^{(k+1)} = A_{ij}^{(k)} - L_{ik} U_{kj} \qquad i, j > k \tag{2.22}$$

so that the complete expression of the elements of $\mathbf{A}^{(k)}$ can be written:

$$A_{ij}^{(k)} = A_{ij} - \sum_{m=1}^{k} L_{im} U_{mj} \qquad i, j > k \tag{2.23}$$

The *elimination form of the inverse* is obtained from Equation (2.19):

$$\mathbf{A}^{-1} = \mathbf{U}^{-1} \mathbf{L}^{-1} \tag{2.24}$$

In practice, the calculation of $\mathbf{U}^{-1}$ and $\mathbf{L}^{-1}$ is never explicitly made. The results of the elimination are usually overwritten on the storage initially occupied by $\mathbf{A}$, in the form of a table which represents two different matrices and is sometimes called a *table of factors* (Tinney and Walker, 1967):

$$\begin{matrix} (D_1)_{11}^{-1} & U_{12} & U_{13} \ldots \\ (L_1^{\mathrm{C}})_{21} & (D_2)_{22}^{-1} & U_{23} \\ (L_1^{\mathrm{C}})_{31} & (L_2^{\mathrm{C}})_{32} & (D_3)_{33}^{-1} \\ \vdots & & \end{matrix} \tag{2.25}$$

First, let us examine how this table is formed. By Equation (2.16), the lower triangle is formed simply by leaving the elements $A_{ik}^{(k)}$ where they are just before elimination; these elements are precisely those which will be eliminated in step k. The diagonal of the table is formed by leaving, at each step k, the reciprocal of the diagonal element of row k. The reciprocal is obtained at the time that row k is normalized, because it is computationally faster to calculate the reciprocal and to multiply all row elements by it, than to divide the row elements by the diagonal element. Besides, it is convenient to have the reciprocals directly available when the table is used for back-substitution. In the upper triangle, the elements of **U** are left as they are obtained in the course of the elimination, as indicated by Equation (2.18). A numerical example of a table of factors is given in Section 2.15.

Now, let us examine how the table of factors is used. Its most common application is the solution of System (2.1) by means of:

$$\mathbf{x} = \mathbf{A}^{-1}\mathbf{b} \tag{2.26}$$

which, using (2.24), is written:

$$\mathbf{x} = \mathbf{U}^{-1}\mathbf{L}^{-1}\mathbf{b} \tag{2.27}$$

From Equation (2.20) we have:

$$\mathbf{L}^{-1} = (\mathbf{L}_n^{\mathrm{C}})^{-1}\mathbf{D}_n^{-1} \ldots (\mathbf{L}_2^{\mathrm{C}})^{-1}\mathbf{D}_2^{-1}(\mathbf{L}_1^{\mathrm{C}})^{-1}\mathbf{D}_1^{-1} \tag{2.28}$$

The matrices $\mathbf{D}_k^{-1}$ are directly available from the table. The matrices $(\mathbf{L}_k^{\mathrm{C}})^{-1}$ are also directly available, because, by Property 2.4(d), their off-diagonal elements are those of $\mathbf{L}_k^{\mathrm{C}}$ with the signs reversed. Thus, **b** can easily be pre-multiplied by $\mathbf{L}^{-1}$ using the table, a procedure usually called *forward substitution*. In order to obtain **x** we need to pre-multiply the result by $\mathbf{U}^{-1}$. For this purpose, we consider **U** to be equal to the product of n upper column elementary matrices:

$$\mathbf{U} = \mathbf{U}_n^{\mathrm{C}} \ldots \mathbf{U}_2^{\mathrm{C}}\mathbf{U}_1^{\mathrm{C}} \tag{2.29}$$

By Property 2.4(e), this product is obtained by superposition; therefore, the elements of the matrices $\mathbf{U}_k^{\mathrm{C}}$ are those stored in the upper triangle of the table (2.25). We have:

$$\mathbf{U}^{-1} = (\mathbf{U}_1^{\mathrm{C}})^{-1}(\mathbf{U}_2^{\mathrm{C}})^{-1} \ldots (\mathbf{U}_n^{\mathrm{C}})^{-1} \tag{2.30}$$

and the product of $\mathbf{U}^{-1}$ and $\mathbf{L}^{-1}\mathbf{b}$ can be obtained because the off-diagonal elements of $(\mathbf{U}_k^{\mathrm{C}})^{-1}$ are those of $\mathbf{U}_k^{\mathrm{C}}$, stored in the table, with their signs reversed (Property 2.4(d)). This procedure is usually called *backward substitution*. Forward and backward substitution are discussed in more detail in Section 2.13.

The same procedure just described can be used to pre-multiply any matrix by $\mathbf{A}^{-1}$. It is also useful to recall that the factors of which **L** and **U** are composed are stored in the table. Therefore, the product of $\mathbf{A} = \mathbf{LU}$ by any vector or matrix can be obtained using the table. It is even possible to use the table for solving certain two-way hybrid systems where the vector of unknowns is $(b_1, b_2, \ldots, b_k, x_{k+1}, \ldots, x_n)$ rather than **x**. Such systems have been considered by Tinney and Walker (1967).

If we want to solve $\mathbf{Ax} = \mathbf{b}$ for only one or a few right-hand vectors **b**, we do not need to form the complete table of factors; we can simply augment **A** by **b**, perform all elimination operations on the augmented matrix, and finally perform the backward substitution on the resulting column vector.

The form (2.5) can be obtained from Equation (2.19) if $\mathbf{L}' = \mathbf{L}\mathbf{D}^{-1}$, where $\mathbf{L}'$ results lower triangular with unit diagonal if **D** is a diagonal matrix of which the elements are, precisely, the diagonal elements of **L**. From Equation (2.20) we obtain:

$$\mathbf{D} = \mathbf{D}_1\mathbf{D}_2 \ldots \mathbf{D}_n \tag{2.31}$$

and the elements of **D** are the reciprocals of the diagonal elements of the table (2.25). This result is particularly important when **A** is symmetric, because then $\mathbf{L}' = \mathbf{U}^{\mathrm{T}}$ and

$$\mathbf{A} = \mathbf{U}^{\mathrm{T}}\mathbf{D}\mathbf{U}. \tag{2.32}$$

In this case, it is not necessary to compute the lower triangle of the table (2.25), which is just the transpose of the upper triangle. Elimination is restricted to the upper triangle and main diagonal, and almost half the storage and labour are saved. Of course, the actual procedure poses certain algorithmic difficulties, mainly due to the fact that the elements of the lower triangle of **A**, which must be eliminated, are not represented in the computer memory. This point is examined at length in Section 7.23 for matrices stored in sparse row-wise format.

2.8. Gauss elimination by rows

For sparse matrices stored in row-wise format the elimination by rows is much more efficient than by columns. The same result is obtained and the same number of operations is performed in both cases. The improved efficiency is due to the fact that the elements of the matrix are used in the natural order in which they are stored. The Gauss elimination of a matrix **A** by rows is performed in n steps. At the beginning of the kth step, we have a matrix $\mathbf{A}^{(k)}$ with zeros in rows 1 to $k-1$ to the left of the diagonal and ones in positions 1 to $k-1$ of the diagonal. The following example illustrates the case $n = 6$, $k = 4$:

$$\mathbf{A}^{(4)} = \begin{array}{c|cccccc|} & 1 & 2 & 3 & 4 & 5 & 6 \\ 1 & 1 & x & x & x & x & x \\ 2 & & 1 & x & x & x & x \\ 3 & & & 1 & x & x & x \\ 4 & x & x & x & x & x & x \\ 5 & x & x & x & x & x & x \\ 6 & x & x & x & x & x & x \end{array} \tag{2.33}$$

The kth step consists of the elimination of the nonzeros of row k to the left of the diagonal by subtraction of convenient multiples of each of the rows 1 to $k - 1$, in that order. Row k is then normalized by dividing all its elements by the diagonal element. Let us examine in more detail the three initial steps of this algorithm.

At step 1, we divide the elements of row 1 of $\mathbf{A}$ by the diagonal element (1, 1).

At step 2, we eliminate element (2, 1) by subtracting a multiple of the first row from the second. Then, we normalize the second row by dividing all its elements by the diagonal element (2, 2).

At step 3, we eliminate the element in position (3, 1) by subtracting a multiple of the first row from the third. Then we eliminate the element (3, 2) by subtracting a multiple of the second row from the third row, and finally we divide the third row by its diagonal element. And so on.

It can easily be verified that this procedure produces exactly the same result as elimination by columns (Tinney and Walker, 1967), which was described in Section 2.7. For example, all the elements of row 1 to the right of the diagonal are obtained by normalization of row 1 in both algorithms. All the elements of row 2 to the right of the diagonal are obtained, in both cases, by subtraction of the *same* multiple of row 1 and normalization of the derived row 2. All the elements of row 3 to the right of the diagonal are obtained, in both cases, by subtraction of the *same* multiples of rows 1 and 2 (which are identical in both cases) from row 3 and subsequent normalization of row 3. The only difference between the two algorithms is the order in which the eliminations are performed, but the same upper triangular unit diagonal matrix $\mathbf{U}$ of Equation (2.17) is finally obtained in both cases.

Each of the eliminations performed by the row algorithm in step k is equivalent to pre-multiplication by a left row elementary matrix $(\mathbf{L}_k^{\mathrm{R}})^{-1}$, while each normalization is equivalent to pre-multiplication by a diagonal elementary matrix $\mathbf{D}_k^{-1}$. Since the product of all $(\mathbf{L}_k^{\mathrm{R}})^{-1}$ and $\mathbf{D}_k^{-1}$ is a lower triangular matrix $\mathbf{L}'$, we can formally represent the Gauss elimination by rows as follows:

$$\mathbf{L}'\mathbf{A} = \mathbf{U} \tag{2.34}$$

Comparing this expression with Equation (2.17) we obtain

$$(\mathbf{L}')^{-1} = \mathbf{L} \tag{2.35}$$

We have therefore obtained the same triangularization $\mathbf{A} = \mathbf{LU}$ as in the column algorithm. And, again, the storage of $\mathbf{L}$ and $\mathbf{U}$ is obtained as a table of factors (see (2.25)), simply by leaving the elements in the lower triangle in their final form just before elimination, those in the upper triangle as and where they are obtained, and the inverses of the final diagonal elements just before normalization on the diagonal.

2.9. Gauss–Jordan elimination

The algorithm for Gauss–Jordan elimination by columns is similar to that for Gauss elimination by columns, the main difference being that, at the beginning of step k, the matrix $\mathbf{A}^{(k)}$ has zeros in it columns 1 to $k-1$ both above and below the diagonal. The following example shows $\mathbf{A}^{(k)}$ for the case $n=6$, $k=3$:

$$\mathbf{A}^{(3)} = \begin{array}{c|cccccc|} & 1 & 2 & 3 & 4 & 5 & 6 \\ \hline 1 & 1 & & x & x & x & x \\ 2 & & 1 & x & x & x & x \\ 3 & & & x & x & x & x \\ 4 & & & x & x & x & x \\ 5 & & & x & x & x & x \\ 6 & & & x & x & x & x \end{array} \tag{2.36}$$

The kth step consists of the elimination of the nonzeros on column k of $\mathbf{A}^{(k)}$ *both above and below the diagonal.* Row k is first normalized by dividing all its elements by the diagonal element. Then, convenient multiples of the normalized row k are subtracted from all those rows which have a nonzero on column k either above or below the diagonal. The matrix $\mathbf{A}^{(k+1)}$ is thus obtained with zeros on its k initial columns. This process is continued until, at the end of step n, the identity matrix $\mathbf{A}^{(n+1)} \equiv \mathbf{I}$ is obtained. The kth step of Gauss–Jordan elimination by columns is equivalent to pre-multiplication of $\mathbf{A}^{(k)}$ by $\mathbf{D}_k^{-1}$ and by the complete column elementary matrix $(\mathbf{T}_k^{\mathrm{C}})^{-1}$:

$$\mathbf{A}^{(k+1)} = (\mathbf{T}_k^{\mathrm{C}})^{-1}\mathbf{D}_k^{-1}\mathbf{A}^{(k)} \tag{2.37}$$

where $\mathbf{A}^{(1)} \equiv \mathbf{A}$ and:

$$(D_k)_{kk} = A_{kk}^{(k)} \tag{2.38a}$$

$$(T_k^{\mathrm{C}})_{ik} = A_{ik}^{(k)} \qquad \text{for all } i \neq k. \tag{2.38b}$$

Thus, we have:

$$(\mathbf{T}_n^{\mathrm{C}})^{-1}\mathbf{D}_n^{-1} \ldots (\mathbf{T}_2^{\mathrm{C}})^{-1}\mathbf{D}_2^{-1}(\mathbf{T}_1^{\mathrm{C}})^{-1}\mathbf{D}_1^{-1}\mathbf{A} = \mathbf{I}. \tag{2.39}$$

The factorized form of $\mathbf{A}$ is

$$\mathbf{A} = \mathbf{D}_1\mathbf{T}_1^{\mathrm{C}}\mathbf{D}_2\mathbf{T}_2^{\mathrm{C}} \ldots \mathbf{D}_n\mathbf{T}_n^{\mathrm{C}}, \tag{2.40}$$

and the *product form of the inverse* in terms of column matrices is:

$$\mathbf{A}^{-1} = (\mathbf{T}_n^{\mathrm{C}})^{-1}\mathbf{D}_n^{-1} \ldots (\mathbf{T}_2^{\mathrm{C}})^{-1}\mathbf{D}_2^{-1}(\mathbf{T}_1^{\mathrm{C}})^{-1}\mathbf{D}_1^{-1}. \tag{2.41}$$

The close relationship between this expression and the elimination form of the inverse, Expression (2.24), will be discussed in Section 2.10. The results of the elimination are usually recorded as a table of factors:

$$\begin{matrix} (D_1)_{1\,1}^{-1} & (T_2^{\mathrm{C}})_{1\,2} & (T_3^{\mathrm{C}})_{1\,3} \cdots \\ (T_1^{\mathrm{C}})_{2\,1} & (D_2)_{2\,2}^{-1} & (T_3^{\mathrm{C}})_{2\,3} \\ (T_1^{\mathrm{C}})_{3\,1} & (T_2^{\mathrm{C}})_{3\,2} & (D_3)_{3\,3}^{-1} \\ & \vdots & \end{matrix} \tag{2.42}$$

By Equation (2.38), this table is formed simply by leaving each off-diagonal $A_{ik}^{(k)}$ where it is obtained. The diagonal is obtained, as in Gauss elimination, by storing the reciprocal of the diagonal elements used to normalize each row. The lower triangle and diagonal of this table are thus identical to those of Gauss table. Expressions (2.40) and (2.41) indicate how to use the table (2.42). When solving linear equations by means of $\mathbf{x} = \mathbf{A}^{-1}\mathbf{b}$, Equation (2.41) is used, with the matrices $(\mathbf{T}_k^{\mathrm{C}})^{-1}$ obtained from the table by reversing the signs of the off-diagonal elements of column k (Property 2.4(d)). The matrices $\mathbf{D}_k^{-1}$ are directly available from the table. The product of $\mathbf{A}$ with any matrix or vector can also be computed using the table, as indicated by Equation (2.40).

Gauss–Jordan elimination can also be performed by rows. The version by columns requires the addition of multiples of row k to all other rows in order to cancel the off-diagonal elements of column k. This process can be understood conceptually as the construction of new equations which are linear combinations of the original ones. On the other hand, in Gauss–Jordan elimination by rows, we add multiples of *column* k to all other columns, in such a way that the off-diagonal elements of *row* k become zero. This process can be viewed as the construction of new *unknowns* which are linear combinations of the original ones and which satisfy linear equations with some zero coefficients. Alternatively, we can forget about the system of linear equations and view the row algorithm as the triangularization of $\mathbf{A}^{\mathrm{T}}$, the transpose of $\mathbf{A}$, by columns. Doing this, we obtain the equivalent of Expression (2.41):

$$(\mathbf{A}^{\mathrm{T}})^{-1} = (\mathbf{T}_n'^{\mathrm{C}})^{-1}(\mathbf{D}_n')^{-1} \ldots (\mathbf{T}_2'^{\mathrm{C}})^{-1}(\mathbf{D}_2')^{-1}(\mathbf{T}_1'^{\mathrm{C}})^{-1}(\mathbf{D}_1')^{-1}, \tag{2.43}$$

which by transposition and using $(\mathbf{A}^{\mathrm{T}})^{-1} = (\mathbf{A}^{-1})^{\mathrm{T}}$ yields:

$$\mathbf{A}^{-1} = (\mathbf{D}_1')^{-1}(\mathbf{T}_1'^{\mathrm{R}})^{-1}(\mathbf{D}_2')^{-1}(\mathbf{T}_2'^{\mathrm{R}})^{-1} \ldots (\mathbf{D}_n')^{-1}(\mathbf{T}_n'^{\mathrm{R}})^{-1} \tag{2.44}$$

Equation (2.44) is the product form of the inverse in terms of row matrices. The elimination by rows is equivalent to multiplying $\mathbf{A}$ *from the right* by Expression (2.44). The nontrivial elements of the matrices of Expression

(2.44) are recorded as a table of factors in the usual way, and the table can be used to solve linear equations or to multiply either $\mathbf{A}$ or $\mathbf{A}^{-1}$ by any matrix or vector.

2.10. Relation between the elimination form of the inverse and the product form of the inverse

From the preceding section it should be clear that Gauss–Jordan elimination by columns can be performed equally well if we first eliminate all nonzeros from the lower triangle of $\mathbf{A}$, and then all nonzeros from the upper triangle of $\mathbf{A}$. In fact, when we start at the upper left-hand corner of $\mathbf{A}$, we can eliminate lower and upper portions of columns in any order, provided only that upper portions are eliminated in order, lower portions are also eliminated in order, and the upper portion of any column k is eliminated *after* the lower portion of the preceding column. This statement holds true due to the fact that a row $k+1$ is obtained in final form immediately after the lower portions of columns 1 to k have been eliminated and row $k+1$ has been normalized; row $k+1$ can then be used either immediately or at any later stage to eliminate the upper portion of column $k+1$, provided that the upper portions of columns 1 to k have been previously eliminated. These facts can be stated formally using the properties of the elementary matrices (Section 2.4). We use Property 2.4(c) to express $\mathbf{T}_k^C$ as follows:

$$\mathbf{T}_k^C = \mathbf{L}_k^C \mathbf{U}_k^C, \tag{2.45}$$

where $\mathbf{U}_k^C$ is formed with the upper part of $\mathbf{T}_k^C$, and $\mathbf{L}_k^C$ with the lower part of $\mathbf{T}_k^C$, and thus $\mathbf{L}_k^C$ is identical to Equation (2.16); from Equation (2.39) we get:

$$(\mathbf{U}_n^C)^{-1}(\mathbf{L}_n^C)^{-1}\mathbf{D}_n^{-1} \ldots (\mathbf{U}_2^C)^{-1}(\mathbf{L}_2^C)^{-1}\mathbf{D}_2^{-1}(\mathbf{U}_1^C)^{-1}(\mathbf{L}_1^C)^{-1}\mathbf{D}_1^{-1}\mathbf{A} = \mathbf{I} \tag{2.46}$$

Now, by Properties 2.4(a) and 2.4(b) we know that $(\mathbf{U}_i^C)^{-1}$, which is an upper column elementary matrix, commutes with any $\mathbf{D}_j^{-1}$ or $(\mathbf{L}_k^C)^{-1}$ when $i < j, k$; therefore, Equation (2.46) can be written:

$$[(\mathbf{U}_n^C)^{-1} \ldots (\mathbf{U}_2^C)^{-1}(\mathbf{U}_1^C)^{-1}][(\mathbf{L}_n^C)^{-1}\mathbf{D}_n^{-1} \ldots (\mathbf{L}_2^C)^{-1}\mathbf{D}_2^{-1}(\mathbf{L}_1^C)^{-1}\mathbf{D}_1^{-1}\mathbf{A}] = \mathbf{I}. \tag{2.47}$$

The second square parenthesis in Equation (2.47) is equal to $\mathbf{U}$ by Equation (2.17). Therefore:

$$(\mathbf{U}_n^C)^{-1} \ldots (\mathbf{U}_2^C)^{-1}(\mathbf{U}_1^C)^{-1} = \mathbf{U}^{-1} \tag{2.48}$$

Equation (2.48) is a factorization of $\mathbf{U}^{-1}$ in terms of the upper column elementary matrices $(\mathbf{U}_k^C)^{-1}$; the products in Equation (2.48) are calculated by superposition (Property 2.4(e)); thus, if the nontrivial columns of the matrices $(\mathbf{U}_k^{\mathrm{C}})^{-1}$ were stored in table form, the resulting array would be identical to the matrix $\mathbf{U}^{-1}$ itself. Now, the upper triangle of the Gauss–Jordan table of factors is formed with the nontrivial columns of the matrices $\mathbf{U}_k^{\mathrm{C}}$, as shown by Equations (2.38) and (2.45); these columns differ from those of the matrices $(\mathbf{U}_k^{\mathrm{C}})^{-1}$ only in the algebraic signs of the off-diagonal elements (Property 2.4(d)). We thus reach the conclusion that the upper triangle of the Gauss–Jordan table is identical to $\mathbf{U}^{-1}$ with all off-diagonal signs reversed. Besides, comparing Equation (2.38b) in the case $i > k$, with Equation (2.16), we conclude that the lower triangle of the Gauss–Jordan table is identical to the lower triangle of $\mathbf{L}$, as for the table of factors of the elimination form of the inverse. These points are illustrated numerically in Section 2.13. We now raise the question as to which of the two tables of factors is sparser, Equation (2.25) for the elimination form of the inverse or Equation (2.42) for the product form of the inverse. Clearly, the comparison is between $\mathbf{U}$ and $\mathbf{U}^{-1}$. The question was investigated by Brayton *et al.* (1970), who found that if the diagonal elements of $\mathbf{A}$ are nonzero, then $\mathbf{U}^{-1}$ will never require less storage than $\mathbf{U}$. This is one of the reasons why Gauss elimination, in any of its forms, is used almost universally for the direct solution of linear equations.

2.11. Cholesky factorization of a symmetric positive definite matrix

When $\mathbf{A}$ is symmetric positive definite, there exists a unique decomposition

$$\mathbf{A} = \mathbf{U}^{\mathrm{T}}\mathbf{U} \tag{2.49}$$

where $\mathbf{U}$ is upper triangular with positive diagonal elements (Property 7 of Section 2.2). In this section we examine how Factorization (2.49) can be obtained directly. We also deduce some bounds which play an important role in the error analysis of symmetric elimination. Let us write the given matrix $\mathbf{A}$ in the partitioned form:

$$\mathbf{A} = \begin{vmatrix} \alpha & \mathbf{b}^{\mathrm{T}} \\ \mathbf{b} & \mathbf{B} \end{vmatrix} \tag{2.50}$$

where $\alpha \equiv A_{11} > 0$ and $\mathbf{B}$ is symmetric of order $n-1$.

Now, $\mathbf{A} \equiv \mathbf{A}^{(1)}$ can be factorized as follows:

$$\mathbf{A} = \begin{vmatrix} \alpha^{1/2} & \mathbf{0}^{\mathrm{T}} \\ \mathbf{b}/\alpha^{1/2} & \mathbf{I} \end{vmatrix} \begin{vmatrix} 1 & \mathbf{0}^{\mathrm{T}} \\ \mathbf{0} & \mathbf{A}^{(2)} \end{vmatrix} \begin{vmatrix} \alpha^{1/2} & \mathbf{b}^{\mathrm{T}}/\alpha^{1/2} \\ \mathbf{0} & \mathbf{I} \end{vmatrix} \tag{2.51}$$

where $\mathbf{0}$ is the null column vector, and

$$\mathbf{A}^{(2)} = \mathbf{B} - \frac{\mathbf{b}}{\alpha^{1/2}} \frac{\mathbf{b}^{\mathrm{T}}}{\alpha^{1/2}} \tag{2.52}$$

is a matrix of order $n - 1$.

Clearly, $\mathbf{A}^{(2)}$ is symmetric; we can also prove that it is positive definite. For this purpose, we use the form (2.50) for $\mathbf{A}$ and write Equation (2.6) with:

$$\mathbf{y} = \begin{vmatrix} y_1 \\ \mathbf{z} \end{vmatrix} \tag{2.53}$$

where $\mathbf{z}$ is any non null vector of order $n - 1$. The result is:

$$\mathbf{y}^{\mathrm{T}}\mathbf{A}\mathbf{y} = \alpha y_1^2 + 2y_1\mathbf{z}^{\mathrm{T}}\mathbf{b} + \mathbf{z}^{\mathrm{T}}\mathbf{B}\mathbf{z} > 0 \tag{2.54}$$

If we now take $y_1 = -\mathbf{z}^{\mathrm{T}}\mathbf{b}/\alpha$ and use Equation (2.52) we obtain:

$$\mathbf{z}^{\mathrm{T}}\mathbf{A}^{(2)}\mathbf{z} > 0 \tag{2.55}$$

and since $\mathbf{z}$ is any vector, this proves that $\mathbf{A}^{(2)}$ is positive definite.

Since $\mathbf{A}^{(2)}$ is symmetric positive definite, it can be factorized in the same way as $\mathbf{A}$, Equation (2.51). A symmetric positive definite matrix $\mathbf{A}^{(3)}$ of order $n - 2$ is obtained, which can in turn be factorized. The procedure is repeated until a matrix $\mathbf{A}^{(n)}$ of order 1, a number, is obtained. All the matrices of the sequence $\mathbf{A}^{(1)} \equiv \mathbf{A}, \mathbf{A}^{(2)}, \ldots, \mathbf{A}^{(n)}$ are symmetric positive definite, and $\mathbf{A}^{(k)}$ is of order $n - \mathrm{k} + 1$. At the end of the procedure the following expression is obtained for $\mathbf{A}$:

$$\mathbf{A} = \mathbf{L}_1'^{\mathrm{C}}\mathbf{L}_2'^{\mathrm{C}} \ldots \mathbf{L}_n'^{\mathrm{C}}\mathbf{U}_n'^{\mathrm{R}} \ldots \mathbf{U}_2'^{\mathrm{R}}\mathbf{U}_1'^{\mathrm{R}} \tag{2.56}$$

where $\mathbf{L}_i'^{\mathrm{C}}$ and $\mathbf{U}_i'^{\mathrm{R}}$ are matrices of the type defined in Section 2.3 but with the ith diagonal element positive and in general different from 1, and $\mathbf{L}_i'^{\mathrm{C}} = (\mathbf{U}_i'^{\mathrm{R}})^{\mathrm{T}}$. The details are left to the reader, who will immediately realize that the final form, Equation (2.49), is obtained by simple superposition.

The practical implementation of the Cholesky algorithm for sparse matrices is, however, quite different. It will be discussed later in Section 2.12. The discussion in this section was given because it lends itself to finding bounds for the elements of the matrices $\mathbf{A}^{(k)}$. These bounds are in turn necessary for the error analysis of Cholesky factorization, presented in Chapter 3, and for the justification of the most important property of Cholesky algorithm: that diagonal pivoting is numerically stable for symmetric positive definite matrices.

Let us now find bounds for the absolute values of the elements of the matrices $\mathbf{A}^{(k)}$. By Property 5 of Section 2.2 we know that, since $\mathbf{A}^{(k)}$ is symmetric positive definite:

$$|A_{ij}^{(k)}| \leqslant a_k \qquad \text{for all } i, j \tag{2.57}$$

where a_k is the largest diagonal element of $\mathbf{A}^{(k)}$. Now, from Equation (2.52), it is evident that the diagonal elements of each $\mathbf{A}^{(k)}$, which are all positive by Property 4 of Section 2.2, are constructed by subtracting non-negative numbers from the corresponding diagonal elements of $\mathbf{A}^{(k-1)}$, which are also all positive. Thus (Wilkinson, 1961):

$$a_1 \geqslant a_2 \geqslant \ldots \geqslant a_n, \tag{2.58}$$

where a_k is the largest diagonal element of $\mathbf{A}^{(k)}$. Finally, we may state the fact that $a \equiv a_1$ is the upper bound for all the elements of all the $\mathbf{A}^{(k)}$:

$$|A_{ij}^{(k)}| \leqslant a \qquad \text{for all } i, j, k. \tag{2.59}$$

Equation (2.59) tells us that no element of any of the reduced matrices $\mathbf{A}^{(k)}$ can exceed in magnitude the value a of the largest diagonal element of the original matrix $\mathbf{A}$.

2.12. Practical implementation of Cholesky factorization

In practice, since $\mathbf{A}$ is symmetric, only its diagonal and upper triangle are kept in memory. The matrices $\mathbf{A}^{(k)}$ are never explicitly constructed. The upper triangular factor $\mathbf{U}$ is directly developed in separate storage, rather than overwriting on $\mathbf{A}$, because it is usually less sparse than $\mathbf{A}$ and requires a special data structure. Although we cannot talk of the Cholesky method as "elimination", because we are not in fact eliminating anything, we will see that the algorithm is almost identical to Gauss elimination.

Looking at Equation (2.51) we realize that, once the square root of $A_{11}^{(1)}$ is obtained and the remaining elements of row 1 are divided by this value, row 1 of $\mathbf{U}$ is complete. Then, we can calculate the elements of row 1 of $\mathbf{A}^{(2)}$, using Equation (2.52), and immediately obtain the square root of $A_{11}^{(2)}$ and divide the remaining elements of the first row of $\mathbf{A}^{(2)}$ by this value; this gives us the complete second row of $\mathbf{U}$. Note that the elements of $\mathbf{b}^{\mathrm{T}}/\alpha^{1/2}$ have already been computed and are stored as the first row of $\mathbf{U}$; thus only multiplications and subtractions are necessary when using Equation (2.52). Note also that this step is exactly analogous to Gauss elimination of A_{21}, using A_{11} as pivot, although A_{11} is not unity in this case.

Now, we proceed to row 3 of $\mathbf{A}$, and use Equation (2.52) to obtain row 2 of $\mathbf{A}^{(2)}$. This is analogous to elimination of A_{31}. Next, still for row 3 of $\mathbf{A}$, we perform the computations necessary to obtain row 1 of $\mathbf{A}^{(3)}$; this is analogous to elimination of A_{32}. We take the square root of the diagonal element just obtained and divide the remaining elements of the row by this value. This produces the complete row 3 of **U** in final form. Proceeding in this way we obtain **U** in exactly the same way as if we were performing Gauss elimination, the only difference being that, at the end of each step, instead of storing the reciprocal of the diagonal element and multiplying the off-diagonal elements by that value, we store the reciprocal of the square root of the diagonal element and multiply the off-diagonal elements of the row by this square root. The table of factors, representing the Cholesky factorization (2.49), consists of the upper triangle of **U** and the reciprocals of the diagonal elements of **U**. We neither store nor operate on elements in the lower triangle of **A**. If we call $\mathbf{D}^{1/2}$ the diagonal matrix formed with the (positive) diagonal elements of **U**, we can write $\mathbf{U} = \mathbf{D}^{1/2}\mathbf{U}'$, where $\mathbf{U}'$ is upper triangular with unit diagonal (unlike **U**); Equation (2.49) can then be written:

$$\mathbf{A} = \mathbf{U}'^{\mathrm{T}}\mathbf{D}\mathbf{U}', \tag{2.60}$$

where $\mathbf{D} = (\mathbf{D}^{1/2})^2$ is diagonal with positive diagonal elements. It is now easy to compare Cholesky factorization with Gauss elimination. In fact, Equation (2.60), obtained by Cholesky factorization, is identical to Equation (2.5) for a symmetric **A**, obtained by Gauss elimination. The diagonal of the Cholesky table is the matrix $\mathbf{D}^{-1/2}$, the upper triangle is the upper triangle of **U**. The diagonal of the Gauss table is $\mathbf{D}^{-1}$, the upper triangle is that of $\mathbf{U}'$.

A numerical example of Cholesky factorization is given in Section 2.15, and algorithms for obtaining the form (2.60), requiring no square roots, with **A** stored in sparse row-wise format, are explicitly given in Fortran in Chapter 9.

2.13. Forward and backward substitution

Solving the linear system, Equation (2.1), is a simple matter when the triangular factorization of **A**, Equation (2.2), is available. The solution is obtained by solving Equation (2.3) for **w**, and then Equation (2.4) for **x**. These equations are reproduced here for clarity:

$$\mathbf{L}\mathbf{w} = \mathbf{b}, \tag{2.61}$$

$$\mathbf{U}\mathbf{x} = \mathbf{w}. \tag{2.62}$$

If **A** is symmetric positive definite and its Cholesky factorization $\mathbf{A} = \mathbf{U}^{\mathrm{T}}\mathbf{U}$ was obtained, the procedure is the same except that $\mathbf{U}^{\mathrm{T}}$ is used in place of **L**. If the factorization of a general **A** is $\mathbf{A} = \mathbf{L}\mathbf{D}\mathbf{U}$, then three steps are necessary, the intermediate one being the trivial solution of a linear system with a diagonal matrix **D** of coefficients.

The solution of (2.61) is called *forward substitution*. Since **L** is lower triangular the first equation has the form:

$$L_{11}w_1 = b_1,$$

where $L_{11} \neq 0$ because we have assumed that **A** is nonsingular. Thus $w_1 = b_1/L_{11}$. Now we can subtract w_1 times the first column of **L** from **b**. What remains of Equation (2.61) is a triangular system of order $n - 1$, with the trailing principal minor of **L** as the matrix of coefficients. Now w_2 can be calculated, and the argument can be applied recurrently, proceeding forward, until the complete solution **w** is obtained. The procedure, of course, is equivalent to pre-multiplication of **b** by $\mathbf{L}^{-1}$, Equation (2.28). If n_L is the number of off-diagonal nonzeros of **L**, forward substitution requires n divisions, n_L multiplications and n_L additions.

With **w** available, System (2.62) can be solved by *backward substitution* or *backsubstitution*. Since we have assumed that **U** is unit diagonal, the last equation of (2.62) has the form:

$$x_n = w_n$$

so that x_n is known. We subtract its product by the last column of **U** from **w** and obtain a triangular system of order $n - 1$ with the leading principal minor of **U** as the matrix of coefficients. Proceeding recurrently backwards the final solution **x** is obtained, the procedure being equivalent to pre-multiplication of **w** by $\mathbf{U}^{-1}$, Equation (2.30). If n_U is the number of off-diagonal nonzeros of **U**, backsubstitution requires n_U multiplications and n_U additions. Forward and backward substitution algorithms for sparse triangular matrices stored in row-wise format are explicitly given in Fortran in Chapter 9.

2.14. Cost considerations

In sparse matrix technology, it is important to know the size of the storage required and the number of operations performed by an algorithm. With this information at hand the user can calculate the effective cost of execution, taking into account the charging algorithm of the installation. In the case of triangular factorization and solution by forward and backward substitution, the basic theorems were given by Rose (1972) for sparse symmetric matrices, and by Bunch and Rose (1974) for general sparse matrices, while the effect of specific storage schemes was considered by Bunch (1974b) (where a minor misprint exists on page 851, but the correct result is given in our Table 2.1).

Table 2.1 Storage and operation count for factorization. All summations extend from $i = 1$ up to $i = n - 1$, both values included. See text for details.

A	Multiplications and divisions	Additions	Storage
Full symmetric	$\frac{1}{6}n^3 + \frac{1}{2}n^2 - \frac{2}{3}n$	$\frac{1}{6}n^3 - \frac{1}{6}n$	$\frac{1}{2}n^2 + \frac{1}{2}n$
Band symmetric	$\frac{1}{2}\beta(\beta + 3)n - \frac{1}{3}\beta^3 - \beta^2 - \frac{2}{3}\beta$	$\frac{1}{2}\beta(\beta + 1)n - \frac{1}{3}\beta^3 - \frac{1}{2}\beta^2 - \frac{1}{6}\beta$	$(\beta + 1)n - \frac{1}{2}\beta^2 - \frac{1}{2}\beta$
Sparse symmetric	$\sum r_i^U(r_i^U + 3)/2$	$\sum r_i^U(r_i^U + 1)/2$	$n + \sum r_i^U$
Full unsymmetric	$\frac{1}{3}n^3 - \frac{1}{3}n$	$\frac{1}{3}n^3 - \frac{1}{2}n^2 + \frac{1}{6}n$	n^2
Band unsymmetric, diagonal pivoting	$(\beta + 1)\beta n - \frac{2}{3}\beta^3 - \beta^2 - \frac{1}{3}\beta$	$\beta^2 n - \frac{2}{3}\beta^3 - \frac{1}{2}\beta^2 + \frac{1}{6}\beta$	$(2\beta + 1)n - \beta^2 - \beta$
Band unsymmetric, partial pivoting	$\leqslant (2\beta + 1)\beta n - \frac{13}{6}\beta^3 - \frac{3}{2}\beta^2 - \frac{1}{3}\beta$	$\leqslant 2\beta^2 n - \frac{13}{6}\beta^3 - \beta^2 + \frac{1}{6}\beta$	$\leqslant (3\beta + 1)n - \frac{5}{2}\beta^2 - \frac{3}{2}\beta$
Sparse unsymmetric	$\sum (r_i^U + 1)c_i^L$	$\sum r_i^U c_i^L$	$n + \sum (r_i^U + c_i^L)$

The theorems give storage size and number of operations in terms of:

r_i^U = number of off-diagonal nonzeros in row i of $\mathbf{U}$;

c_j^L = number of off-diagonal nonzeros in column j of $\mathbf{L}$;

n = order of the matrix.

Divisions are counted as multiplications and subtractions as additions. Fill-ins are also counted as additions, and accidental cancellations are neglected. It would be desirable to express the results in terms of properties of the *original* matrix **A** and be able to compute the cost before elimination starts. This task will be undertaken for symmetric matrices in Chapter 4.

The results are given in Tables 2.1 and 2.2 for several cases. When **A** is symmetric, $r_i = c_i$ and both storage and labour can be almost halved, as discussed at the end of Section 2.7. For a full matrix all elements are considered as nonzeros even if the value is zero. Also elements inside the band of a banded matrix are considered nonzeros. In both cases it is possible to by-pass operations involving zeros, thus actually performing less arithmetic than the tables indicate. But this requires an additional test to be performed on every element and the final cost may increase rather than decrease if the proportion of zeros is low.

For a full matrix, $r_i^U = c_i^L = n - 1$. In this case the results in Tables 2.1 and 2.2 are given in terms of n, a property of the original matrix.

For a banded matrix, r_i^U and c_i^L can also be calculated in terms of properties of the original matrix. Both semibands are of the same width β, and the bandwidth is $2\beta + 1$. Pivots are taken orderly from the diagonal when "diagonal pivoting" is specified, and fill-in may occur only inside the band. However, when the matrix is unsymmetric or indefinite, it is usually necessary to select the pivot at step k from the kth subcolumn, and then bring it to the diagonal by means of the interchange of two rows (see Section 1.12).

Table 2.2 Operation count for forward and backsubstitution. All summations extend from $i = 1$ up to $i = n - 1$, both values included. See text for details.

A	Multiplications	Additions
Full symmetric or unsymmetric	n^2	$n^2 - n$
Band symmetric or band unsymmetric with diagonal pivoting	$(2\beta + 1)n - \beta^2 - \beta$	$2\beta n - \beta^2 - \beta$
Sparse symmetric	$n + 2\sum r_i^U$	$2\sum r_i^U$
Band unsymmetric, partial pivoting	$\leqslant (3\beta + 1)n - \frac{5}{2}\beta^2 - \frac{3}{2}\beta$	$3\beta n - \frac{5}{2}\beta^2 - \frac{3}{2}\beta$
Sparse unsymmetric	$n + \sum (r_i^U + c_i^L)$	$\sum (r_i^U + c_i^L)$

The required storage consists of a lower semiband of width β and an upper semiband of width at most 2β. This case is specified as "diagonal pivoting" in Tables 2.1 and 2.2, where only upper bounds for storage and operations are given because the actual width of the upper semiband may be less than 2β.

In Table 2.1, the factorization is $\mathbf{A} = \mathbf{LU}$ for a general $\mathbf{A}$, or $\mathbf{A} = \mathbf{U}^{\mathrm{T}}\mathbf{DU}$ for a symmetric $\mathbf{A}$. The storage includes all elements considered as nonzeros, but does not include overhead storage, which may be appreciable if linked schemes or sparse formats are employed. Additional n locations are required for forward or backsubstitution in all cases. Results for factorization and solution are given separately because applications may require the factorization of a given matrix just once and then the solution of many linear systems with different right-hand sides.

2.15. Numerical examples

In this section, the various forms of factorization of a matrix discussed in this chapter are demonstrated by means of numerical examples. Consider the matrix:

$$\mathbf{A} = \begin{vmatrix} 2 & 1 & 1 \\ 2 & 3 & -1 \\ 1 & 1 & 4 \end{vmatrix}$$

Using Gauss elimination (either way, by rows or by columns), the factorization $\mathbf{A} = \mathbf{LU}$ is obtained:

$$\mathbf{A} = \begin{vmatrix} 2 & & \\ 2 & 2 & \\ 1 & \frac{1}{2} & 4 \end{vmatrix} \begin{vmatrix} 1 & \frac{1}{2} & \frac{1}{2} \\ & 1 & -1 \\ & & 1 \end{vmatrix}$$

and the corresponding table of factors, Equation (2.25), is:

$$\text{Gauss table} = \begin{vmatrix} \frac{1}{2} & \frac{1}{2} & \frac{1}{2} \\ 2 & \frac{1}{2} & -1 \\ 1 & \frac{1}{2} & \frac{1}{4} \end{vmatrix}$$

The matrix $\mathbf{U}^{-1}$ is computed using the upper triangle of the table, as indicated by Equation (2.30):

$$\mathbf{U}^{-1} = \begin{vmatrix} 1 & -\frac{1}{2} & -1 \\ & 1 & 1 \\ & & 1 \end{vmatrix}$$

A factorization of the form $\mathbf{A} = \mathbf{L}'\mathbf{D}\mathbf{U}$ with $\mathbf{L}'$ lower triangular with unit diagonal can be obtained from $\mathbf{A} = \mathbf{L}\mathbf{U}$ by writing $\mathbf{L}'\mathbf{D} = \mathbf{L}$ (Equation 2.5). The result is:

$$\mathbf{A} = \begin{vmatrix} 1 & & \\ 1 & 1 & \\ \frac{1}{2} & \frac{1}{4} & 1 \end{vmatrix} \begin{vmatrix} 2 & & \\ & 2 & \\ & & 4 \end{vmatrix} \begin{vmatrix} 1 & \frac{1}{2} & \frac{1}{2} \\ & 1 & -1 \\ & & 1 \end{vmatrix}$$

When Gauss–Jordan elimination by columns is used, the factorization $\mathbf{A} = \mathbf{D}_1\mathbf{T}_1^C\mathbf{D}_2\mathbf{T}_2^C\mathbf{D}_3\mathbf{T}_3^C$ of Equation (2.40) is obtained, as follows:

$$\mathbf{A} = \begin{vmatrix} 2 & & \\ & 1 & \\ & & 1 \end{vmatrix} \begin{vmatrix} 1 & & \\ 2 & 1 & \\ 1 & & 1 \end{vmatrix} \begin{vmatrix} 1 & & \\ & 2 & \\ & & 1 \end{vmatrix}$$

$$\times \begin{vmatrix} 1 & \frac{1}{2} & \\ & 1 & \\ & \frac{1}{2} & 1 \end{vmatrix} \begin{vmatrix} 1 & & \\ & 1 & \\ & & 4 \end{vmatrix} \begin{vmatrix} 1 & & 1 \\ & 1 & -1 \\ & & 1 \end{vmatrix}$$

and the corresponding table of factors, Equation (2.42), is:

$$\text{Gauss–Jordan table of column factors} = \begin{vmatrix} \frac{1}{2} & \frac{1}{2} & 1 \\ 2 & \frac{1}{2} & -1 \\ 1 & \frac{1}{2} & \frac{1}{4} \end{vmatrix}$$

As discussed in Section 2.10, the lower triangle of this table is identical with the lower triangle of the Gauss factor $\mathbf{L}$, while the upper triangle is identical with that of $\mathbf{U}^{-1}$ with the algebraic signs reversed.

Performing Gauss–Jordan elimination on $\mathbf{A}$ by rows is equivalent to performing Gauss–Jordan elimination on $\mathbf{A}^T$, the transpose of $\mathbf{A}$, by columns. The factorization $\mathbf{A}^T = \mathbf{D}'_1\mathbf{T}'^C_1\mathbf{D}'_2\mathbf{T}'^C_2\mathbf{D}'_3\mathbf{T}'^C_3$ is obtained:

$$\mathbf{A}^T = \begin{vmatrix} 2 & & \\ & 1 & \\ & & 1 \end{vmatrix} \begin{vmatrix} 1 & & \\ 1 & 1 & \\ 1 & & 1 \end{vmatrix} \begin{vmatrix} 1 & & \\ & 2 & \\ & & 1 \end{vmatrix}$$

$$\times \begin{vmatrix} 1 & 1 & \\ & 1 & \\ & -2 & 1 \end{vmatrix} \begin{vmatrix} 1 & & \\ & 1 & \\ & & 4 \end{vmatrix} \begin{vmatrix} 1 & & \frac{1}{4} \\ & 1 & \frac{1}{4} \\ & & 1 \end{vmatrix}$$

which, by transposition, yields the corresponding factorization $\mathbf{A} = \mathbf{T}_3'^{\mathrm{R}}\mathbf{D}_3'\mathbf{T}_2'^{\mathrm{R}}\mathbf{D}_2'\mathbf{T}_1'^{\mathrm{R}}\mathbf{D}_1'$

$$\mathbf{A} = \begin{vmatrix} 1 & & \\ & 1 & \\ \frac{1}{4} & \frac{1}{4} & 1 \end{vmatrix} \begin{vmatrix} 1 & & \\ & 1 & \\ & & 4 \end{vmatrix} \begin{vmatrix} 1 & & \\ 1 & 1 & -2 \\ & & 1 \end{vmatrix}$$

$$\times \begin{vmatrix} 1 & & \\ & 2 & \\ & & 1 \end{vmatrix} \begin{vmatrix} 1 & 1 & 1 \\ & 1 & \\ & & 1 \end{vmatrix} \begin{vmatrix} 2 & & \\ & 1 & \\ & & 1 \end{vmatrix}$$

The table of factors is, for this case:

$$\text{Gauss–Jordan table of row factors} = \begin{vmatrix} \frac{1}{2} & 1 & 1 \\ 1 & \frac{1}{2} & -2 \\ \frac{1}{4} & \frac{1}{4} & \frac{1}{4} \end{vmatrix}$$

Finally, let us consider a symmetric positive definite matrix:

$$\mathbf{B} = \begin{vmatrix} 2 & 1 & 1 \\ 1 & 3 & 2 \\ 1 & 2 & 4 \end{vmatrix}.$$

The **LU** factorization is, for this case:

$$\mathbf{B} = \begin{vmatrix} 2 & & \\ 1 & \frac{5}{2} & \\ 1 & \frac{3}{2} & \frac{13}{5} \end{vmatrix} \begin{vmatrix} 1 & \frac{1}{2} & \frac{1}{2} \\ & 1 & \frac{3}{5} \\ & & 1 \end{vmatrix},$$

while the $\mathbf{U}^{\mathrm{T}}\mathbf{D}\mathbf{U}$ factorization is:

$$\mathbf{B} = \begin{vmatrix} 1 & & \\ \frac{1}{2} & 1 & \\ \frac{1}{2} & \frac{3}{5} & 1 \end{vmatrix} \begin{vmatrix} 2 & & \\ & \frac{5}{2} & \\ & & \frac{13}{5} \end{vmatrix} \begin{vmatrix} 1 & \frac{1}{2} & \frac{1}{2} \\ & 1 & \frac{3}{5} \\ & & 1 \end{vmatrix}.$$

The Cholesky factorization $\mathbf{B} = \mathbf{U}'^{\mathrm{T}}\mathbf{U}'$, where $\mathbf{U}'$ is upper triangular but not unit diagonal, can be obtained either by taking the square root of the elements of $\mathbf{D}$, or using Equation (2.51) three times as discussed in Section

2.11, or following the procedure normally used in practical implementations of the algorithm, which was discussed in Section 2.12. In either case the result is:

$$\mathbf{B} = \left|\begin{array}{ccc} 2^{1/2} & & \\ (\frac{1}{2})^{1/2} & (\frac{5}{2})^{1/2} & \\ (\frac{1}{2})^{1/2} & (\frac{9}{10})^{1/2} & (\frac{13}{5})^{1/2} \end{array}\right| \left|\begin{array}{ccc} 2^{1/2} & (\frac{1}{2})^{1/2} & (\frac{1}{2})^{1/1} \\ & (\frac{5}{2})^{1/2} & (\frac{9}{10})^{1/2} \\ & & (\frac{13}{5})^{1/2} \end{array}\right| .$$

Matrix **B** is diagonally dominant. In Section 6.3 its eigenvalues will be calculated.

CHAPTER 3

Numerical Errors in Gauss Elimination

3.1. Introduction

Several elimination algorithms, particularly Gauss elimination, were examined in detail in Chapter 2. When the operations necessary to solve

$$\mathbf{A}\mathbf{x} = \mathbf{b} \tag{3.1}$$

are carried out using floating point arithmetic, numerical errors are introduced due to round-off or truncation. Errors then grow as the algorithm progresses, and unless something is done to prevent excessive growth, they may seriously impair the accuracy of the resulting solution or even lead to a complete loss of significance. Consider the following example, where $-9 \leqslant a \leqslant 9$ and the computations are performed using a floating accumulator which keeps only one digit:

$$\mathbf{A} = \begin{vmatrix} 0.1 & 1 \\ 1 & a \end{vmatrix}.$$

If 0.1 is used as pivot and fl stands for "floating point operation", we obtain:

$$\text{fl}\begin{vmatrix} 0.1 & 1 \\ 0 & a-10 \end{vmatrix} = \begin{vmatrix} 0.1 & 1 \\ 0 & -10 \end{vmatrix}.$$

The value of a has disappeared and the result is completely independent of it. This is due to a bad choice of pivot. If the rows of **A** were permuted:

$$\mathbf{A}' = \begin{vmatrix} 1 & a \\ 0.1 & 1 \end{vmatrix}$$

the result would be obtained, correct to working precision:

$$\mathrm{fl}\begin{vmatrix} 1 & a \\ 0 & 1 - 0.1a \end{vmatrix} = \begin{vmatrix} 1 & a \\ 0 & 1 \end{vmatrix}.$$

In Chapter 2, pivots were chosen orderly along the diagonal of the matrix, and the question of whether any other alternative deserved consideration was not raised. In fact, at step k, any nonzero element of the active part of $\mathbf{A}^{(k)}$ can be the pivot. We recall that the active submatrix of $\mathbf{A}^{(k)}$ contains all elements $A_{ij}^{(k)}$ with $i, j \geqslant k$. As the example shows, we may either select different elements of the active submatrix as pivots, or we may alternatively reorder the equations and unknowns in such a way that the pivots fall orderly along the diagonal. Both procedures are mathematically equivalent, but only the first is computationally acceptable because it avoids moving data in the computer memory. For the sake of simplicity in the mathematical description we will assume that reordering of the rows and columns of **A** is represented by the permutation matrices **P** and **Q** to form the matrix

$$\mathbf{A}' = \mathbf{PAQ}, \tag{3.2}$$

and that elimination with diagonal pivoting is performed on $\mathbf{A}'$, but that the reordering is never performed in the computer. Thus, instead of solving Equation (3.1), we will actually think of solving

$$(\mathbf{PAQ})(\mathbf{Q}^{\mathrm{T}}\mathbf{x}) = (\mathbf{Pb}), \tag{3.3}$$

where $\mathbf{QQ}^{\mathrm{T}} = \mathbf{I}$ because **Q** is a permutation matrix.

The freedom in the selection of **P** and **Q** can be used not only to ensure numerical stability and improve accuracy, but also to preserve the sparsity of the triangular factors **L** and **U**. Constraints imposed by stability are discussed in this chapter, and sparsity is the subject of Chapters 4 and 5. The question as to how both conditions can be met, especially difficult when **A** is indefinite, is also discussed in those chapters.

Norms are commonly used as global estimators of the "size" of a vector or matrix. The following vector norm will be used for a real vector **x** with n components, when $1 \leqslant p \leqslant \infty$:

$$p\text{-norm} \qquad \|\mathbf{x}\|_p = \left(\sum_{i=1}^{n} |x_i|^p\right)^{1/p}. \tag{3.4}$$

In particular, for $p = 1$ or $p = \infty$:

$$\text{1-norm} \qquad \|\mathbf{x}\|_1 = \sum_{i=1}^{n} |x_i| \tag{3.5}$$

$$\infty\text{-norm} \qquad \|\mathbf{x}\|_\infty = \max_{1 \leqslant i \leqslant n} |x_i|. \tag{3.6}$$

The following matrix norms will be used for a real n by n matrix $\mathbf{A}$:

$$\text{1-norm} \qquad \|\mathbf{A}\|_1 = \max_j \sum_{i=1}^{n} |A_{ij}| \tag{3.7}$$

$$\infty\text{-norm} \qquad \|\mathbf{A}\|_\infty = \max_i \sum_{j=1}^{n} |A_{ij}|. \tag{3.8}$$

The following inequalities hold for 1-norms and ∞-norms:

$$\|\mathbf{x} + \mathbf{y}\| \leqslant \|\mathbf{x}\| + \|\mathbf{y}\|; \tag{3.9}$$

$$\|\mathbf{Ax}\| \leqslant \|\mathbf{A}\| \, \|\mathbf{x}\|; \tag{3.10}$$

$$\|\mathbf{AB}\| \leqslant \|\mathbf{A}\| \, \|\mathbf{B}\|. \tag{3.11}$$

Hölder's inequality holds for two vectors, $\mathbf{x}$ and $\mathbf{y}$, when $(1/p) + (1/q) = 1$ and $1 \leqslant p, q \leqslant \infty$:

$$|\mathbf{x}^{\mathrm{T}}\mathbf{y}| \leqslant \|\mathbf{x}\|_p \|\mathbf{y}\|_q. \tag{3.12}$$

3.2. Numerical errors in floating point operations

When a floating point number is stored in the memory of a computer, only a certain fixed number of digits is kept (e.g. six hexadecimal digits, or equivalently 24 binary digits in single precision Fortran). When an operation is performed between two numbers a and b stored in memory, the result may have to be rounded or truncated before it can fit into the desired memory location. For this type of error, bounds are usually set as follows:

$$\mathrm{fl}(a \circ b) = (a \circ b)(1 + \varepsilon) \tag{3.13}$$

where $\circ$ represents one of the elementary operations $+$, $-$, $\times$ or $\div$, $(a \circ b)$ is the exact result of the operation, $\mathrm{fl}(a \circ b)$ is the result obtained after performing the floating point operation and truncating or rounding if necessary, and $|\varepsilon| \leqslant \varepsilon_{\mathrm{M}}$, the machine precision; for example $\varepsilon_{\mathrm{M}} = 2^{-t}$ for a computer which uses t bit numbers and rounds off the result. We employ the usual algebraic notation to represent exact calculations and the symbol fl for calculations performed using floating point arithmetic.

Although the model of floating point arithmetic represented by Equation (3.13) is somewhat over-simplified (see, e.g., Parlett, 1980, p. 23), it is sufficient for our purposes and has been widely used (Wilkinson, 1965).

In the following section we will need a bound for the error which is made when the product of two numbers l and u is subtracted from a third number a to calculate b using floating point arithmetic:

$$b = \text{fl}(a - lu), \tag{3.14}$$

where a, l and u are assumed to be exactly stored in memory and b is the *computed* value. The error, e, is defined by

$$b = a - lu + e, \tag{3.15}$$

where exact arithmetic operations between the stored numbers are implied. We assume that a and b are bounded as follows:

$$|a|, |b| \leqslant a_{\text{M}}. \tag{3.16}$$

From Equations (3.13) and (3.14) we have:

$$b = [a - lu(1 + \varepsilon_1)](1 + \varepsilon_2), \tag{3.17}$$

where

$$|\varepsilon_1|, |\varepsilon_2| \leqslant \varepsilon_{\text{M}}. \tag{3.18}$$

Since we are not assuming any bounds for l or u, we eliminate lu from Equation (3.15) using Equation (3.17), and solve for e:

$$e = b\left[1 - \frac{1}{(1 + \varepsilon_1)(1 + \varepsilon_2)}\right] - a\frac{\varepsilon_1}{1 + \varepsilon_1}. \tag{3.19}$$

Using the bounds for a and b, Equation (3.16), we obtain:

$$|e| \leqslant a_{\text{M}}\left[\left|1 - \frac{1}{(1 + \varepsilon_1)(1 + \varepsilon_2)}\right| + \left|\frac{\varepsilon_1}{1 + \varepsilon_1}\right|\right]. \tag{3.20}$$

Using the bounds for ε_1 and ε_2 given by Equation (3.18), and assuming that $\varepsilon_{\text{M}} < 1$, we obtain after some analysis:

$$|e| \leqslant a_{\text{M}}\varepsilon_{\text{M}}\frac{1}{1 - \varepsilon_{\text{M}}}\left(\frac{1}{1 - \varepsilon_{\text{M}}} + 2\right). \tag{3.21}$$

We will now assume that the precision of the computer is at least $\varepsilon_{\text{M}} \leqslant 0.002$ (equivalent to 9 bits). This assumption is fulfilled in all normal cases. Then:

$$\frac{1}{1 - \varepsilon_{\text{M}}}\left(\frac{1}{1 - \varepsilon_{\text{M}}} + 2\right) < 3.01,$$

and the final bound for e is:

$$|e| < 3.01\varepsilon_M a_M. \tag{3.22}$$

It is worth noting that not much is gained using higher precision for addition alone, as done by certain programs which accumulate inner products in double precision while multiplications are carried out in single precision. If, for example, we take $|\varepsilon_1| \leqslant \varepsilon_M$ and $|\varepsilon_2| \leqslant \varepsilon_M^2$ in place of Equation (3.18), we get:

$$|e| < 2.01\varepsilon_M a_M. \tag{3.23}$$

To improve the accuracy it is necessary to perform both addition and multiplication in double precision, and then round the final result for storing.

The result given by Equation (3.22) was obtained without assuming any bounds for l or u, although of course the magnitude of the product lu is bound by $2a_M + |e|$ due to Equations (3.15) and (3.16). Our procedure is essentially the same as that employed by Reid (1971b). In the next section, when Equation (3.22) is used for step k of Gauss elimination by columns, a and b will represent elements of the reduced matrices $\mathbf{A}^{(k)}$ and $\mathbf{A}^{(k+1)}$, respectively, while l and u will be elements of $\mathbf{L}$ and $\mathbf{U}$, and a_M will be an upper bound for all relevant elements of all the reduced matrices. Now, Equation (2.21) shows that the elements of $\mathbf{L}$ are equal to certain elements of each $\mathbf{A}^{(k)}$, which means that, in the case of our particular application, l is bounded by a_M, and in fact all elements of $\mathbf{L}$ are bounded by a_M.

The same is not true of u, the elements of $\mathbf{U}$, obtained by Equation (2.18), which can be large if the pivot $A_{kk}^{(k)} \equiv (D_k)_{kk} \equiv L_{kk}$ is small.

There exists an alternative formulation (Bunch, 1974b) where, essentially, a bound σ is used for the elements of $\mathbf{U}$, and those of $\mathbf{L}$ and $\mathbf{A}^{(k)}$ are bounded by a_M. Thus, in Equation (3.15), $|a|, |b|, |l| \leqslant a_M$, and $|u| \leqslant \sigma$. Elimination of a from Equations (3.15) and (3.17) yields:

$$e = b\frac{\varepsilon_2}{1 + \varepsilon_2} - lu\varepsilon_1, \tag{3.24}$$

from which, using Equation (3.18) and $\varepsilon_M \leqslant 0.002$ we easily obtain:

$$|e| < (\sigma + 1.003)\varepsilon_M a_M. \tag{3.25}$$

The bound for $|e|$ given by Equation (3.25) involves the product σa_M, the appearance of which is due to the presence of the product lu in Equation (3.24). Both σ and a_M can be large in practice (except if partial pivoting by columns is used, selecting the largest element from row k, in which case $\sigma = 1$ but a_M may become too large). In fact all strategies used for improving accuracy try to avoid an excessive growth of the elements of the matrices during elimination. In this context, the bound given by Equation (3.22) is less restrictive and will be used in this book.

Equation (3.15) and the entire presentation of this Section and the next one, are forms of Wilkinson's *backward error analysis*, extensively used in the literature and extolled by many authors, for example Parlett (1980, p. 97).

3.3. Numerical errors in sparse factorization

Let us consider an element A_{ij} of a matrix $\mathbf{A}$ on which Gauss elimination by columns is performed with the pivots being selected directly along the diagonal. Elimination by columns is considered only to fix ideas, but it must be emphasized that the methods and results hold equally well for elimination by rows, and with slight changes for Cholesky factorization. We think in terms of storing at the same location the element $A_{ij}^{(k)}$ of each of the reduced matrices $\mathbf{A}^{(k)}$, where $\mathbf{A}^{(1)} \equiv \mathbf{A}$. At a certain step k, where $k < \min(i, j)$, we divide row k by the pivot $A_{kk}^{(k)}$ and store $U_{kj} \equiv A_{kj}^{(k+1)} = A_{kj}^{(k)}/A_{kk}^{(k)}$ in place of $A_{kj}^{(k)}$. The operation performed on $A_{ij}^{(k)}$ during step k using floating point arithmetic is (see Fig. 3.1):

$$A_{ij}^{(k+1)} = A_{ij}^{(k)} - L_{ik}U_{kj} + e_{ij}^{(k)}, \tag{3.26}$$

where $L_{lk} = A_{lk}^{(k)}$ for $l \geqslant k$. The notation used in Equation (3.26) is consistent with Equations (2.18) and (2.21) of Chapter 2. The error $e_{ij}^{(k)}$ made by the floating point computations can be bounded using the results of the preceding section. For this purpose we define $a_{ij} = \max_k |A_{ij}^{(k)}|$, so that:

$$|A_{ij}^{(k)}| \leqslant a_{ij} \tag{3.27}$$

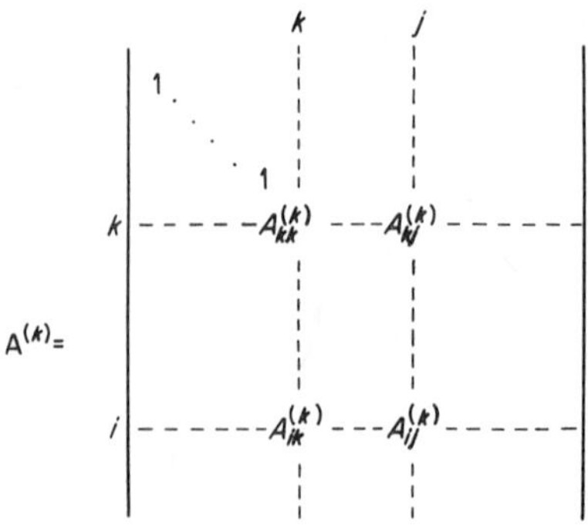

Figure 3.1 The matrix $\mathbf{A}^{(k)}$ just before the kth step of Gauss elimination by columns.

for $k \leqslant \min(i, j)$. In particular, for $k = 1$, the bound holds for the elements of the original matrix $\mathbf{A} \equiv \mathbf{A}^{(1)}$. As anticipated in the preceding section, Equation (3.27) implies a bound for the elements of $\mathbf{L}$, but not for those of $\mathbf{U}$. In fact, when $i \geqslant j = k$, $L_{ik} = A_{ik}^{(k)}$ by Equation (2.21), and $|L_{i\,k}|$ is bounded by $a_{i\,k}$. On the other hand, if $k = i < j$, $U_{k\,j} = A_{kj}^{(k)}/L_{k\,k}$ by Equations (2.16) and (2.18), so that the product $|L_{k\,k}U_{k\,j}|$ is bounded by $a_{k\,j}$, but $U_{k\,j}$ has no bound and can be large.

When Equation (3.27) holds, Equation (3.26) satisfies the same conditions as Equation (3.15) with $a_{\mathrm{M}} = a_{i\,j}$, and we can set a bound for the error using Equation (3.22):

$$|e_{ij}^{(k)}| \leqslant 3.01\varepsilon_{\mathrm{M}} a_{ij} \tag{3.28}$$

for $k < \min(i, j)$ and provided $\varepsilon_{\mathrm{M}} < 0.002$.

If an element of $\mathbf{A}$ is zero and no fill-in occurs at that location during elimination, the corresponding element of $\mathbf{L}$ or $\mathbf{U}$ will be exactly equal to zero. Furthermore, no operations have been performed on that element and no error has been contributed by Equation (3.26). We must make a distinction between this case and the case of an element of $\mathbf{L}$ or $\mathbf{U}$ which is equal to zero due to accidental cancellation, and to which an error has been contributed because one or more fill-ins took place at that location. Such an element will be considered as a nonzero. Accidental cancellation is rare (except in certain specific cases), and it would not be rewarding to take it explicitly into account. Thus, a nonzero is an element either different from zero or equal to zero due to cancellation, while a zero is an element originally zero and where no fill-in took place.

We now note that if either $L_{i\,k}$ is zero or $U_{k\,j}$ is zero, or both, no operation is performed in $A_{i\,j}^{(k)}$ in Equation (3.26), and

$$e_{ij}^{(k)} = 0. \tag{3.29}$$

Equation (3.26) is an *exact* relation between *computed* numbers; it gives no indication of the total error affecting the computed value of $A_{i\,j}^{(k+1)}$, because, if such an error were to be evaluated, then the errors affecting each of the computed numbers $A_{i\,j}^{(k)}$, L_{ik} and U_{kj} would have to be taken into account; the error $e_{ij}^{(k)}$ for which bounds were obtained is just the difference between the computed value of $A_{ij}^{(k+1)}$ and the value of $A_{ij}^{(k+1)}$ which would be obtained if exact arithmetic operations were performed with the computed numbers $A_{ij}^{(k)}$, L_{ik} and U_{kj}.

An important property of sparse elimination is described by Equation (3.29): the fact that, since only a few operations are performed on each element, the final error bounds are kept low. This property is what makes the direct solution of a very large sparse system feasible without an excessive accumulation of numerical errors. In order to make systematic use of it we define the matrix of integers n_{ij}:

$$n_{ij} = \sum_{k=1}^{m} n_{ij}^{(k)}, \tag{3.30}$$

where:

$$n_{ij}^{(k)} = 1 \text{ if both } L_{ik} \text{ and } U_{kj} \text{ are nonzeros.}$$

$$n_{ij}^{(k)} = 0 \text{ otherwise}$$

$$m = \min(i, j)$$

We will also use the following definitions:

r_i^L = number of off-diagonal nonzeros in row i of **L**.

c_i^L = number of off-diagonal nonzeros in column i of **L**.

r_i^U = number of off-diagonal nonzeros in row i of **U**.

c_i^U = number of off-diagonal nonzeros in column i of **U**.

n_L = number of nonzeros in **L**, including diagonal; $n_L = \sum r_i^L + n = \sum c_i^L + n$.

n'_U = number of off-diagonal nonzeros in **U**; $n'_U = \sum r_i^U = \sum c_i^U$.

It is useful to have bounds for n_{ij} available. Then:

$$n_{ij} \leqslant \min(r_i^L, c_j^U) + 1. \tag{3.31}$$

Since $r_i^L \leqslant i - 1$ and $c_j^U \leqslant j - 1$ we also have the weaker bound:

$$n_{ij} \leqslant \min(i, j) \tag{3.32}$$

which can also be obtained directly from Equation (3.30) by noting that $n_{ij}^{(k)} \leqslant 1$ and the summation has m terms. Expressions of n_{ij} for full and band matrices are given in Table 3.1, and numerical examples are shown in Fig. 3.2 for several cases.

We now return to the analysis of Equation (3.26). Each time that at step k the product $L_{ik}U_{kj}$ is computed and subtracted from the element at position (i, j), an error $e_{ij}^{(k)}$ is added to that element. If $j > i$, the last step in which the element is modified is $i - 1$, while at step i it is divided by the diagonal element L_{ii} and stored as U_{ij}. Thus, the operations performed on an element for which $j > i$ are:

$$[(A_{ij} - L_{i1}U_{1j} + e_{ij}^{(1)} - L_{i2}U_{2j} + e_{ij}^{(2)} - \ldots$$
$$- L_{i,i-1}U_{i-1,j} + e_{ij}^{(i-1)})/L_{ii}] \times (1 + \varepsilon) = U_{ij} \tag{3.33}$$

(a)

	1	2	3	4	5	6
1	1	1	1	1	1	1
2	1	2	2	2	2	2
3	1	2	3	3	3	3
4	1	2	3	4	4	4
5	1	2	3	4	5	5
6	1	2	3	4	5	6

(b)

	1	2	3	4	5	6	7	8	9
1	1	1	1	1					
2	1	2	2	2	1				
3	1	2	3	3	2	1			
4	1	2	3	4	3	2	1		
5		1	2	3	4	3	2	1	
6			1	2	3	4	3	2	1
7				1	2	3	4	3	2
8					1	2	3	4	3
9						1	2	3	4

(c)

	1	2	3	4	5	6	7	8	9	10	11	12
1	1	1	1	1	1	1	1					
2	1	2	2	2	2	2	2	1				
3	1	2	3	3	3	3	3	2	1			
4	1	2	3	4	4	4	4	3	2	1		
5		1	2	3	4	4	4	4	3	2	1	
6			1	2	3	4	4	4	4	3	2	1
7				1	2	3	4	4	4	4	3	2
8					1	2	3	4	4	4	4	3
9						1	2	3	4	4	4	4
10							1	2	3	4	4	4
11								1	2	3	4	4
12									1	2	3	4

Figure 3.2 Values of n_{ij} defined by Equation (3.30) for: (a) a full matrix of order $n = 6$; (b) a band matrix of order $n = 9$ and half-bandwidth $\beta = 3$; (c) a band matrix of order $n = 12$, lower band of width $\beta = 3$ and upper band of width $2\beta = 6$.

where the factor $(1 + \varepsilon)$ takes into account the error introduced when division by L_{ii} is performed, according to Equation (3.13). Equation (3.33) can be written:

$$A_{ij} + \sum_{k=1}^{i-1} e_{ij}^{(k)} = \sum_{k=1}^{i} L_{ik}U_{kj} - L_{ii}U_{ij}\frac{\varepsilon}{1+\varepsilon} \tag{3.34}$$

where, in the particular case of $i = 1$, the summation on the left-hand side must be omitted.

We define the error matrix $\mathbf{E}$ with elements E_{ij} given by

$$E_{ij} = \sum_{k=1}^{i-1} e_{ij}^{(k)} + L_{ii}U_{ij}\frac{\varepsilon}{1+\varepsilon} \tag{3.35}$$

when $j > i$ (the remaining elements are defined in Equation (3.39) below). A bound for the elements of $\mathbf{E}$ can be set as follows. Using $|\varepsilon| \leqslant \varepsilon_M \leqslant 0.002$ and the fact that $|L_{i\,i}U_{i\,j}| \leqslant a_{i\,j}$ by Equation (3.27), we obtain:

$$\left| L_{i\,i}U_{i\,j}\frac{\varepsilon}{1+\varepsilon} \right| < 1.003\varepsilon_M a_{i\,j} < 3.01\varepsilon_M a_{i\,j}. \tag{3.36}$$

Now, if $U_{i\,j}$ is a nonzero, the number of subtrahends in Equation (3.33) is exactly $n_{i\,j} - 1$ (since $L_{i\,i} \neq 0$ and thus in Equation (3.30) $n_{i\,j}^{(i)} = 1$). The summation in Equation (3.35) contains $n_{i\,j} - 1$ terms, each bounded by $3.01\varepsilon_M a_{i\,j}$ according to Equation (3.22). On the other hand, if $U_{i\,j}$ is zero, then no fill-in took place there and $n_{i\,j}^{(k)} = 0$ for $k < i$; besides $n_{i\,j}^{(i)} = 0$ because $U_{i\,j} = 0$; thus $n_{i\,j} = 0$. In either case, for $j > i$:

$$|E_{i\,j}| \leqslant 3.01\varepsilon_M a_{i\,j} n_{i\,j}. \tag{3.37}$$

A similar reasoning is followed for the case $j \leqslant i$. The operations performed on $A_{i\,j}$ are:

$$A_{i\,j} - L_{i\,1}U_{1\,j} + e_{i\,j}^{(1)} - L_{i\,2}U_{2\,j} + e_{i\,j}^{(2)} - \ldots - L_{i,\,j-1}U_{j-1,\,j} + e_{i\,j}^{(j-1)} = L_{ij} \tag{3.38}$$

Equation (3.38) expresses the fact that the result of the operations is stored as $L_{i\,j}$. For $j \leqslant i$ we define:

$$E_{i\,j} = \sum_{k=1}^{j-1} e_{i\,j}^{(k)}. \tag{3.39}$$

If $L_{i\,j}$ is a nonzero, and since $U_{j\,j} = 1 \neq 0$ and $n_{i\,j}^{(j)} = 1$ in Equation (3.30), the summation in Equation (3.39) contains $n_{i\,j} - 1$ terms. If $L_{i\,j}$ is zero, then no fill-in occurred at that location, $n_{i\,j} = 0$, and $E_{i\,j} = 0$. Thus, using Equation (3.28) we have for $j \leqslant i$:

$$|E_{i\,j}| \leqslant 3.01\varepsilon_M a_{i\,j} n_{i\,j}. \tag{3.40}$$

Finally, using Equation (3.35) in Equation (3.34), and Equation (3.39) in Equation (3.38), we can write:

$$\mathbf{LU} = \mathbf{A} + \mathbf{E} \tag{3.41}$$

where, for all i, j:

$$|E_{i\,j}| \leqslant 3.01\varepsilon_M a_{i\,j} n_{i\,j}. \tag{3.42}$$

A somewhat less tight but more tractable bound can be obtained if a_M is the largest $a_{i\,j}$, so that

$$|A_{ij}^{(k)}| \leqslant a_M \tag{3.43}$$

for all i, j and $k \leqslant \min\,(i, j)$. Then:

$$|E_{ij}| \leqslant 3.01\varepsilon_M a_M n_{ij}. \tag{3.44}$$

A norm of $\mathbf{E}$ serves as a global estimator of the "size" of the error matrix. From Equations (3.7) and (3.8) we have obtained the bounds for $\|\mathbf{E}\|_1$ and $\|\mathbf{E}\|_\infty$ which are given in Table 3.1 for sparse, full and band matrices. Bounds for the norms of $\mathbf{L}$ will be necessary for Section 3.4. They can easily be obtained from Equation (3.43) and are listed in Table 3.1 for the different cases of interest.

3.4. Numerical errors in sparse substitution

Forward and backward substitution were discussed in Section 2.13. Forward substitution, or solution of $\mathbf{Lw} = \mathbf{b}$, can be viewed as an algorithm with n steps, where a sequence of vectors $\mathbf{b}^{(1)} \equiv \mathbf{b}, \mathbf{b}^{(2)}, \ldots, \mathbf{b}^{(n)}$ is computed; $\mathbf{b}^{(k+1)}$ and $\mathbf{b}^{(k)}$ have their k initial components identical. Step k, $k = 1, 2, \ldots, n$, is:

$$\begin{aligned} w_k &= (b_k^{(k)}/L_{kk})(1+\varepsilon) \\ b_i^{(k+1)} &= b_i^{(k)} - L_{ik}w_k + f_i^{(k)}; \qquad i = k+1, \ldots, n \end{aligned} \tag{3.45}$$

where ε and $f_i^{(k)}$ are the corresponding errors. As usual $|\varepsilon| \leqslant \varepsilon_M \leqslant 0.002$. Let $b_{Mi} = \max_k |b_i^{(k)}|$, so that:

$$|b_i^{(k)}| \leqslant b_{Mi}; \qquad 1 \leqslant i \leqslant n,\ 1 \leqslant k \leqslant i \tag{3.46}$$

Actually, Equation (3.46) holds for $1 \leqslant k \leqslant n$. Then, from Equation (3.22):

$$|f_i^{(k)}| \leqslant 3.01\varepsilon_M b_{Mi}; \qquad k < i. \tag{3.47}$$

Vectors $\mathbf{b}$ and $\mathbf{w}$ are considered full. The operations performed on an element b_i are:

$$[(b_i - L_{i1}w_1 + f_i^{(1)} - \ldots - L_{i,i-1}w_{i-1} + f_i^{(i-1)})/L_{ii}](1+\varepsilon) = w_i \tag{3.48}$$

which can be written:

$$b_i + \sum_{k=1}^{i-1} f_i^{(k)} = \sum_{k=1}^{i} L_{ik}w_k - L_{ii}w_i\frac{\varepsilon}{1+\varepsilon}, \tag{3.49}$$

where the summation in the left-hand side must be omitted if $i = 1$. Since $|L_{ii}w_i| = |b_i^{(i)}| \leqslant b_{Mi}$, we have

$$\left|L_{ii}w_i\frac{\varepsilon}{1+\varepsilon}\right| \leqslant 1.003\varepsilon_M b_{Mi} < 3.01\varepsilon_M b_{Mi}. \tag{3.50}$$

Table 3.1 Bounds for the norms of **L**, expressions for n_{ij} (see Equation (2.16)), and bounds for the norms of the error matrix **E** for the factorization $\mathbf{LU} = \mathbf{A} + \mathbf{E}$, where all matrices are of order n. The bandwidth of band matrices is assumed not to exceed n.

A	Bounds for **L**	n_{ij}	Error bounds for factorization
Sparse	$\|\mathbf{L}\|_1 \leqslant a_M \left(\max_j c_j^L + 1 \right)$	$\sum_{k=1}^{m} n_{ij}^{(k)}$	$\|E\|_1 \leqslant 3.01 \varepsilon_M a_M \max_j \sum_{i=1}^{n} n_{ij}$
	$\|\mathbf{L}\|_\infty \leqslant a_M \left(\max_i r_i^L + 1 \right)$	$m = \min(i, j)$	$\|E\|_\infty \leqslant 3.01 \varepsilon_M a_M \max_i \sum_{j=1}^{n} n_{ij}$
Full	$\|\mathbf{L}\|_1 \leqslant a_M n$	$\min(i, j)$	$\|E\|_1, \|E\|_\infty \leqslant \frac{3.01}{2} \varepsilon_M a_M n \times (n + 1)$
	$\|\mathbf{L}\|_\infty \leqslant a_M n$		
Band $\|\beta\backslash\beta\backslash\|$	$\|\mathbf{L}\|_1 \leqslant a_M(\beta + 1)$ $\|\mathbf{L}\|_\infty \leqslant a_M(\beta + 1)$	$\max[0, \min(i, j, i - j + \beta + 1, j - i + \beta + 1)]$	$\|E\|_1, \|E\|_\infty \leqslant 3.01 \varepsilon_M a_M \times (\beta + 1)^2$
Band $\|\beta\backslash 2\beta\backslash\|$	$\|\mathbf{L}\|_1 \leqslant a_M(\beta + 1)$ $\|\mathbf{L}\|_\infty \leqslant a_M(\beta + 1)$	$\max[0, \min(i, j, i - j + 2\beta + 1, j - i + \beta + 1, \beta + 1)]$	$\|E\|_1, \|E\|_\infty \leqslant 3.01 \varepsilon_M a_M \times (\beta + 1)(2\beta + 1)$

We recall that r_i^L is the number of off-diagonal nonzeros in row i of $\mathbf{L}$. We define the error vector $\delta\mathbf{b}$ with components

$$\delta b_i = \sum_{k=1}^{i-1} f_i^{(k)} + L_{ii} w_i \frac{\varepsilon}{1+\varepsilon}; \qquad i > 1$$

$$\delta b_1 = L_{1\,1} w_1 \frac{\varepsilon}{1+\varepsilon}. \tag{3.51}$$

Then, the computed result $\mathbf{w}$ satisfies the exact relation

$$\mathbf{Lw} = \mathbf{b} + \delta\mathbf{b} \tag{3.52}$$

where, from Equations (3.47) and (3.50), the following bounds hold for the components of $\delta\mathbf{b}$:

$$|\delta b_i| \leqslant 3.01 \varepsilon_M b_{Mi} (r_i^L + 1). \tag{3.53}$$

A less tight but simpler bound is obtained if b_M is the absolute value of the largest element of all the vectors $\mathbf{b}^{(k)}$, so that $b_{Mi} \leqslant b_M$ and:

$$|b_i^{(k)}| \leqslant b_M; \qquad i = 1, 2, \ldots, n; \qquad k \leqslant i. \tag{3.54}$$

Then:

$$|\delta b_i| \leqslant 3.01 \varepsilon_M b_M (r_i^L + 1). \tag{3.55}$$

Backward substitution is the solution of $\mathbf{Ux} = \mathbf{w}$. It can be viewed as an algorithm with n steps, where the sequence of vectors $\mathbf{w}^{(n)} \equiv \mathbf{w}$, $\mathbf{w}^{(n-1)}, \ldots, \mathbf{w}^{(2)}, \mathbf{w}^{(1)}$ is computed, with $\mathbf{w}^{(k)}$ and $\mathbf{w}^{(k-1)}$ having their components k to n identical. Step k, $k = n, n-1, \ldots, 1$, is:

$$x_k = w_k^{(k)}$$

$$w_i^{(k-1)} = w_i^{(k)} - U_{i\,k} x_k + g_i^{(k)}; \qquad i = 1, \ldots, k-1, \tag{3.56}$$

where $g_i^{(k)}$ is the error introduced by the floating point computation. The operations performed on an element w_i, $i < n$, are:

$$w_i - U_{i\,n} x_n + g_i^{(n)} - U_{i,n-1} x_{n-1} + g_i^{(n-1)} - \ldots - U_{i,i+1} x_{i+1} + g_i^{(i+1)} = x_i \tag{3.57}$$

or:

$$w_i + \sum_{k=i+1}^{n} g_i^{(k)} = \sum_{k=i}^{n} U_{i\,k} x_k; \qquad i < n. \tag{3.58}$$

Thus, if we define the error vector $\delta\mathbf{w}$:

$$\delta w_i = \sum_{k=i+1}^{n} g_i^{(k)}; \qquad i < n$$

$$\delta w_n = 0, \tag{3.59}$$

we have the following exact relation between the computed numbers:

$$\mathbf{Ux} = \mathbf{w} + \delta\mathbf{w}. \tag{3.60}$$

In order to obtain bounds for $\delta\mathbf{w}$, we let $w_{\mathrm{M}i} = \max_k |w_i^{(k)}|$, so that:

$$|w_i^{(k)}| \leqslant w_{\mathrm{M}i}; \qquad 1 \leqslant i \leqslant n; \qquad i \leqslant k \leqslant n. \tag{3.61}$$

In particular, for $k = i$, $w_i^{(i)} = x_i$, so that $|x_i| \leqslant w_{\mathrm{M}i}$. We also let w_{M} be the largest $w_{\mathrm{M}i}$; therefore:

$$|w_i^{(k)}| \leqslant w_{\mathrm{M}}; \qquad i = 1, 2, \ldots, n; \qquad k \geqslant i \tag{3.62}$$

Then, using Equation (3.22):

$$|g_i^{(k)}| \leqslant 3.01\varepsilon_{\mathrm{M}} w_{\mathrm{M}i}; \qquad k > i \tag{3.63}$$

and

$$|\delta w_i| \leqslant 3.01\varepsilon_{\mathrm{M}} w_{\mathrm{M}i} r_i^U, \tag{3.64}$$

where r_i^U is the number of off-diagonal nonzeros in row i of $\mathbf{U}$. Alternatively, using Equation (3.62):

$$|\delta w_i| \leqslant 3.01\varepsilon_{\mathrm{M}} w_{\mathrm{M}} r_i^U. \tag{3.65}$$

Finally, we consider the residual

$$\mathbf{r} = \mathbf{Ax} - \mathbf{b} \tag{3.66}$$

obtained when the solution $\mathbf{x}$ of System (3.1) is computed using floating point arithmetic. Using Equations (3.41), (3.52) and (3.60), we obtain:

$$\mathbf{r} = -\mathbf{Ex} + \mathbf{L}\,\delta\mathbf{w} + \delta\mathbf{b}. \tag{3.67}$$

Taking the 1-norm or the ∞-norm, we have:

$$\|\mathbf{r}\| \leqslant \|\mathbf{E}\|\,\|\mathbf{x}\| + \|\mathbf{L}\|\,\|\delta\mathbf{w}\| + \|\delta\mathbf{b}\|. \tag{3.68}$$

From Equation (3.62) we obtain bounds for the norms of $\mathbf{x}$:

$$\|\mathbf{x}\|_1 \leqslant n w_{\mathrm{M}}$$

$$\|\mathbf{x}\|_\infty \leqslant w_{\mathrm{M}}. \tag{3.69}$$

Bounds for the norms of $\mathbf{E}$ and $\mathbf{L}$ are given in Table 3.1. Bounds for the norms of $\delta\mathbf{w}$ and $\delta\mathbf{b}$ were obtained from Equations (3.65) and (3.55), respectively, and are listed in Table 3.2. Thus, a bound for $\|\mathbf{r}\|$ can be computed using Equation (3.68).

Table 3.2 Values of some parameters and bounds for the norms $\delta\mathbf{b}$ and $\delta\mathbf{w}$ for forward and backward substitution.

A	Parameters defined in Section 3.4	Forward substitution	Backward substitution
Sparse	See Section 3.4	$\|\delta\mathbf{b}\|_1 \leqslant 3.01\varepsilon_M b_M n_L$	$\|\delta\mathbf{w}\|_1 \leqslant 3.01\varepsilon_M w_M n'_U$
		$\|\delta\mathbf{b}\|_\infty \leqslant 3.01\varepsilon_M b_M \left(\max_i r_i^L + 1\right)$	$\|\delta\mathbf{w}\|_\infty \leqslant 3.01\varepsilon_M w_M \max_i r_i^U$
Full	$r_i^L = i - 1$	$\|\delta\mathbf{b}\|_1 \leqslant \frac{3.01}{2}\varepsilon_M b_M n(n+1)$	$\|\delta\mathbf{w}\|_1 \leqslant \frac{3.01}{2}\varepsilon_M w_M n(n-1)$
	$r_i^U = n - i$ $n_L = n(n+1)/2$ $n'_U = n(n-1)/2$	$\|\delta\mathbf{b}\|_\infty \leqslant 3.01\varepsilon_M b_M n$	$\|\delta\mathbf{w}\|_\infty \leqslant 3.01\varepsilon_M w_M (n-1)$
Band	$r_i^L = \min(i-1, \beta)$ $r_i^U = \min(n-i, \beta)$	$\|\delta\mathbf{b}\|_1 \leqslant 3.01\varepsilon_M b_M (n-\beta/2)(\beta+1)$	$\|\delta\mathbf{w}\|_1 \leqslant 3.01\varepsilon_M w_M (n-\beta/2-1/2)\beta$
$\|\backslash\beta\backslash\beta\backslash\|$	$n_L = (n-\beta/2)(\beta+1)$ $n'_U = (n-\beta/2-1/2)\beta$	$\|\delta\mathbf{b}\|_\infty \leqslant 3.01\varepsilon_M b_M (\beta+1)$	$\|\delta\mathbf{w}\|_\infty \leqslant 3.01\varepsilon_M w_M \beta$
Band	$r_i^L = \min(i-1, \beta)$ $r_i^U = \min(n-i, 2\beta)$	$\|\delta\mathbf{b}\|_1 \leqslant 3.01\varepsilon_M b_M (n-\beta/2)(\beta+1)$	$\|\delta\mathbf{w}\|_1 \leqslant 3.01\varepsilon_M w_M (2n-2\beta-1)\beta$
$\|\backslash\beta\backslash 2\beta\backslash\|$	$n_L = (n-\beta/2)(\beta+1)$ $n'_U = (2n-2\beta-1)\beta$	$\|\delta\mathbf{b}\|_\infty \leqslant 3.01\varepsilon_M b_M (\beta+1)$	$\|\delta\mathbf{w}\|_\infty \leqslant 6.02\varepsilon_M w_M \beta$

The residual $\mathbf{r}$ has another interpretation. Let $\tilde{\mathbf{x}}$ be the exact solution of Equation (3.1); then $\mathbf{A}\tilde{\mathbf{x}} = \mathbf{b}$ and

$$\mathbf{r} = \mathbf{A}(\mathbf{x} - \tilde{\mathbf{x}}). \tag{3.70}$$

Therefore

$$\|\mathbf{x} - \tilde{\mathbf{x}}\| = \|\mathbf{A}^{-1}\mathbf{r}\| \leqslant \|\mathbf{A}^{-1}\|\,\|\mathbf{r}\| \tag{3.71}$$

and a bound for $\|\mathbf{x} - \tilde{\mathbf{x}}\|$ can be found when $\|\mathbf{A}^{-1}\|$ is available.

3.5. The control of numerical errors

In Equation (3.41), $\mathbf{A}$ is the given matrix, assumed to be exactly stored in the computer memory. $\mathbf{L}$ and $\mathbf{U}$ are computed triangular matrices. Equation (3.41) expresses the fact that the exact product between $\mathbf{L}$ and $\mathbf{U}$ is not equal to $\mathbf{A}$ but to $\mathbf{A} + \mathbf{E}$, where $\mathbf{E}$ is an error matrix. Equation (3.42) provides bounds for the elements of $\mathbf{E}$ in terms of the parameters ε_{M}, a_{ij} and n_{ij}. Acting upon these parameters we can improve the accuracy of the solution. Conversely, a bad choice may produce inaccurate results or even a complete loss of significance if some elements of $\mathbf{E}$ turn out to be much larger than the corresponding elements of $\mathbf{A}$.

Let us first examine a_{ij}, which was defined by Equation (3.27). To keep a_{ij} low we must avoid an excessive growth of the elements of the successive matrices $\mathbf{A}^{(k)}$. This is usually achieved by a convenient *scaling* of the original matrix $\mathbf{A}$ and by *pivot selection* in the course of elimination. Scaling will be considered in Section 3.7. Assuming for the moment that all elements of $\mathbf{A}$ are of comparable size, it is clear from Equation (3.26) that element growth can be prevented by requiring the successive pivots $A_{kk}^{(k)}$ to be large numbers. To discuss this point further we must state the concept of pivot selection more precisely. At the beginning of step k of elimination, $\mathbf{A}^{(k)}$ is available and a pivot is required to compute $\mathbf{A}^{(k+1)}$. The pivot need not necessarily be the element $A_{kk}^{(k)}$. We may choose any element $A_{ij}^{(k)} \neq 0$ with $i, j \geqslant k$, and then interchange row i with row k and column j with column k to bring $A_{ij}^{(k)}$ to position (k, k) (see Fig. 3.1). These interchanges introduce no conceptual difficulties in the elimination algorithm. Of course we do not need actually to perform the interchanges in the computer memory: we merely attach permutation vectors to the rows and columns, and record there the interchanges. Formally, when Equation (3.1) is the given system of linear equations, we solve Equation (3.3), where the permutation matrices $\mathbf{P}$ and $\mathbf{Q}$ contain all the information on row and column interchanges.

The bounds a_{ij} for the elements $A_{ij}^{(k)}$ may depend critically on the proper choice of $\mathbf{P}$ and $\mathbf{Q}$. On the other hand, when the factorization $\mathbf{PAQ} = \mathbf{LU}$ is computed, it is also known that the sparsity patterns of **L** and **U** may depend very strongly on the choice of **P** and **Q**. In some cases **P** and **Q** may be selected before elimination actually starts, in other cases their final forms are obtained during elimination, but in all cases both sparsity and error considerations are made.

Pivot selection strategies are examined in the next section. However, it is worth mentioning here the important case where **A** is symmetric positive definite. If a is the value of the largest diagonal element of **A** and diagonal pivoting is used, then Equation (2.59) shows that no element of any $\mathbf{A}^{(k)}$ will exceed a in absolute value. Thus, all that is needed to maintain numerical stability is that pivots be taken from the diagonal, while the order in which they are taken can be decided on sparsity grounds alone. The simplicity of this rule gave rise to the important developments discussed in Chapter 4.

To continue with the analysis of the error bounds given by Equation (3.42), we consider the machine precision ε_M. If the computer uses binary arithmetic and a real number is represented with a t-bit mantissa and an exponent, then $\varepsilon_M = 2^{-t}$. The total storage required for a set of real numbers is approximately proportional to t, and for computers where t can be changed the execution times of the elementary operations may also be roughly proportional to t. Thus, in the worst case, the total cost for computing **L** and **U** is proportional to t^2. On the other hand, the error decreases exponentially when t increases. This shows that a large improvement in the accuracy can be obtained at relatively little extra cost by using higher precision arithmetic, a fact which is not completely self-evident but has seldom been mentioned in the sparse matrix literature. For example, if t is increased from 24 to 56 bits, which correspond to single and double precision in IBM machines, the cost grows by a factor of about 4 or less while the error bound decreases by a factor of $2^{32} \cong 4 \times 10^9$. Of course the cost may grow further if more storage means using peripheral devices.

Finally, we turn our attention to the parameters n_{ij}, defined by Equation (3.30). The effect of these parameters on the error bounds, Equation (3.42), is also important. n_{ij} is bounded by $\min(i, j)$ and attains the bound for a full matrix, which means that if **A** is large and **L** and **U** are not sufficiently sparse, some of the n_{ij} may be large numbers and impair the error bounds. Besides, $n_{ij} - 1$ is the number of times an element A_{ij} is changed in the course of elimination; if elements are allowed to grow at each step, some a_{ij} may become too large in Equation (3.42) unless the n_{ij} are sufficiently small, which in turn requires **L** and **U** to be sufficiently sparse. Thus, when we try to retain sparsity, we are improving the error bounds, in addition of course to the other advantages of sparseness. This fact has been stressed by a number of authors (Tewarson, 1971; Duff, 1972, 1974a, 1977; Bunch, 1974b; Bunch and Rose, 1976; Gear, 1975). Of course sparsity alone cannot guarantee numerical stability and pivots must still be selected in such a way that an excessive growth of a_{ij} is prevented. It is in this sense that sparsity-preserving algorithms are usually regarded as a means for saving storage and computation, but it must be borne in mind that they also provide important improvements for the accuracy of the solution.

3.6. Numerical stability and pivot selection

We will now examine the most common pivot selection strategies for Gauss elimination, and their relation with numerical stability. We recall that the *active submatrix* at step k contains all $A_{ij}^{(k)}$ with $i \geqslant k, j \geqslant k$. The elements in the active submatrix are called the *active elements*. Four subsets of the elements in the active submatrix will be necessary for the discussion:

S_{pc} The subset of primary candidates. These are the nonzeros of the active submatrix which will be searched. The definition of this set amounts to a delimitation of the extension of the search for a pivot. The purpose of the definition is to reduce labour.

S_{st} A subset of S_{pc} which consists of the elements satisfying some stability condition.

S_{sp} A subset of S_{pc} which consists of the elements satisfying some sparsity preserving criterion.

$S_{piv} = S_{st} \cap S_{sp}$ the set from which the pivot will be chosen. The elements of S_{piv} satisfy both stability and sparsity requirements.

The definitions of S_{st} and S_{sp} need not be independent. Sometimes S_{st} is specified as a subset of S_{sp}, or vice versa. The pivot is chosen from S_{piv}. If S_{piv} contains more than one element, then sparsity considerations are made again to select the final element, because we would like to reduce cost by improving sparsity as much as possible while stability requirements are still met. If at some step S_{piv} happens to be empty, then sparsity requirements must be relaxed, redefining S_{sp}. Clearly, our stability criterion must allow enough freedom for S_{st} to be reasonably large. In practice, the explicit computation of the four sets is normally not necessary, because simplified procedures are available.

In this section, the discussion concentrates on S_{st}. Hints are given concerning S_{sp}, but this last set is discussed at length in Chapters 4 and 5.

The most important particular case is that of a symmetric positive definite matrix $\mathbf{A}$. In this case, all diagonal elements of $\mathbf{A}$ are positive. If a is the value of the largest diagonal element and all pivots are taken from the diagonal in any order, then $a_{ij} \leqslant a$ for all i, j by Equation (2.59). This means that the elements of successive $\mathbf{A}^{(k)}$ will not grow beyond a, and that the stability conditions will be satisfied, provided diagonal pivots are used. Thus, at step k, S_{st} consists of elements $A_{ii}^{(k)}$ with $i \geqslant k$, which are all positive because the active part of $\mathbf{A}^{(k)}$ is also symmetric and positive definite, and pivots can be chosen on sparsity grounds alone. This strategy is called *diagonal pivoting*, and is the subject of Chapter 4. Diagonal pivoting is formally equivalent to taking $\mathbf{Q} = \mathbf{P}^{\mathrm{T}}$ in Equation (3.3) and performing only symmetric interchanges between the rows and the columns of $\mathbf{A}$. Then all $\mathbf{A}^{(k)}$ are symmetric and $\mathbf{L} = \mathbf{U}^{\mathrm{T}}\mathbf{D}$, so that we can store only the upper (or the lower) triangle of $\mathbf{A}$ and the diagonal of $\mathbf{D}$, and perform the elimination there, thus saving about one half of both storage and computation.

For an indefinite matrix, the search for a pivot cannot be restricted to the diagonal. In *complete pivoting*, the set of primary candidates S_{pc}, at step k, contains all nonzeros of the active submatrix. The nonzero with the largest absolute value, say $A_{ij}^{(k)}$, is taken as the kth pivot and brought to position (k, k) by interchanging row i with row k and column j with column k. S_{st} is $A_{ij}^{(k)}$ alone and S_{sp} must necessarily contain $A_{ij}^{(k)}$. With complete pivoting, the growth of matrix elements is bounded by (Wilkinson, 1961):

$$|A_{ij}^{(k-1)}| \leqslant k^{1/2}[2^1 3^{1/2} \ldots k^{1/(k-1)}]^{1/2} a_0 < 2k^{(\ln k + 2)/4} a_0 \tag{3.72}$$

where $a_0 = \max|A_{ij}|$ and ln stands for natural logarithm. The values of the bounds given in Table 3.3 are useful for reference.

Table 3.3

k	$k^{1/2}[2^1 \ldots k^{1/(k-1)}]^{1/2}$	$2k^{(\ln k + 2)/4}$
100	3.57×10^3	4.01×10^3
1000	8.65×10^6	9.59×10^6
2000	1.51×10^8	1.68×10^8
5000	9.61×10^9	1.06×10^{10}
10 000	2.93×10^{11}	3.25×10^{11}

The true upper bound is much smaller. This strategy guarantees a tight bound for a_{ij} in Equation (3.27), but it is not satisfactory from the point of view of sparsity because no freedom is allowed for controlling the fill-in. Complete pivoting is recommended only for small dense matrices when numerical stability is at a premium.

Partial pivoting consists of selecting the element of maximum absolute value from a certain column (or row) in the active submatrix, and then performing the necessary interchanges. The pivotal line (a line is either a row or a column) is chosen on sparsity grounds. Thus, S_{pc} contains all active nonzeros, because the entire active submatrix must be inspected in order to find the pivotal line. S_{sp} contains, precisely, the nonzeros of the pivotal line.

S_{st} is, in this case, a subset of S_{sp}: it contains just the element of S_{sp} with the largest absolute value. So does S_{piv}. From Equation (3.26) (disregarding $e_{ij}^{(k)}$), or from Fig. 3.1, we may deduce the following relation, valid when partial pivoting is used:

$$|A_{ij}^{(k+1)}| \leqslant 2 \max_{i,j} |A_{ij}^{(k)}|. \tag{3.73}$$

This ensures that elements can grow by a factor of not more than 2 at each step, and that the overall growth is limited to 2^{ν}, where $\nu = \max(n_{ij}) - 1$ is the maximum number of operations on an individual element (Gear, 1975). The actual growth, however, is likely to be much smaller, so that if good error bounds are to be obtained we need to monitor the size of the matrix elements or to use some good estimator. This point is discussed in Section 3.7.

Partial pivoting allows some advantage to be taken of sparsity, but it is still too rigid a scheme. A more versatile scheme can be obtained without seriously impairing the results by using *threshold pivoting* (Reid, 1971b, 1977). In threshold pivoting all nonzeros of the active submatrix are primary candidates and belong to S_{pc}. A *tolerance* u is chosen in the range $0 < u \leqslant 1$, and S_{st} is defined to be the set of all nonzeros $A_{ij}^{(k)}$ of S_{pc} which satisfy one of the following conditions:

$$|A_{ij}^{(k)}| \geqslant u \max_{k \leqslant p \leqslant n} |A_{pj}^{(k)}| \tag{3.74a}$$

$$|A_{ij}^{(k)}| \geqslant u \max_{k \leqslant q \leqslant n} |A_{iq}^{(k)}|. \tag{3.74b}$$

S_{sp} is defined independently, usually using some form of Markowitz criterion to be discussed in Chapter 5. The final pivot is selected from $S_{piv} = S_{st} \cap S_{sp}$, again using sparsity considerations, and brought to position (k, k) by means of interchanges. If S_{piv} results empty, then S_{st} must be enlarged by reducing the value of u. In practice, however, the procedure works differently: an element is selected from S_{pc}, the best from the point of view of sparsity. This element is then tested for conditions (3.74) and accepted as pivot if one of them is satisfied. The element is rejected if (3.74) is not met and a new one is selected, again from sparsity conditions, but this situation is relatively rare and the additional search contributes little to the overall cost provided a reasonable value of u is used. The selection $u = 1$ corresponds to partial pivoting. The choice of u was found not to be very critical and a value $u = 0.25$ was recommended. The value $u = 0.1$ allows good retention of both sparsity and accuracy (Duff, 1977), but a value as low as $u = 0.01$ can be used if $\nu = \max(n_{ij}) - 1$ is a small number, as happens in linear programming (Tomlin, 1972).

From Equation (3.26), disregarding $e_{ij}^{(k)}$ and when Equations (3.74) are fulfilled, we deduce:

$$|A_{ij}^{(k+1)}| \leqslant (1 + u^{-1}) \max_{i,j} |A_{ij}^{(k)}|. \tag{3.75}$$

This ensures that the growth of matrix elements per step is limited to the factor $(1 + u^{-1})$, and the overall growth is bounded by $(1 + u^{-1})^{\nu}$ (Gear, 1975). The actual growth is normally much smaller and must be monitored, or an estimator must be used (see Section 3.7). Threshold pivoting is very popular and is used in most production codes.

Two alternative pivotal strategies were proposed by Zlatev (1980). The strategies depend on a stability parameter u in the range $0 < u \leqslant 1$ and a parameter p which determines the number of rows of the active submatrix to be searched at stage k, where $1 \leqslant p \leqslant n - k + 1$. Both p and u are fixed numbers and values of p as small as 3 may give good results. The set S_{pc} of primary candidates consists of the nonzeros of p rows of the active submatrix. The selection of the p rows is made trying to improve sparsity, for example they may be the p rows with fewest nonzeros at stage k. The stability condition used to determine which elements of S_{pc} belong to S_{st} is the same as in threshold pivoting by rows, Equation (3.74b). S_{sp} is defined as a subset of S_{st}, using the following criterion which produces a local optimization of sparsity: an element $A_{ij}^{(k)}$ of S_{st} belongs to S_{sp} when $\mu_{ij} \equiv (r_i - 1)(c_j - 1) = \mu$, where $\mu = \min_{i,j} (\mu_{ij})$, r_i is the number of active nonzeros in row i at stage k, and c_j is the number of active nonzeros in column j at stage k. In other words, S_{sp} contains all nonzeros of S_{st} for which the product of other active nonzeros in the same row and other active nonzeros in the same column, at the beginning of the step, is a minimum. In this case, S_{piv} coincides with S_{sp}.

Zlatev's strategy is to choose as pivot any element of S_{piv}. The *improved Zlatev's strategy* is to choose the element of S_{piv} with the largest absolute value. In normal cases, both strategies give about the same accuracy, but the improved one gives best results in difficult cases because bad pivotal sequences permitted by the first strategy are avoided.

When **A** is symmetric but indefinite and we wish to preserve symmetry, we may take for pivot any diagonal element which satisfies, say, the stability condition for threshold pivoting, Equation (3.74), and some sparsity criterion. However, such an element may not exist, as shown by the following example (Wilkinson, 1965):

$$\mathbf{A} = \begin{vmatrix} 0 & 1 \\ 1 & 0 \end{vmatrix},$$

for which elimination with diagonal pivoting fails at the first step. It is worth mentioning here two stable procedures which preserve symmetry. The methods employ congruence transformations rather than elimination. In the case of a full matrix, both the number of operations and the storage can be reduced to about one half of that required by Gauss elimination with interchanges, which would destroy symmetry. The first method, proposed by Parlett and Reid (1970) and reformulated by Aasen (1971), reduces the given matrix to symmetric band form with bandwidth $2\beta + 1 = 3$ (tridiagonal form). The resulting tridiagonal system is then solved by Gauss elimination with interchanges, losing the symmetry. The other method, called *block diagonal pivoting* (Bunch, 1971; Bunch and Parlett, 1971) takes pivots from the diagonal but uses 2×2 principal submatrices as pivots when no good scalar pivot is available. In this case, the matrix is reduced to block diagonal form. The two methods, together with a third approach, were discussed by Bunch (1974a) in both the full and band cases, though neither method would preserve the band structure. Bunch's method was tested by Duff and Reid (1976) in the sparse case, and satisfactory results were reported. It was further discussed by Duff (1978).

Applications exist where elimination is performed on **A** at the same time that **A** is being assembled. This is the case of the Frontal and Multi-frontal strategies, used mainly in connection with the Finite Element and Finite Difference methods, but also in more general contexts. In such cases, S_{pc} is restricted at each step to the part of **A** which is fully assembled. In the symmetric positive definite case, pivots are taken from the diagonal. In the symmetric indefinite case, Bunch's method of block diagonal pivoting can be used with either 1×1 or 2×2 blocks as pivots. These modern and important techniques are discussed further in Chapter 4.

3.7. Monitoring or estimating element growth

When threshold pivoting with a tolerance u is employed, individual elements of the matrix **A** may grow in the course of elimination by a factor as high as $(1 + u^{-1})^{\nu}$, where ν is the number of operations performed on that element. However, the actual growth is usually much smaller in practice. Since we need values for a_{ij}, Equation (3.27), if we wish to know how accurate our solution is, we either have to monitor the growth of the elements or use a good estimator. Monitoring is usually done in terms of a single parameter a such that $|A_{ij}^{(k)}| \leqslant a$ for all i, j, k, which can easily be calculated during elimination. The weak form of the error bound, Equation (3.44), can be used in this case. Monitoring requires extra instructions in the inner loop of the program, and sometimes does not give a true indication of some errors because the a_{ij} are not explicitly obtained, while the upper bound a may be too high. A good estimator may be advantageous in such cases. We will describe the estimator suggested by Erisman and Reid (1974). Using Inequality (3.12) and the fact that $|a+b| \leqslant |a| + |b|$ for any a, b, in Equation (2.23), the following bound is obtained:

$$|A_{ij}^{(k)}| \leqslant |A_{ij}| + \|L_{i1}, L_{i2}, \ldots, L_{ik}\|_p \|U_{1j}, U_{2j}, \ldots, U_{kj}\|_q \qquad (3.76)$$

for $k < i, j \leqslant n$. This bound can be conveniently used in practice with $p = 1$ and $q = \infty$, or vice versa. In the first case:

$$|A_{ij}^{(k)}| \leqslant |A_{ij}| + l_i^{(k)} u_j^{(k)} \qquad (3.77)$$

where, for $k < i, j \leqslant n$:

$$l_i^{(k)} = \sum_{m=1}^{k} |L_{im}|, \qquad u_j^{(k)} = \max_{1 \leqslant m \leqslant k} |U_{mj}|. \qquad (3.78)$$

The parameters $l_i^{(k)}$ and $u_j^{(k)}$ may be accumulated in two real arrays of n positions each as the elimination progresses, and used to see whether any element of $\mathbf{A}^{(k)}$ has become too large. If the growth proves unsatisfactory it will normally be necessary to start the elimination again with a higher value of the tolerance u, although the method of Stewart (1974) for pivot modification can also be used. In this way growth monitoring has not only been taken out of the inner loop of the program, but it is even possible to perform the test once every 10 or 50 steps, because $l_i^{(k)}$ and $u_j^{(k)}$ both increase monotonically as k increases. Of course, as noted previously, if $\mathbf{A}$ is symmetric and positive definite, and diagonal pivoting is used, no growth takes place and growth monitoring is not necessary.

3.8. Scaling

It often happens in practice that all the elements of the given matrix $\mathbf{A}$ are of comparable size. Elimination can then proceed directly. However, if this is not the case, some form of *scaling* is necessary before elimination starts, to obtain an accurate factorization. Scaling is usually done by multiplying the rows and the columns of $\mathbf{A}$ by suitable scale factors. To state it formally: if the system of equations is $\mathbf{Ax} = \mathbf{b}$, we find two diagonal matrices $\mathbf{R}$ and $\mathbf{C}$, and solve:

$$(\mathbf{RAC})(\mathbf{C}^{-1}\mathbf{x}) = (\mathbf{Rb}). \qquad (3.79)$$

The simplest method (Van der Sluis, 1970) is known as *equilibration*. A matrix $\mathbf{B}$ is said to be *row equilibrated* with respect to the p-norm if $\|\mathbf{e}_i^{\mathrm{T}}\mathbf{B}\|_p = 1$ for all i and $\mathbf{e}_i$ is the ith column of the identity matrix $\mathbf{I}$. $\mathbf{B}$ is *column equilibrated* when $\|\mathbf{Be}_j\|_p = 1$ for all j. Van der Sluis' method is to determine $\mathbf{R}$ in such a way that $\mathbf{RA}$ is row equilibrated with respect to some norm, and then to determine **C** in such a way that **RAC** is column equilibrated. Note that **RAC** is usually not row equilibrated. This simple procedure may, however, lead to poor results (Curtis and Reid, 1972). A variant of this method, called *balancing*, is obtained when $\mathbf{C} = \mathbf{R}^{-1}$, and **C** is determined in such a way that sums of the magnitudes of elements in corresponding rows and columns are made nearly equal (Parlett and Reinsch, 1969). **C** is determined iteratively and its elements are powers of the radix β of the machine in order to prevent scaling from introducing round-off errors. Balancing is used mainly for unsymmetric eigenanalysis, because it has the property of preserving the eigenvalues (Smith *et al.*, 1976, p. 200). The effect of equilibration is that of improving the condition number of the matrix (Wilkinson, 1965, p. 192).

A better scaling procedure was suggested by Hamming (1971). The diagonal elements of **R** and **C** are defined as follows:

$$R_{ii} = \beta^{-r_i}; \qquad C_{ii} = \beta^{-c_i}, \tag{3.80}$$

where β is the machine radix ($\beta = 2$ for binary machines), so that an element of **RAC** is $A_{ij}\beta^{-r_i-c_j}$. Hamming suggests reducing the range of values spanned by the elements of **RAC** by computing ρ_i and γ_j such that

$$\sum_{A_{ij}\neq 0} (\log_\beta|A_{ij}| - \rho_i - \gamma_j)^2 \tag{3.81}$$

is minimized, and then taking for r_i and c_j the nearest integers to ρ_i and γ_j, respectively. Scaling by integer powers of the radix ensures that no rounding errors are introduced. However, when β is large, the scaling may be very coarse, and it might then be better to take $r_i = \rho_i$ and $c_j = \gamma_j$ to get a finer scaling. This procedure is not expensive to implement. Curtis and Reid (1972) report good results and use the method of conjugate gradients to solve (3.81), which normally requires 7 to 10 sweeps through the matrix. Tosovic (1973) also reports good results. A similar method was proposed by Fulkerson and Wolfe (1962). They use linear programming to minimize

$$\max_{A_{ij}\neq 0} |\log_\beta|A_{ij}| - \rho_i - \gamma_j|, \tag{3.82}$$

but Curtis and Reid (1972) found that this gives poorer results than Hamming's suggestion.

Skeel (1981) points out that, when partial pivoting is used in combination with equilibration and S_{sp} at stage k is fixed, it is possible to force practically any choice of pivots by scaling the matrix in one way or another. Skeel shows that column pivoting with row equilibration satisfies the same type of error bound as does row pivoting without equilibration, and vice versa. He also shows that, in situations where the norm of the residual $\|\mathbf{r}\|$, Equation (3.66), is important, the error for column pivoting without equilibration is as small as one might reasonably expect, but that column equilibration is needed if row pivoting is employed.

CHAPTER 4

Ordering for Gauss Elimination: Symmetric Matrices

4.1. Introduction: Statement of the problem

In this chapter we examine how sparsity if affected when Gauss elimination is performed on a symmetric sparse matrix **A** and the triangular factorization of **A** is obtained either in the form:

$$\mathbf{A} = \mathbf{U}^{\mathrm{T}}\mathbf{D}\mathbf{U} \tag{4.1}$$

or

$$\mathbf{A} = \mathbf{U}'^{\mathrm{T}}\mathbf{U}', \tag{4.2}$$

where **U** is upper triangular with unit diagonal, **D** is diagonal, **U**′ is upper triangular, and **U** and **U**′ have the same nonzero pattern. The elements of **U** (or of **U**′) are calculated in the course of the elimination, and new nonzero elements result at positions of **U** which correspond to zeros in **A**. Cancellations may also occur, but they are rare in practice except in some special cases which deserve particular consideration. Following the usual practice, we will neglect cancellations. Thus, every element which is nonzero in **A** is also nonzero in **U**. Therefore, the nonzero pattern of **U** consists of all positions which contain nonzeros in the upper triangle of **A**, plus the *fill-in*, which is the set of positions of the additional nonzeros generated during the elimination. Note that we are only concerned with the positions of the nonzeros, not with their values.

There are three strong reasons why fill is undesirable:

(1) Storage must be allocated for the new nonzeros. The amount of fill may be very great. A particularly perverse example, often quoted in the literature (e.g. Reid, 1977, p. 109; Duff, 1977, p. 504) is a matrix with full first row, first column and main diagonal and zeros elsewhere: if the elements of the first column are eliminated, nonzeros are introduced in all the remaining positions of the matrix. When **A** is symmetric and positive definite, the amount of fill and the positions of the new nonzeros can be determined before elimination starts. The necessary storage can then be allocated. However, when **A** is indefinite, this cannot be done, and the storage allocation problem is much harder.

(2) The computer time required to achieve the factorization increases rapidly when the amount of fill increases, because many more arithmetic operations are required. Usually, the amount of storage and the operation count together determine whether a problem is at all tractable by direct methods. The range of problems for which direct methods are applicable is thus closely related to our ability to reduce fill-in.

(3) Error bounds increase when the amount of fill increases, as shown by Equation (3.42) of Chapter 3, where n_{ij}, defined by Equation (3.30), is a measure of the sparseness of **U**. Many authors have pointed out the crucial importance of the fact that an element of **A** is only operated upon a few times, thus preventing excessive error accumulation. On the other hand, the prevention of error growth must be considered as one of the objectives pursued by the fill-reducing algorithms, a point of view which has not been sufficiently stressed in the literature. Too much fill may mean too much error and may force the use of an iterative method rather than a direct one to solve a large system of equations.

Nowadays much is known about the origin of fill and efficient procedures have been devised to reduce its amount. All procedures take advantage of the freedom which exists for the selection of the pivots. When **A** is positive definite pivots can be selected from the diagonal, as discussed in Section 3.6. Alternatively, the rows and columns of **A** can be permuted in any way which preserves symmetry, and then elimination can be performed pivoting sequentially on the diagonal elements. A well known fact is that the amount of fill-in may depend drastically on the permutation selected. For example, consider the perverse matrix just mentioned, the one with full first row, first column and main diagonal, and zeros elsewhere: if the first and last columns are interchanged, and the first and last rows are also interchanged, the new structure will have nonzeros only in the last row, last column and diagonal, and elimination will produce no fill-in at all.

Let us state our problem explicitly. We wish to solve

$$\mathbf{Ax} = \mathbf{b} \tag{4.3}$$

with $\mathbf{A}$ sparse and symmetric. If $\mathbf{P}$ is a permutation matrix, and thus $\mathbf{P}^{\mathrm{T}}\mathbf{P} = \mathbf{I}$, the system of linear equations (4.3) can be written:

$$\mathbf{PAP}^{\mathrm{T}}\mathbf{Px} = \mathbf{Pb} \tag{4.4}$$

or, if $\mathbf{y} = \mathbf{Px}$ and $\mathbf{c} = \mathbf{Pb}$,

$$\mathbf{By} = \mathbf{c}, \tag{4.5}$$

where $\mathbf{B} = \mathbf{PAP}^{\mathrm{T}}$ is the permuted form of $\mathbf{A}$ and is also sparse and symmetric. Besides, if $\mathbf{A}$ is positive definite, $\mathbf{B}$ is also positive definite. However, the amount of fill-in and the number of operations required to factorize $\mathbf{B}$ depend on $\mathbf{P}$. Our concern is to find a *convenient* $\mathbf{P}$, or alternatively a *convenient ordering* or numbering of the rows and columns of $\mathbf{A}$, eventually different from the natural ordering given by the original matrix, before solving the permuted system $\mathbf{By} = \mathbf{c}$.

An ordering is said to be optimum with respect to fill if it results in the least possible fill-in. An ordering is said to be optimum with respect to operation count if it results in the least possible number of operations. If $\mathbf{A}$ is of order n there are $n!$ different orderings, one or more of which are optimum with respect to fill, and one or more of which are optimum with respect to operation count. One would like to find such optimum orderings, but unfortunately this seems to be very difficult and no efficient algorithms exist for the purpose. Existing procedures are heuristic and usually attempt to find orderings for which the fill-in and the operation count are low, without guaranteeing a true minimum.

Graph theory is an extremely useful tool for the analysis of algorithms which operate on matrices. We give some basic notions in Section 4.2, but the interested reader can find more material, for example, in the books by König (1950) or Harary (1969). Band and profile methods are discussed in Sections 4.5 and 4.6. These methods regard fill-in in a global manner, and confine it to certain areas of the matrix. In Section 4.7 we give the graph-theoretical background necessary for the understanding of the remaining sections, where methods which look at fill-in in more detail are discussed. It is difficult to compare methods because the efficiency of a method depends on the problem or class of problems for which it is being used. Some references relevant to this question are given in the corresponding sections. Most of the chapter deals with positive definite matrices, but symmetric indefinite matrices are examined in Section 4.17.

Software based on the methods discussed in this chapter is available. See for example the Software Catalog (Heath, 1982), and Duff (1978).

4.2. Basic notions of graph theory

A *graph* $G = (V, E)$ consists of a set V of *vertices* $u, v, w, \ldots$, together with a set E of *edges*, where an edge is a pair (u, v) of vertices of V. We will use vertical bars to indicate the number of elements or *cardinality* of a set; thus $|V|$ is the number of vertices and $|E|$ is the number of edges in G. When no distinction is made between (u, v) and (v, u), we say that edges are represented by unordered pairs and that the graph is *undirected*. If, however, the pairs which represent edges are ordered, the graph is a *directed graph* or a *digraph*. An undirected graph may also be regarded as a digraph for which, if (u, v) is an edge, then also (v, u) is an edge. A graph with n vertices is said to be *labelled* (*ordered*, *numbered*) when the vertices are in a one-to-one correspondence with the integers $1, 2, \ldots, n$. We will often refer to vertices by their numbers in a labelled graph, and if α is the correspondence between vertices and numbers, we will sometimes use the notation $G_\alpha = (V, E, \alpha)$ for the labelled graph.

A graph may be associated with any matrix $\mathbf{A}$. If $\mathbf{A}$ is square of order n, A_{ij} are its elements, and the diagonal elements A_{ii} are all different from zero, then the graph is undirected and contains n labelled vertices $v_1, v_2, \ldots, v_n$, and (v_i, v_j) is an edge of the graph if and only if $A_{ij} \neq 0$. A diagonal element A_{ii} which is different from zero corresponds to a *loop* or *selfedge* (v_i, v_i), and the assumption that $A_{ii} \neq 0$ for all i implies that all selfedges are present in the graph. When this is true, it is not usually necessary to take selfedges explicitly into account. In Chapter 5 we will discuss digraphs and other types of graphs which are usually associated with unsymmetric matrices. The present chapter is concerned only with symmetric matrices having a zero-free diagonal, and the analysis is restricted to undirected graphs. Figure 4.1 shows a symmetric matrix and its corresponding labelled graph. Storage of graph representations in the computer memory was considered in Section 1.4.

The graph of a symmetric matrix remains unchanged if a symmetric permutation is performed on the matrix, only the labelling of the vertices changes. This invariance property is what makes graphs interesting in sparse

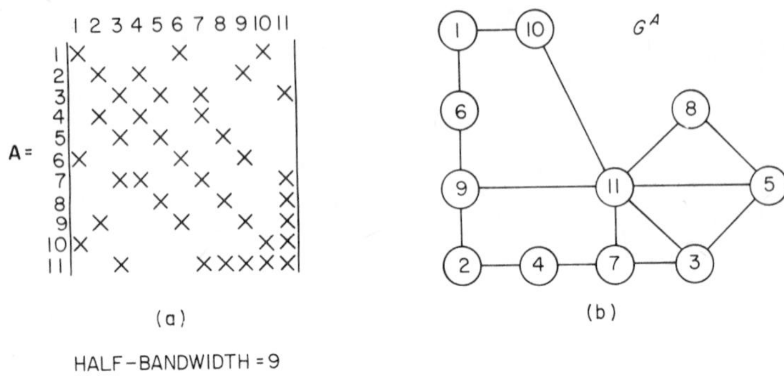

Figure 4.1 The structure of a symmetric sparse matrix and the corresponding labelled undirected graph.

matrix technology. Explicitly, if **A** is a symmetric matrix and $\mathbf{B} = \mathbf{PAP}^T$, where **P** is a permutation matrix (see Section 2.6), and if G_A and G_B are the graphs associated with **A** and **B**, respectively, then G_A and G_B are identical except for the labelling of their vertices.

If vertices are mapped into points and edges into simple curves in the plane, a *planar embedding* of the graph is obtained. A representation of a graph on paper such as the one shown in Fig. 4.1(b) is a planar embedding. A graph is *planar* when an embedding exists such that no two edges intersect. Matrices with planar graphs are important because they are known to have good orderings for Gauss elimination. The graph of Fig. 4.1(b) is planar.

A *subgraph* $G' = (V', E')$ of $G = (V, E)$ is a graph which consists of some or all vertices of G and some of the edges of G: $V' \subseteq V$, $E' \subset E$. The subgraph is a *section graph* when V' consists of only some of the vertices of G, and E' consists of all edges (u, v) of G such that both u and v are in V':

$$V' \subset V$$

$$E' = \{(u, v) \in E | u \in V' \quad \text{and} \quad v \in V'\} \tag{4.6}$$

where {} indicates "set". In Fig. 4.1(b), vertices 3, 5, 7, 8 and 11, together with edges (3, 5), (5, 8), (8, 11), (11, 7), (3, 7) and (3, 11) are a section graph.

If (u, v) is an edge, vertices u and v are said to be *adjacent*. The edge (u, v) is said to be *incident* to the vertex u and to the vertex v. The *degree* of a vertex is the number of edges incident to it. If W is a subset of the vertices of G, the *adjacent set* of W, denoted by Adj(W), is the set of all vertices not in W which are adjacent to vertices in W. Namely, given $G = (V, E)$ and $W \subset V$:

$$\text{Adj}(W) = \{u \in V - W | \exists v \in W \ni (u, v) \in E\}$$

where $V - W$ is the set of all vertices of V which are not in W. In Fig. 4.1, the vertices 1 and 6 are adjacent, and both are of degree 2. If W is the set of vertices (1, 6), then Adj(W) = (9, 10). A subgraph is a *clique* when every pair of vertices is adjacent. In Fig. 4.1, the subgraph (3, 7, 11) is a clique.

A *path* is an ordered set of distinct vertices $(u_1, u_2, \ldots, u_{m+1})$ such that u_i and u_{i+1} are adjacent for $i = 1, 2, \ldots, m$. m is the *length* of the path. A path of length m may also be regarded as an ordered set of m edges (u_1, u_2), $(u_2, u_3), \ldots, (u_m, u_{m+1})$. We say that two given vertices u and v are *connected by a path* if a path exists having u and v as its end points. A path is a *cycle* when $u_1 = u_{m+1}$. The *distance* $d(u, v)$ between two vertices u and v is the length of the shortest path connecting them. Given a vertex u, the largest distance between u and any other vertex of the graph is called the *eccentricity* $e(u)$ of the vertex u. The largest eccentricity of any vertex in a graph is the *diameter* of the graph. A *peripheral* vertex is one for which the eccentricity is equal to the diameter of the graph. Many sparse matrix algorithms which operate on the graph associated with the matrix, require a "starting" vertex having a large eccentricity. A peripheral vertex would be ideal for this purpose; unfortunately, however, no efficient algorithm is known which finds peripheral vertices. On the other hand, a good algorithm exists (Gibbs *et al.*, 1976) for finding *pseudoperipheral* vertices. A pseudoperipheral vertex u is defined by the condition that, if v is any vertex for which $d(u, v) = e(u)$, then $e(v) = e(u)$. This definition guarantees that the eccentricity of a pseudoperipheral vertex is "large", usually close to the diameter of the graph. In Fig. 4.1, vertices 1 and 3 are connected by the path (1, 10, 11, 3) of length 3, and also by the path (1, 6, 9, 11, 3) of length 4. The distance between 1 and 3 is thus 3. The path (5, 8, 11, 3, 5) is a cycle. The diameter of the graph is 4, and the peripheral vertices are 1, 2, 4, 5 and 6, because their eccentricity is 4. In this example, all pseudoperipheral vertices are true peripheral vertices, a situation which may presumably happen frequently in practice.

A graph is *connected* if every pair of vertices is connected by a path. Otherwise the graph is *disconnected*. A disconnected graph consists of two or more *connected components*. A *separator* is a set of vertices, the removal of which, together with their incident edges, disconnects an otherwise connected graph or connected component. A separator is *minimal* if no proper subset of it is a separator. A vertex which is itself a separator is called a *cutvertex*. The graph of Fig. 4.1 is connected. The set of vertices (7, 11) is a minimal separator, their removal leaving two connected components: (3, 5, 8) and (10, 1, 6, 9, 2, 4).

Given a subset of vertices $W \subset V$, the *span of* W, Span(W), consists of the union of W and all those vertices which are connected with vertices in W. If W is a single vertex v, Span(v) is the connected component containing v, but more in general Span(W) consists of all those connected components which contain any vertex of W.

The notion of reachable sets has proved to be very useful for the study of Gaussian elimination (George and Liu, 1978a). Given a graph and a subset S of vertices, if u and v are two distinct vertices which do not belong to S, we say that *v is reachable from u through S* when u and v are connected by a path which is either of length 1 (u and v are adjacent) or is composed entirely of vertices which belong to S (except, of course, the endpoints u and v). Given S and $u \notin S$, the *reachable set* Reach(u, S) of u through S is defined to be the set of all vertices which are reachable from u through S. Note that when S is empty, or when u does not belong to Adj(S), then Reach(u, S) = Adj(u). In Fig. 4.1, if we choose $S = (7, 3)$, then Reach(5, S) = (8, 11, 4), and Reach(8, S) = Adj(8) = (5, 11). Note also that u itself does not belong to Reach(u, S).

Graphs may be partitioned in several ways. A *partitioning* is obtained when the vertices are grouped into disjoint subsets $S_0, S_1, \ldots, S_m$. If the graph is disconnected and the subsets are the connected components, a *component partitioning* is obtained. When vertices are partitioned into levels, a *level structure* is obtained; this important class of partitionings, which we discuss in Section 4.3, is used in connection with many sparse matrix algorithms.

An undirected graph which is connected and has no cycles is called a *tree*. Trees are important in our context because a matrix of which the graph is a tree can be rearranged in such a way that it suffers no fill during Gauss elimination (Parter, 1961). In a tree there is exactly one path connecting any two given vertices (Berge, 1962). A tree is *rooted* when a vertex r is designated to be the root. The unique path which connects the root r with any other vertex u of the tree is used to establish an ancestor–descendant relation between the vertices: if v belongs to such a path, v is an *ancestor* of u, and u is a *descendant* of v. If u and v are adjacent, v is the *father* of u, and u is the *son* of v. If u and v are ancestors of w, we say that u is an *older* (*younger*) ancestor of w than v if the distance $d(r, u)$ between the root r and u is shorter (longer) than the distance $d(r, v)$. The root r is the oldest ancestor of any vertex in the rooted tree. The *pedigree* of a vertex is the set of its ancestors and the *offspring* is the set of its descendants.

As for any graph, a tree can be labelled by numbering its vertices. Different numbering schemes can be adopted and have useful properties (Aho *et al.*, 1976). The *monotone ordering* is important in our context: it is one for which each vertex is numbered before its father.

A partitioning of a graph which is not a tree can be used to generate a new graph, called the *quotient graph*, which is a tree. This idea forms the basis of a method for exploiting the desirable features of trees in the case of matrices having graphs which are not trees. Let the set of vertices V of a graph G be partitioned into the disjoint subsets $S_1, S_2, \ldots, S_m$. The quotient graph has the m sets S_i as *composite vertices*, and its edges are defined by the condition that (S_i, S_j) is an edge if and only if two vertices $u \in S_i$ and $v \in S_j$ can be found such that u and v are adjacent in G. When the quotient graph is a tree, it is called a *quotient tree*, and the corresponding partitioning a *tree partitioning*. Figure 4.2 shows a graph, its level structure and its quotient tree. A monotone ordering is also indicated by the numbers near the circles. An

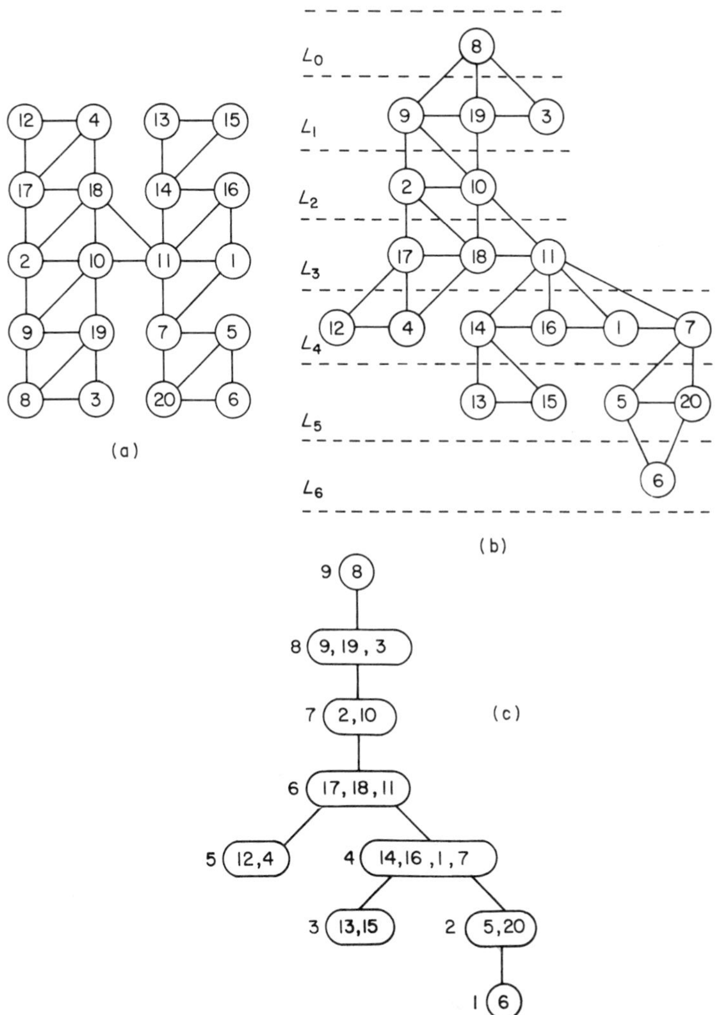

Figure 4.2 An undirected graph (a), its level structure (b), and the corresponding quotient tree (c). A monotone ordering of the quotient tree is also indicated in (c).

algorithm for finding a tree partitioning of a general graph, due to George (1977) is given in Section 4.9.

Given a connected graph $G = (V, E)$ a *spanning tree* $T = (V, E')$ is a subgraph which is a tree and contains all the vertices of G. A spanning tree can be obtained by searching the graph and breaking cycles by deleting edges without disconnecting the graph. A convenient procedure for doing this is depth-first search (Tarjan, 1972), to be discussed in Section 4.14. A spanning tree of the graph of Fig. 4.1 is shown in Fig. 4.3. A set of trees with no common vertices which span a graph is called a *spanning forest*. A spanning forest is obtained if cycles are broken in a disconnected graph.

An important source of sparse matrix problems is the Finite Element method (Zienkiewicz, 1977), and several ideas discussed in this chapter have originated in connection with that field. In the simplest version of the method, a differential equation is solved in a region of plane or space by dividing the region into finite elements which have nodes at the corners and may have additional nodes at the boundary or interior. A sparse matrix **A** is then constructed, in which a row and a column correspond to each node in the grid, and $A_{ij} \neq 0$ if and only if nodes i and j belong to the same finite element. Consider now the graph associated with matrix **A**, which is the *finite element graph*. There is a one-to-one correspondence between vertices of the graph and nodes of the grid. Two vertices are connected by an edge only if the corresponding nodes belong to the same finite element; thus, the graph has a clique corresponding to each element. The grid itself can be considered to represent another graph, called the *skeleton* of the finite element graph. The finite element graph is then obtained from the skeleton by adding all possible edges between nodes which belong to the same element.

If the problem to be solved by the Finite Element method is two-dimensional, the grid is two-dimensional and the skeleton graph is planar. If the elements are three-noded triangles, the finite element graph coincides

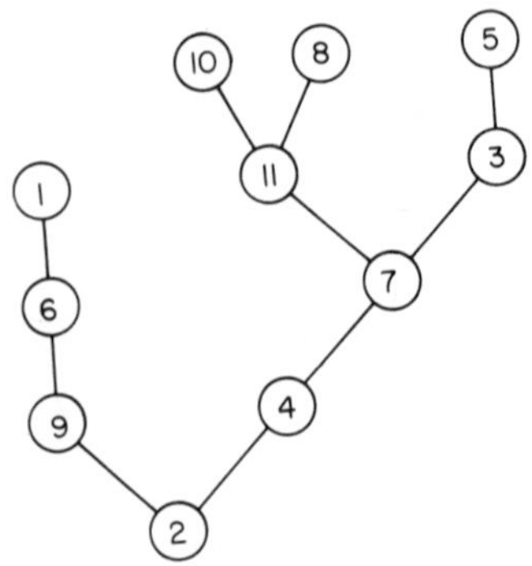

Figure 4.3 Spanning tree for the graph shown in Fig. 4.1(b).

with the skeleton and is also planar. However, any other type of element, even simple four-noded quadrilaterals, produces a graph which is not planar. A graph which is not planar but has a planar skeleton, is called an *almost-planar graph*. The definition can easily be extended to three dimensions. Almost-planar and almost-three-dimensional graphs will be used in Section 4.12 in connection with generalized nested dissection.

In the next sections we will discuss some graph theoretical algorithms which are important for sparse matrix technology.

4.3. Breadth-first search and adjacency level structures

In the preceding section we have mentioned that a graph $G = (V, E)$ can be partitioned by grouping the vertices into disjoint subsets. *Adjacency level structures* or simply *level structures* are a very important class of partitionings. A level structure $L_0, L_1, \ldots, L_m$ with $m + 1$ levels is obtained when the subsets are defined in such a way that:

$$\begin{aligned} &\text{Adj}(L_i) \subseteq L_{i-1} \cup L_{i+1}, \qquad 0 < i < m \\ &\text{Adj}(L_0) \subseteq L_1 \\ &\text{Adj}(L_m) \subseteq L_{m-1}. \end{aligned} \tag{4.7}$$

m is the *length* of the level structure, and the *width* is defined as the maximum number of vertices in any level. In a level structure, each L_i, $0 < i < m$, is a separator of the graph. A level structure is said to be *rooted* at L_0 if $L_0 \subset V$ is given and each of the remaining sets is the adjacent of the union of the preceding sets:

$$L_i = \text{Adj}\left(\bigcup_{j=0}^{i-1} L_j\right), \qquad i > 0 \tag{4.8}$$

If L_0 is a single vertex u, i.e. $L_0 = \{u\}$, we say that the level structure is *rooted at vertex u*.

A *search* is a procedure by which we visit the vertices and edges of a graph $G = (V, E)$ in some sequence. The sequence in which the vertices are visited can be used to order the graph, and the properties of edges discovered during the search can be used to sort edges into classes. Many graph-theoretical algorithms employ this technique, in particular some used in sparse matrix technology. Examples are the algorithm of Gibbs for finding pseudo-peripheral vertices and the dissection algorithms of George for symmetric matrices. A search is initiated at some arbitrarily chosen vertex s. The remaining vertices are then visited in a sequence established by some rule.

The search is *breadth-first* when we explore all edges incident to a current vertex before moving to a new vertex. The search is *depth-first* if we explore just one of the edges and take the vertex reached by the edge as the new current vertex. Depth-first search is considered in Section 4.14. In this section we examine the use of breadth-first search to generate a rooted level structure. Breadth-first search sorts vertices into levels and marks edges as either *tree arcs* or *cross-links*. Level L_0 is the starting vertex s alone. At a certain stage during the search we have identified all vertices in a certain level L_i. All vertices in preceding levels have been visited before and we also mark vertices in L_i as visited. Then for some $v \in L_i$, we examine the edges which lead from v to other vertices. If an edge reaches an unvisited vertex w, w belongs to level L_{i+1} and the edge is a tree arc. If an edge reaches a visited vertex x, then (v, x) is a cross-link. This visited vertex may only belong either to L_i or L_{i+1}, thus cross-links can only connect vertices in the same level or in adjacent levels. Tree arcs only connect vertices in adjacent levels, and there may be no connection between a vertex in level L_j and another vertex in level L_k if $|j - k| > 1$. Thus, each level i, $1 < i < m$, is a separator. Furthermore, a spanning tree is obtained, given by the set V of vertices of the original graph and the edges which are tree arcs. The algorithm, due to Rose *et al.* (1976), uses a queue (see Section 1.2) to store vertices in the order in which they are found. Consider the graph $G = (V, E)$ and let V_v be the set of visited vertices and E_t be the set of edges which are tree arcs. Explicitly, the algorithm is as follows:

Step 1 (Initialization). Initialize queue to contain the starting vertex s. Set: level $(s) = 0$, $V_v \leftarrow \{s\}$ and $E_t \leftarrow \emptyset$.

Step 2 (Form partition member). If queue is empty, stop. Otherwise remove the vertex v at the rear of the queue and find the set S of unvisited vertices adjacent to v:

$$S \leftarrow \text{Adj}(v) \cap (V - V_v)$$

Step 3 (Sort vertices and edges). If $S = \emptyset$ go to Step 2. Otherwise, for each $w \in S$ do the following:
(3a) add w to the front of the queue.
(3b) set level $(w) =$ level $(v) + 1$.
(3c) mark (v, w) as a tree arc: $E_t \leftarrow E_t \cup (v, w)$.
(3d) mark w as visited: $V_v \leftarrow V_v \cup \{w\}$.

Step 4 (Loop). Go to Step 2.

At the end of the algorithm, all vertices for which level$(v) = i$ are in level L_i, and all edges in $E - E_t$ are cross-links. For an example of the application of the algorithm consider the graph shown in Fig. 4.1(b), and choose 10 as the starting vertex. Initially, 10 is the only vertex in the queue and level$(10) = 0$.

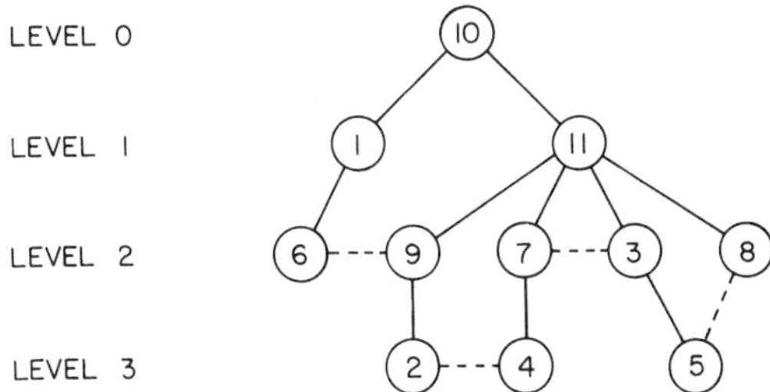

Figure 4.4 Level structure for the graph of Fig. 4.1(b), obtained by breadth-first search. The tree arcs of the spanning tree are shown with full lines. Cross-links are shown with dotted lines.

10 is removed from the queue and its adjacent set is found to be $S = \{1, 11\}$, both vertices unvisited. Thus we set level(1) = 1, level(11) = 1 and mark the edges (10, 1) and (10, 11) as tree arcs. Vertices 1 and 11 are added to the front of the queue.

Now, since 10 was removed from the queue, we find vertex 1 at the rear. We remove 1 and find that its only adjacent unvisited vertex is 6. Thus level(6) = 2 and (1, 6) is a tree arc. Next comes 11 from the rear of the queue. Its set of adjacent unvisited vertices is $S = \{9, 7, 3, 8\}$. These vertices are inscribed in level 2, and the edges leading to them from vertex 11 are marked as tree arcs. The reader can finish the construction of the level structure, which is shown complete in Fig. 4.4. The spanning tree is defined by the tree arcs shown with full lines. Dotted lines indicate cross-links. There are $|V| - 1 = 10$ tree arcs, and $|E| - |V| + 1 = 4$ cross-links. The length of the level structure is $m = 3$ and the width is 5. Note that the set of vertices $\{1, 11\}$ in level 1 is a separator of the graph. The set $\{6, 9, 7, 3, 8\}$ in level 2 is also a separator.

4.4. Finding a pseudoperipheral vertex and a narrow level structure of a graph

This algorithm is due to Gibbs *et al.* (1976). Although originally intended for reducing the bandwidth and profile of a sparse matrix, it is now widely used for finding a vertex with a large eccentricity. Several important sparse matrix algorithms require such a vertex (in the graph associated with the matrix) as a starting vertex. The Gibbs algorithm starts at a node r which is of minimum degree, and is thus likely to have a large eccentricity, and finds the level structure rooted at r. Now, if v is a vertex of the last level, the length of the level structure is the distance between r and v, which is in turn equal to the eccentricity of r. The eccentricity of v, however, is *at least* equal to the length of the level structure, and may be larger, in which case the eccentricity of v would be larger than that of r. Thus, the algorithm constructs the level structures rooted at the vertices of the last level sorted in order of ascending degree until a longer structure is found. The procedure is repeated until all possible structures have the same length, in which case r is a pseudoperipheral vertex. In practice, computer time can be saved by rejecting very wide structures as soon as they are detected (Crane *et al.*, 1975). Another time-saving modification was proposed by George (1977). In the level structure rooted at r, there may be many vertices in the last level; George proposes to pick as representatives the lowest degree vertex of each of the connected components in which the last level may be partitioned. The modified algorithm will certainly find a vertex with a high eccentricity, although it may not strictly satisfy the definition of a pseudoperipheral vertex. In detail, the modified algorithm is as follows:

Step 1 Find a vertex r of minimum degree.
Step 2 Generate the level structure rooted at r.
Step 3 Find all the connected components in the section graph corresponding to the deepest level of the current level structure.
Step 4 For each component find a vertex of minimum degree and generate its rooted level structure. Reject very wide level structures as soon as they are detected. If for some v, the level structure is longer than the one rooted at r, put $r \leftarrow v$ and go to Step 3.
Step 5 r is a vertex with a high eccentricity.

For the graph shown in Fig. 4.1, one possible starting vertex with minimum degree $= 2$, is 10. The level structure rooted at vertex 10 has length 3 (see example in Section 4.3). Vertices 2, 4 and 5 are in the deepest level. We pick 2 from the first connected component 2, 4, and find that the level structure rooted at 2 has length 4. Thus, 2 is better than 10. In the last level of the structure rooted at 2 we find vertex 5 alone. The level structure rooted at 5 also has length 4, and thus 2 is the vertex we were in search of. In this case we have found a true peripheral vertex (the diameter of the graph is 4), a result which may frequently be achieved in practice.

4.5. Reducing the bandwidth of a symmetric matrix

It has been mentioned in Section 1.5 that the bandwidth of a symmetric matrix depends on the order in which its rows and columns are arranged. In this section we will discuss the *algorithm of Cuthill and McKee* (1969; Cuthill,

1972) which provides a systematic procedure for renumbering the rows and columns in such a way that the permuted matrix has a small bandwidth.

The algorithm operates on the undirected graph associated with the matrix and requires a starting vertex. A labelling is found for the graph, and then rows and columns are permuted in the same way in order to preserve symmetry. The labelling is found as follows. The starting vertex is numbered with a 1. Then, for $i = 1, 2, \ldots, n$, where n is the order of the matrix, all vertices adjacent to vertex i which are still unnumbered, are numbered successively in order of increasing degree.

The starting vertex may be one of minimum degree. George and Liu (1975) and George (1977) have proposed a better strategy: the use of a pseudoperipheral vertex, which can in turn be found using the algorithm of Gibbs discussed in Section 4.4. Other strategies for selecting the starting vertex, or for using more than one starting vertex, have been proposed by Cheng (1973a,b), but they seem to be inferior (George, 1977). Due to its simplicity and effectiveness, the combination of the Cuthill–McKee algorithm with a starting pseudoperipheral vertex has become standard in many computations.

Other algorithms have also been proposed for bandwidth reduction or minimization. The method of Alway and Martin (1965) is a systematic search of permutations which lead to bandwidth reduction, until the theoretical minimum is achieved. Rosen (1968) has proposed a method that interchanges a pair of rows and columns at each step in a straightforward manner. This method is faster than Alway's, but unless a good initial guess is available, it may terminate with a bandwidth far from the minimum (Cuthill and McKee, 1969). Both algorithms are better when used to improve orderings obtained with the Cuthill–McKee algorithm. The algorithm of Arany *et al.* (1971) is a maximum degree method, similar to the method of Cuthill and McKee except that it specifically chooses vertices of high degree in the middle of the level structure. For some matrices it may lead to significant improvements at relatively little computational cost, particularly when the corresponding graph has a cutvertex, which is used as a starting vertex. Algorithms for finding cutvertices have been presented by Paton (1971), Shirey (1969) and Martelli (1973).

Tewarson (1971) has proposed probabilistic methods for permuting an arbitrary sparse matrix to narrow band form and to other desirable forms.

Figure 4.5 shows an example of application of the algorithm of Cuthill and McKee. Consider the symmetric sparse matrix and its associated undirected graph represented in Fig. 4.1. The matrix is of order 11 and has a comparatively large half-bandwidth, equal to 9. The graph was considered in Section 4.2, and it was mentioned there that the peripheral vertices are 1, 2, 4, 5 and 6. Let us take 1 as the starting vertex for the algorithm. This vertex is

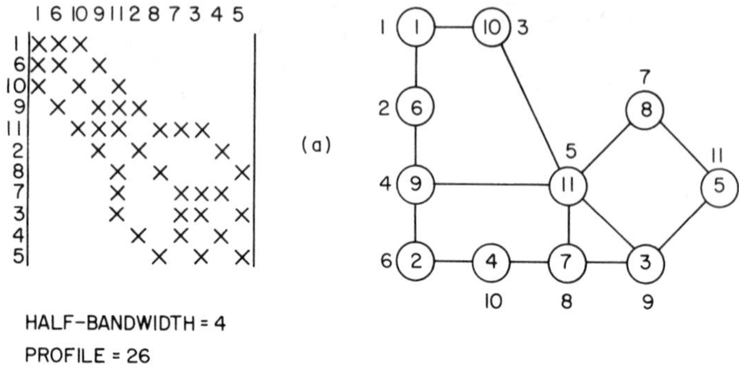

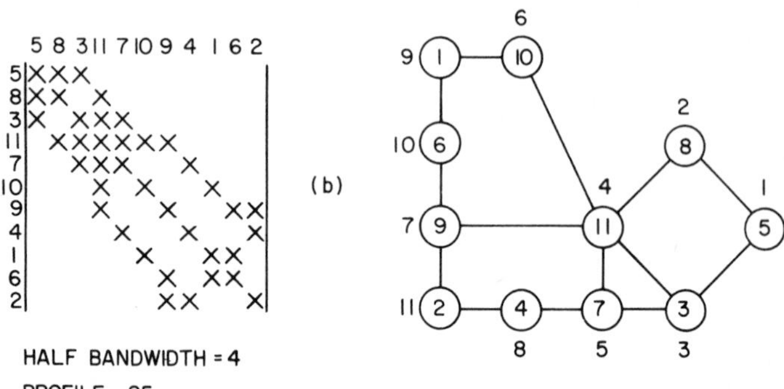

Figure 4.5 Two examples of application of the algorithm of Cuthill and McKee to the graph of Fig. 4.1(b). The permuted matrix and the relabelled graph when: (a) 1 is the starting vertex, and (b) 5 is the starting vertex. Graph relabellings are shown with numbers near the circles, while the numbers inside the circles show the old labelling.

renumbered with a 1, as seen in Fig. 4.5(a), where the original labelling is shown inside the circles, and the new labelling outside. At this point, the set of already numbered vertices is composed of vertex 1 alone. The adjacent vertices are 6 and 10, both of degree 2. The tie is broken in an arbitrary manner, and vertex 6 is labelled with a 2 and vertex 10 with a 3. The next candidates are vertices 9 and 11, of degrees 3 and 5 respectively; thus, 9 is labelled with a 4 and 11 with a 5. The algorithm is continued in the same manner until the complete new labelling is obtained. The labelling and the corresponding permuted matrix are shown in Fig. 4.5(a). The half-bandwidth is now only 4. It is important to notice, however, that a matrix is seldom actually permuted in the computer memory. Instead, all that is done is to store the permutation in an array, say IPER. Then, when row or column i is required, we merely access row or column IPER (i) (Gustavson, 1976a). For our example:

position =	1	2	3	4	5	6	7	8	9	10	11
IPER =	1	6	10	9	11	2	8	7	3	4	5

If we need, for example, row 4 of the matrix of Fig. 4.5(a), we find IPER(4) = 9, and the row we need is row 9 of the original matrix, Fig. 4.1.

Another example of application of the algorithm of Cuthill and McKee is shown in Fig. 4.5(b). This time the peripheral vertex 5 was chosen as the starting vertex. The labelling which is obtained and the corresponding permuted matrix are given in the figure. The permuted matrix also has a half-bandwidth equal to 4.

4.6. Reducing the profile of a symmetric matrix

The profile of a symmetric matrix was defined in Section 1.6 as the number of elements which are inside the envelope of the matrix. It was also mentioned that reducing the profile is highly desirable when the matrix is stored according to Jennings' scheme, and that this can be achieved by reordering the rows and columns. In this section we will discuss some algorithms which can be used for that purpose. The algorithms operate on the graph associated with the matrix.

It has been found (George, 1971) that by reversing the ordering provided by the Cuthill–McKee algorithm discussed in the preceding section, an ordering having a much smaller profile can often be found. This method is known as the *Reverse Cuthill–McKee algorithm*. The bandwidth remains unchanged when the order is reversed, but it has been shown that the profile can never increase (Liu and Sherman, 1975). Examples of this method are given in Fig. 4.6, where the matrices (a) and (b) are the reversed versions of the matrices (a) and (b) of Fig. 4.5, respectively. The profiles are reduced from 26 to 24 in the first case, and from 25 to 23 in the second case. The profile of the original matrix in Fig. 4.1 is 40.

Another important profile-reducing algorithm is due to King (1970). This algorithm operates as follows. Choose a vertex of minimum degree and number it with a 1. The set of vertices now divides into three subsets, A, B and C. A consists of the vertices already numbered. B is the adjacent set to A, $B = \text{Adj}(A)$, and thus consists of all vertices which are adjacent to any vertex of A. C consists of all the remaining vertices. Then, at each stage, number the

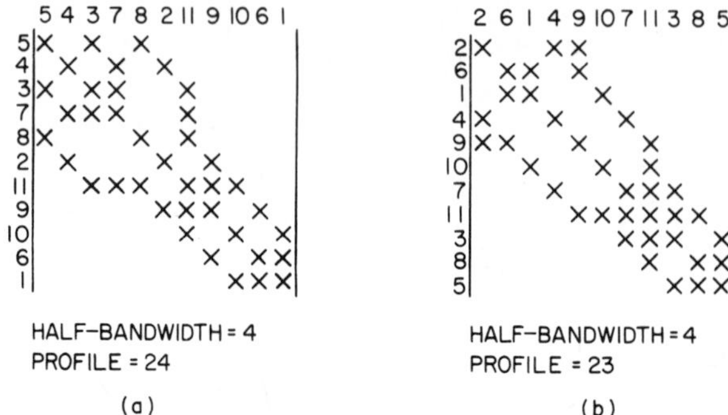

Figure 4.6 Examples of application of the reverse Cuthill–McKee algorithm to the matrices of Fig. 4.5(a) and (b), respectively.

vertex of subset B which causes the smallest number of vertices of subset C to come into subset B, and redefine A, B and C accordingly. When the graph is disconnected, the algorithm can be applied independently to each connected component. Examples of application of this algorithm to the graph of Fig. 4.1 are provided in Fig. 4.7. Minimum degree vertices are 1, 10, 6, 2, 4, 8 and 5. We choose 1 as the starting vertex (1 is also a peripheral vertex), and we label it with a 1. The original labelling is shown inside the circles, and the new labelling outside. At this point, the sets are, in terms of the original labelling:

$$A = \{1\}$$

$$B = \{6, 10\}$$

$$C = \text{remaining vertices}$$

Thus, 6 and 10 are the next candidates. If 6 were numbered, 9 would come into subset B. If 10 were numbered, 11 would come into B. This is a tie, which is arbitrarily broken by numbering 6 with a 2. After this has been done, the subsets are redefined:

$$A = \{1, 6\}$$

$$B = \{9, 10\}$$

$$C = \text{remaining vertices.}$$

Now 10 must be numbered because on doing so only 11 comes into B. The reader can continue the algorithm as an exercise. The resulting permuted matrix is shown in Fig. 4.7(a). It has a profile equal to 19.

When vertex 8, which is of minimum degree but is not peripheral, is chosen as the starting vertex, the ordering of Fig. 4.7(b) is obtained, with a profile

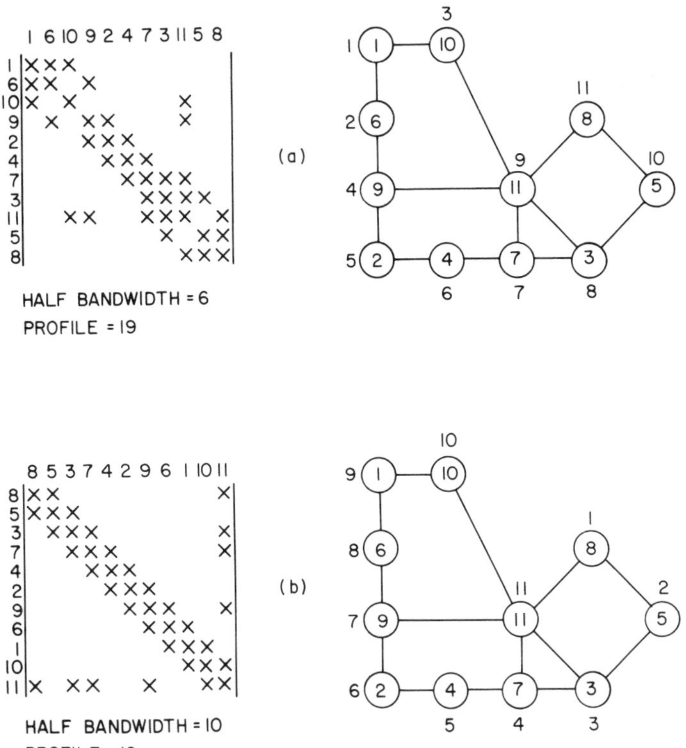

Figure 4.7 Examples of application of the algorithm of King to the graph of Fig. 4.1. The resulting permuted matrices and graph relabellings are shown when: (a) 1 is the starting vertex, and (b) 8 is the starting vertex.

also equal to 19. Other choices are: vertex 4 gives a profile of 22, and either 5 or 10 give 19, although these values may depend on the tie-breaking strategy employed. The half-bandwidths obtained for these three orderings are 6, 5 and 10, respectively, and for the examples of Fig. 4.7 they are 6 and 10, all larger than the half-bandwidth of 4 in Fig. 4.6 obtained by the reverse Cuthill–McKee algorithm. Thus, it appears that by sacrificing the bandwidth a smaller profile may be obtained, a possibility which is not contemplated by the reverse Cuthill–McKee algorith. The reader should not conclude, however, from these simple examples, that King's algorithm is necessarily better than Cuthill–McKee's.

A reverse King algorithm was proposed by Cuthill (1972), but it was found not to do any better than the straightforward King algorithm (Duff, 1977). A variant of King's algorithm was proposed by Levy (1971), in which vertices from both subsets B and C are candidates for labelling at each stage. Levy's method can produce a smaller profile but the computational costs are higher. It has already been mentioned that the algorithm of Gibbs *et al.* (1976), discussed in Section 4.4, can be used for profile minimization.

An integer programming formulation (Gass, 1969) of the profile minimization problem was proposed by Tewarson (1967b). An iterative method for profile minimization was proposed by Akyuz and Utku (1968). This method is slow and costly when used alone and works best when a good initial guess is available (Cuthill, 1972). Thus, it might be used for improving the ordering obtained by some other method.

4.7. Graph-theoretical background of symmetric Gauss elimination

So far we have considered the accumulation of nonzeros in the triangular factor of **A** only in a global manner. We are now interested in describing more sophisticated algorithms which deal with fill-in in detail, and our first concern is the set of rules which establish the actual positions of the nonzeros. Let **A** be a symmetric sparse matrix of order n and $G^A = (V, E)$ its labelled graph, and assume that Gauss elimination by columns is performed on **A** until the factorization $\mathbf{A} = \mathbf{U}^T\mathbf{D}\mathbf{U}$ is obtained. At the beginning of step k all nonzeros in columns $1, 2, \ldots, k-1$ below the diagonal have been eliminated. Multiples of the kth row are then subtracted from all rows which have a nonzero in column k below the diagonal. On doing this new nonzero elements may be introduced in rows $k+1, \ldots, n$ to the right of column k. Cancellations may also occur, producing new zeros, but this is rare in practice except for very special cases, and will be neglected. Consider the active submatrix at step k (we recall that the active submatrix contains all elements $A_{ij}^{(k)}$ with $i, j \geqslant k$). Let G^k be the graph associated with the active submatrix. G^k is an *elimination graph*. Its vertices are the $n-k+1$ last numbered vertices of G^A. It contains all edges connecting those vertices which were present in G^A (since we neglect cancellations), and additional edges corresponding to fill-ins produced during the $k-1$ initial elimination steps. The sequence of graphs $G^1 \equiv G^A, G^2, \ldots$ can be obtained recursively using the following rule (Parter, 1961):

> To obtain G^{k+1} from G^k, delete vertex k and add all possible edges between vertices which are adjacent to vertex k in G^k.

As an example of the application of this rule consider the matrix and graph of Fig. 4.1. Figure 4.8 shows the three initial elimination steps and the

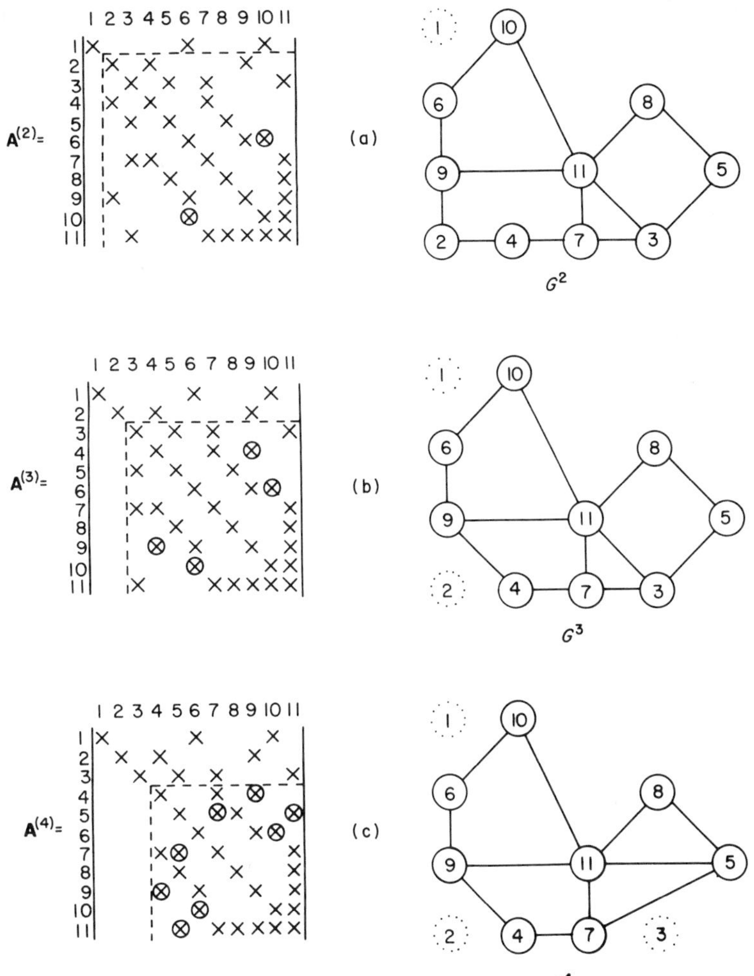

Figure 4.8 The three initial elimination steps and the corresponding elimination graphs for the matrix of Fig. 4.1(a). Fill-ins are encircled.

corresponding elimination graphs. The correspondence between fill-ins and new edges added to the graphs is evident. The reader can finish the exercise.

In terms of graph theory, Parter's rule says that the adjacent set of vertex k becomes a clique when vertex k is eliminated. Thus, Gauss elimination generates cliques systematically. Later, as elimination progresses, cliques grow or sets of cliques join to form larger cliques, a process known as *clique amalgamation* (Duff, 1981a, p. 3). Cliques have very useful properties. A clique with m vertices has $m(m-1)/2$ edges, but it can be represented in the computer memory by storing a list of the vertices, without any reference to edges, using for example lists of integers as discussed in Section 1.3. Cliques represented in this way can be amalgamated in a time proportional to the number of vertices. With regard to the matrix, a clique corresponds to a full principal submatrix, and storing the list of the vertices in the clique is equivalent to storing merely a list of the lines (rows and columns) which define the submatrix. Since clique formation and amalgamation take place systematically in Gauss elimination, important savings in both storage and labour can be obtained if clique properties are used in the symbolic part of the algorithms. Of course, it is still necessary to store and process the numerical values of all elements in each full submatrix.

The problem of fill-in location can be viewed in a different way. Consider the upper triangular factor **U**. **U** is not symmetric and cannot be associated with an undirected graph, but its nonzero pattern above the diagonal is the same as that of $\mathbf{U} + \mathbf{U}^T$, which does have an undirected graph called the *filled graph* G^F. G^F has n vertices, all edges which were present in G^A, and all additional edges corresponding to fill-ins introduced during factorization. If we call F the set of edges introduced during factorization, where $G^A = (V, E)$ and $F \cap E = \emptyset$, then $G^F = (V, E \cup F)$. The following rule specifies the edges in G^F, and thus the locations of the nonzeros in **U** (Parter, 1961):

> (i, j) is an edge of G^F if and only if (i, j) is an edge of G^A or (i, k) and (j, k) are edges of G^F for some $k < i, j$.

Figure 4.9 shows the structure of $\mathbf{U} + \mathbf{U}^T$ and the filled graph G^F for the matrix of Fig. 4.1(a). (9, 11) is an edge of G^F because (9, 11) is an edge of G^A. (8, 9) is an edge of G^F because (8, 7) and (9, 7) are edges of G^F, and $7 < 8, 9$. Note that (8, 7) and (9, 7) are not edges of G^A. The reader can verify that any two vertices joined by a dashed line in G^F are in turn

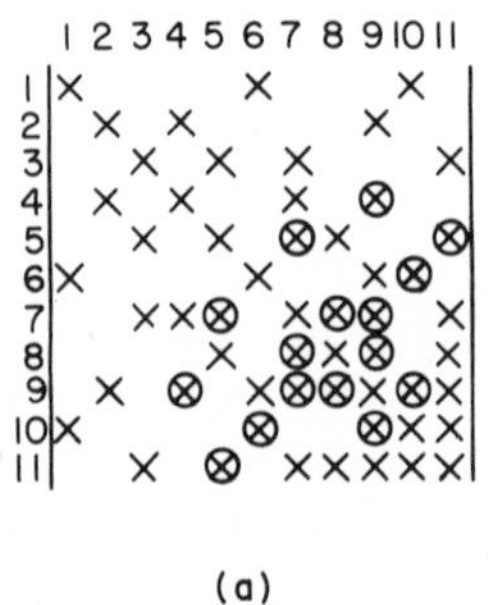

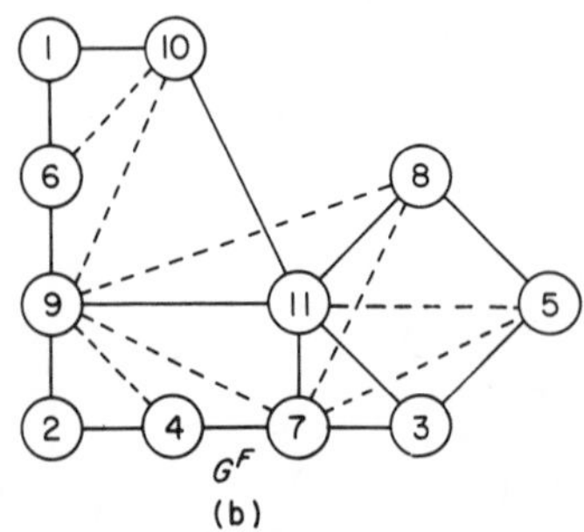

Figure 4.9 The structure of $\mathbf{U} + \mathbf{U}^T$ and the corresponding filled graph for the matrix of Fig. 4.1(a), obtained when elimination is performed in the natural order.

adjacent to another vertex with a lower number. The set F of edges introduced by factorization consists of all edges shown by dashed lines.

Both rules are recursive in nature and cannot give a direct answer to the question of whether a certain edge does or does not belong to G^F (or of whether a given element of **U** is zero or not) unless the elimination is actually carried out or at least simulated. The following theorem, phrased in terms of the concept of reachable sets defined in Section 4.2, gives a direct answer (George and Liu, 1976; Rose *et al.*, 1976):

> Let $i < j$, and let Q_i be the set of all vertices with numbers less than i. Then (v_i, v_j) is an edge of G^F (i.e. U_{ij} is different from zero) if and only if $v_j \in \text{Reach}(v_i, Q_i)$ in the *original* graph G^A.

For example, let us find out whether edge (8, 9) belongs to G^F or not. Since $i = 8$, we have $Q_8 = \{1, 2, 3, 4, 5, 6, 7\}$. The paths (8, 11) and (8, 5, 3, 7, 4, 2, 9), the endpoints of which do not belong to Q_8, show that $\text{Reach}(8, Q_8) = \{9, 11\}$. Thus $9 \in \text{Reach}(8, Q_8)$ and (8, 9) is an edge of G^F. Note that when $i > j$ the rule is valid with i and j interchanged.

There is an important concept closely related to the present context. Recall that a separator S of a graph is a set of vertices, the removal of which leaves the graph disconnected into two or more components, i.e., with no paths joining two vertices in different components. An immediate consequence is that, if the vertices of the separator S are numbered *after* those in one of the components and v_i and v_j belong to different components, then $Q_i \cap S = \emptyset$, v_j does not belong to $\text{Reach}(v_i, Q_i)$, and not only $A_{ij} = 0$ but also $U_{ij} = 0$. Thus, an entire block of zeros is introduced directly into the triangular factor **U**. This property is exploited by dissection techniques, discussed in Sections 4.10 and 4.13. For example, in Fig. 4.1, the separator {9, 11}, which is numbered after the component {2, 4, 7, 3, 5, 8}, causes the fact that none of these vertices are connected with any vertex of the remaining component {6, 1, 10}, as the reader can verify in the graph G^F of Fig. 4.9. The corresponding elements of **U** are all zero. Another example is {7, 11, 8}, which disconnects the sets {3, 5} and {10, 1, 6, 9, 2, 4}, as the reader can also verify.

The following theorem (George and Liu, 1981) characterizes the edges of elimination graphs:

> Let u be a vertex of the elimination graph G^k, and let Q_k be the set of vertices $v_1, v_2, \ldots, v_{k-1}$ (i.e., the vertices of the original graph G^A already eliminated). Then the set of vertices adjacent to u in G^k is the set $\text{Reach}(u, Q_k)$ in the original graph G^A.

For example, consider G^4 in Fig. 4.8(c). We have $Q_4 = \{1, 2, 3\}$. From the graph G^A of Fig. 4.1 we obtain: $\text{Reach}(6, Q_4) = \{9, 10\}$, which is the adjacent set of vertex 6 in G^4. Other cases are left for the reader as an exercise.

4.8. The minimum degree algorithm

In this section we initiate the discussion of algorithms which try to reduce the fill-in caused by elimination when the matrix is symmetric, positive definite and sparse, but has no particular structure (for example, it is not a band matrix). In Section 3.6, it has been shown that any diagonal element $A_{ii}^{(k)}$ with $i \geqslant k$ satisfies the stability condition (belongs to S_{st}) and can be used as the kth pivot. All algorithms discussed in the present chapter employ this property, and select pivots from the diagonal in an order dictated by sparsity considerations alone.

The *minimum degree algorithm* (Tinney, 1969) is the best general purpose pivoting method. It is simple, cheap and effective, and is extensively used, at least for problems which are not too large. It is in fact the symmetric version of the Markowitz algorithm for unsymmetric matrices discussed in Chapter 5. The central idea is to achieve a local minimization of fill-in and number of operations by selecting, at each stage of elimination and among all possible pivots, that row and column which introduces the least number of nonzeros in the triangular factors. Consider Gauss elimination by columns, which can easily be combined with the minimum degree algorithm. At the kth stage of elimination the matrix $\mathbf{A}^{(k)}$ has zeros in columns 1 to $k-1$ below the diagonal, as shown by the examples of Fig. 4.8. Row k is normalized and multiples of it are subtracted from those rows which have a nonzero in column k below the diagonal. These nonzeros become nonzeros of the lower factor $\mathbf{U}^{\mathrm{T}}$, while the nonzeros in row k to the right of the diagonal become nonzeros of the upper factor $\mathbf{U}$. Thus, if we wish to minimize the number of nonzeros introduced in $\mathbf{U}$ or $\mathbf{U}^{\mathrm{T}}$ at step k, all we have to do is to examine the active submatrix (formed by rows k to n and columns k to n of $\mathbf{A}^{(k)}$), select a row (or column) with the minimum number of nonzeros, say row (or column) l, and interchange row l with row k and column l with column k of the complete matrix $\mathbf{A}^{(k)}$ before performing step k of elimination.

For its implementation, the algorithm requires the use of an integer array, say NZ, initialized with the number of off-diagonal nonzeros in each row of $\mathbf{A}$. NZ is updated at each step of elimination. At the beginning of step k, NZ(i) is the number of off-diagonal nonzeros in row i, columns k to n, and for i in the range k to n. A pivotal row with the minimum number of nonzeros is selected by examination of NZ(i), $i = k, \ldots, n$, and the kth step of elimination is performed. NZ is updated during the step. Clearly, it is necessary to update only those positions of NZ which correspond to rows with a nonzero in column k. When one such nonzero is eliminated, say from position (j, k) of the matrix, we subtract 1 from NZ(j) and then we add 1 for each new nonzero introduced in row j. The algorithm can be executed numerically to obtain both the structure of $\mathbf{U}$ and the numerical values of its elements.

Alternatively, when several linear systems have to be solved, all with the same sparseness structure but with different values of the nonzero coefficients, the algorithm can be executed symbolically to determine the ordering and to find the structure of **U**. Then, the ordering and the structure remain fixed, and Gauss elimination is performed numerically as many times as required.

Consider Fig. 4.1 as an example. The array NZ is initialized as follows:

position:	1	2	3	4	5	6	7	8	9	10	11
NZ:	2	2	3	2	2	2	3	2	3	2	5

There are several rows with two off-diagonal nonzeros. Since no tie-breaking strategy has been established, we select any of them, say row 1, and proceed to elimination. Since the nonzeros of column 1 are in rows 6 and 10, we must update NZ(6) and NZ(10) only, subtracting 1 from each of them and adding the number of new nonzeros introduced in each of those rows. The matrix $\mathbf{A}^{(2)}$ which is obtained is shown in Fig. 4.8(a), and the updated NZ is

position:	1	2	3	4	5	6	7	8	9	10	11
NZ:	x	2	3	2	2	2	3	2	3	2	5

where "x" indicates an irrelevant number.

Again, there are several rows with two nonzeros. Selecting arbitrarily row 2, and proceeding to elimination, we obtain the matrix $\mathbf{A}^{(3)}$ of Fig. 4.8(b) and the updated NZ:

position:	1	2	3	4	5	6	7	8	9	10	11
NZ:	x	x	3	2	2	2	3	2	3	2	5

Any row with two nonzeros can be selected, say row 10. The reader can verify that one of the possible minimum degree orderings is the one shown in Fig. 4.10. This ordering results in a fill-in of only 5 elements in the upper triangle of the permuted matrix.

The approach we have just been discussing has the disadvantage that the storage requirements cannot be predicted. An alternative approach based on

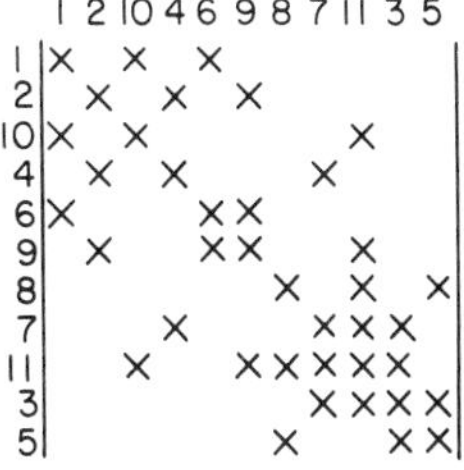

Figure 4.10 A minimum degree ordering for the matrix of Fig. 4.1(a).

graph theory has been proposed by George and Liu (1981), who also gave the corresponding Fortran software. The method uses the graph of the *original* matrix **A** and can thus predict the required storage without actually generating the structure of **U**. At step k, the number of off-diagonal nonzeros in a certain row or column of the active submatrix is the degree of the corresponding vertex in the elimination graph G^k. Hence, what we do at each step is merely to select a vertex of the minimum degree in G^k (this explains the name of the algorithm) and to label it with k, i.e., next for elimination. Now, from Section 4.7 we know that the set of vertices adjacent to a vertex v in G^k is $\text{Reach}(v, Q_k)$, where $Q_k = \{v_1, \ldots, v_{k-1}\}$ is the set of vertices already eliminated and the Reach operator is applied to the *original* graph G^A of **A**. Besides, if v is eliminated at step k, the next elimination graph G^{k+1} is obtained by deleting v from G^k and joining with edges all vertices in $\text{Reach}(v, Q_k)$, where Reach is again applied to the original graph G^A. The vertices in $\text{Reach}(v, Q_k)$ are the only vertices in G^k of which the degree is changed at step k. Thus, no further reference to elimination graphs is necessary. NZ is initialized with the degrees of the vertices in G^A. Then, at step k, a vertex of the minimum degree is selected by inspection of positions k to n of NZ and labelled v_k. The positions of NZ corresponding to vertices in $\text{Reach}(v_k, Q_k)$ are updated. If $u \in \text{Reach}(v_k, Q_k)$, its updated degree is $|\text{Reach}(u, Q_{k+1})|$, where $Q_{k+1} = Q_k \cup \{v_k\} = \{v_1, v_2, \ldots, v_k\}$ and the vertical bars indicate the number of elements in the set they enclose.

Another enhancement of the minimum degree algorithm has been proposed by George and Liu (1981). It is based on the concept of *indistinguishable vertices*. At elimination step k, two unlabelled vertices u and v are said to be indistinguishable if

$$\text{Reach}(u, Q_k) \cup \{u\} = \text{Reach}(v, Q_k) \cup \{v\}. \tag{4.9}$$

A summary of the properties of indistinguishable vertices follows. Indistinguishable vertices have the same degree. If u and v are indistinguishable at step k, they will continue to be indistinguishable at all subsequent steps until one of them is eliminated. Furthermore, if u and v become of minimum degree and u is eliminated at some step, then v becomes again of minimum degree and can be eliminated at the next step without any minimum degree search. These properties are used to improve the efficiency of the algorithm.

Indistinguishable vertices can be identified by means of the following condition. Let C_1 and C_2 be two connected components of the subgraph $G(Q_k)$, at step k, and let

$$\begin{aligned} R_1 &= \text{Adj}(C_1) \\ R_2 &= \text{Adj}(C_2). \end{aligned} \tag{4.10}$$

The vertices in $R_1 \cap R_2$ are the candidates for indistinguishability. Consider the set

$$T = R_1 \cup R_2 \cup C_1 \cup C_2 \tag{4.11}$$

If

$$u \in R_1 \cap R_2 \tag{4.12}$$

and

$$\mathrm{Adj}(u) \subset T, \tag{4.13}$$

then

$$\mathrm{Reach}(u, Q_k) \cup \{u\} = R_1 \cup R_2. \tag{4.14}$$

Thus, all vertices of $R_1 \cap R_2$ having an adjacent set entirely in T are indistinguishable. This condition was not designed to identify all possible sets of indistinguishable vertices, but it usually does. Its main advantage is simplicity and ease of implementation. Besides, if all indistinguishable vertices are eliminated together by numbering them, say, $k, k + 1, \ldots, k + l$, then all corresponding rows in the triangular factor **U** will have the same structure. If Sherman's compressed storage scheme is used, this fact can be exploited to reduce overhead storage (see Section 1.10).

The enhanced algorithm exploits the ideas just exposed. For a graph $G^A = (V, E)$, the algorithm is as follows:

Step 1 (Initialization). Set $S \leftarrow \emptyset$ and find the degrees of all vertices in G^A.
Step 2 (Selection). Select a vertex $u \in V - S$ which is of minimum degree.
Step 3 (Elimination). Let W be the set composed of u and all vertices indistinguishable from u. Number the vertices in W next in the ordering.
Step 4 (Degree update). For $v \in \mathrm{Reach}(u, S) - W$, update the degree of v to $|\mathrm{Reach}(v, S \cup W)|$. Identify indistinguishable vertices in the set $\mathrm{Reach}(u, S) - W$.
Step 5 (Loop or stop). Set $S \leftarrow S \cup W$. If $S = V$ stop, otherwise go to Step 2.

The output from this algorithm, as stated, is the ordering. Besides, in preparation for the generation of the symbolic structure of the upper factor **U**, a table giving the number or nonzeros in each row of **U** can be obtained by storing, at Step 3, the degree of each vertex just before elimination. From a computational point of view such a table is highly desirable because it allows the determination of storage requirements. Notice, however, that after running the algorithm the user may find out that the available storage is insufficient or too expensive, and decide to use other methods. Alternatively, the user may have enough memory available and decide to continue the procedure, in which case the only useful result yet obtained would be the ordering but not the structure of **U**. The user would have to run another algorithm to obtain the structure of **U**.

On the other hand, the standard minimum degree algorithm is much simpler, generates the ordering and the structure of **U** together, and can even generate the corresponding numerical values in the same run. The disadvantage is that the required storage cannot be anticipated. The user must guess. If the assigned storage turns out to be insufficient, the algorithm would stop without informing the size of the total required storage. Nowadays storage is tending to become cheaper, so this handicap may not be a severe one.

When the structure of **U** was not computed by the ordering algorithm, it must be computed separately. This can be done in a time proportional to the number of off-diagonal nonzeros in **U**. The idea (Rose *et al.*, 1976) is better described in terms of reachable sets. As discussed in Section 4.7, the structure of row i of **U** is determined by the set Reach(v_i, Q_i) in the original graph G^A, where $Q_i = \{v_1, v_2, \ldots, v_{i-1}\}$. Thus, we need to determine the sets Reach(v_i, Q_i) for $i = 1, 2, \ldots, n-1$, and this can be done using the following recursive relation. Consider a row k of **U** and call m_k the column index of the first nonzero in that row. In terms of graph theory, m_k is defined by:

$$m_k = \min\{j | v_j \in \text{Reach}(v_k, Q_k)\}. \tag{4.15}$$

Now consider row i of **U**, and let W be the set of all vertices v_k with $k < i$ for which $m_k = i$. In terms of the matrix, W is the set of all those rows which have their first nonzero in column i. Then:

$$\text{Reach}(v_i, S_i) = \text{Adj}(x_i) \cup \left[\bigcup_k \{\text{Reach}(v_k, S_k) | v_k \in W\} \right] - S_{i+1} \tag{4.16}$$

In other words, we merge the nonzeros of the rows in W with the nonzeros of row i in **A** to obtain the nonzeros of row i in **U**. The advantage of this procedure is that other rows with nonzeros in column i of **U** are not taken into account.

Consider, for example, the graph shown in Fig. 4.1, and let us calculate Reach$(7, Q_7)$. Suppose we have available all previous reachable sets:

$$\begin{aligned}
&\text{Reach}(1, S_1) = \{6, 10\}; && m_1 = 6 \\
&\text{Reach}(2, S_2) = \{4, 9\}; && m_2 = 4 \\
&\text{Reach}(3, S_3) = \{5, 7, 11\}; && m_3 = 5 \\
&\text{Reach}(4, S_4) = \{7, 9\}; && m_4 = 7 \\
&\text{Reach}(5, S_5) = \{7, 8, 11\}; && m_5 = 7 \\
&\text{Reach}(6, S_6) = \{9, 10\}; && m_6 = 9
\end{aligned}$$

Thus, $W = \{4, 5\}$, since $m_4 = m_5 = 7$. We have to merge Adj(7) $= \{3, 4, 11\}$ with Reach(4, S_4) and with Reach(5, S_5), and delete vertices with labels 7 or less. We obtain

$$\text{Reach}(7, S_7) = \{8, 9, 11\}$$

which is the correct result. The reader can check all reachable sets by looking at the filled matrix and graph of Fig. 4.9.

4.9. Tree partitioning of a symmetric sparse matrix

A matrix may have a graph which is a tree. If the tree is labelled in the monotone order and the matrix is permuted accordingly, then Gauss elimination with diagonal pivoting can be performed without any fill being produced (Parter, 1961). This important property is demonstrated in Fig. 4.11, where a tree labelled according to the monotone ordering and the corresponding matrix are shown. The reader can easily verify the property. Trees are a particular case of triangulated graphs (Rose, 1970), a class of graphs which suffer no fill.

When the graph of a matrix is not a tree, then it is often possible to find a tree partitioning of the graph, i.e., a partitioning such that the quotient graph is a tree. The composite vertices of the quotient tree correspond to sets of rows and columns of the matrix. Thus the tree partitioning induces a partitioning in the matrix, which becomes a *block matrix*. The block matrix has elements which are matrices, the diagonal blocks being square, and its graph is the quotient tree. In this way the desirable properties of trees can be taken advantage of for general sparse symmetric matrices.

In this section we discuss the *Refined Quotient Tree Algorithm* (George, 1977; George and Liu, 1978b), which is used for finding a tree partitioning of an undirected graph, with as many members as possible. A level structure is a

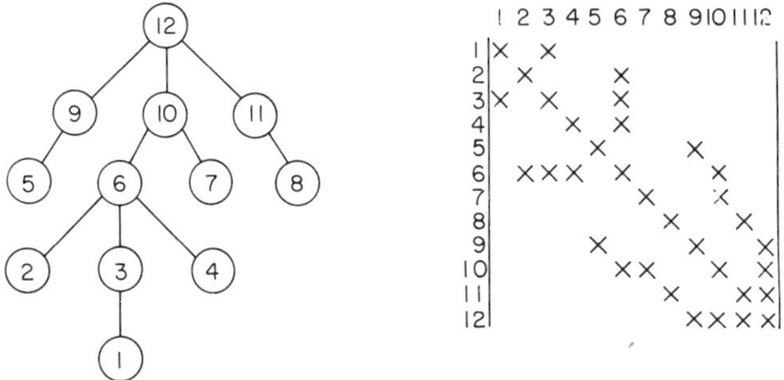

Figure 4.11 A tree with a monotone ordering and the corresponding matrix.

tree partitioning of the graph, in which each level is a partition member and which induces a block tridiagonal partitioning of the matrix. A rooted level structure with many levels is obtained when the root is a pseudoperipheral vertex. The algorithm of George starts with a level structure rooted at a pseudoperipheral vertex and finds a refinement of the partitioning. The refinement is based on the observation that the section graph corresponding to a certain level and all levels below it may not be connected. For example, in Fig. 4.2(b), the section graph formed by levels L_4, L_5 and L_6 has two components, and the section graph formed by levels L_5 and L_6 has again two components. The quotient tree of Fig. 4.2(c) reflects these facts. An algorithm for finding a pseudoperipheral vertex was discussed in Section 4.4.

Consider a graph $G = (V, E)$ and let $L_0, L_1, \ldots, L_m$ be a level structure with $m + 1$ levels rooted at a pseudoperipheral vertex. In order to explain the algorithm of George, we first consider the section graph $G(L_l)$, which consists of all the vertices of level L_l and all those edges having both ends in L_l. $G(L_l)$ may be disconnected. Let S be any subset of vertices of L_l. The set

$$Y = \text{Span}[S, G(L_l)] \tag{4.17}$$

is defined to be the union of S and all those vertices of L_l which are connected with vertices of S by paths entirely in $G(L_l)$. When S is a single vertex v, Y is the connected component of L_l containing v, but in a more general case Y may consist of several connected components of L_l. For example, in Fig. 4.2(b), for $l = 5$, $L_5 = \{13, 15, 5, 20\}$. If $S = \{20\}$, $\text{Span}[S, G(L_5)] = \{5, 20\}$. If $S = \{13, 5\}$, then $\text{Span}[S, G(L_5)] = \{13, 15, 5, 20\}$, which consists of two connected components.

The algorithm uses a stack (see Section 1.2) to store temporarily the subsets S when they cannot be utilized immediately after generation. The subsets S are partially formed partition members awaiting completion. The algorithm is as follows:

Step 0 (Initialization). Find a pseudoperipheral vertex r, generate the level structure $L_0, L_1, \ldots, L_m$ rooted at r, set $l = m$, and choose any vertex v from level L_m. Set $S = \{v\}$ and empty the stack.

Step 1 (Enlarge S and pop stack). If the stack is empty go to Step 2. Otherwise let T be the set of vertices on the top of the stack. If $T \cap L_l$ is empty go to Step 2. Otherwise pop T from the stack and set $S \leftarrow S \cup T$.

Step 2 (Form possible partition member). Determine the set $Y \leftarrow \text{Span}[S, G(L_l)]$. If $\text{Adj}(Y)$ has any vertex in L_{l+1} which has not yet been placed in a partition member, go to Step 5. Otherwise Y is a new partition member.

Step 3 (Internal numbering of new partition member). Number $Y - S$ using the reverse Cuthill–McKee algorithm. Then number S in any order.

Step 4 (Next level). Set $l \leftarrow l - 1$. If $l < 0$ stop. Otherwise determine the set $S \leftarrow \text{Adj}(Y) \cap L_l$ and go to Step 1.

Step 5 (Partially formed partition member). Push S onto the stack. Pick a vertex v_{l+1} which is adjacent to Y and is in L_{l+1} and trace a path v_{l+1}, $v_{l+2}, \ldots, v_{l+t}$, where each v_{l+i} is in level L_{l+i} and v_{l+t} is such that the path cannot be prolonged to a deeper level, i.e., v_{l+t} has no adjacent vertex in L_{l+t+1}. Let $S \leftarrow \{v_{l+t}\}$ and $l \leftarrow l + t$ and go to Step 1.

At the beginning of Step 3, the set S consists of all vertices of Y which are adjacent to any vertex in L_{l+1}. Thus, the set $Y - S$, if not empty, consists of all vertices of Y which are not adjacent to any vertex in L_{l+1}. Numbering $Y - S$ first and according to the reverse Cuthill–McKee algorithm has the effect of reducing the profile of the diagonal blocks of the matrix, which can then be conveniently stored using Jenning's scheme (Section 1.6). The order in which the partition members are found directly provides a monotone labelling of the quotient tree, as required by the theorem of Parter.

For an example of the application of the algorithm consider the graph of Fig. 4.2(a). If $r = 8$, a peripheral vertex, is chosen as the root, the level structure of Fig. 4.2(b) is obtained. The first set S found at Step 1 is $S = \{6\}$; at Step 2, $Y = \{6\}$, and vertex 6 alone becomes the first partition member and is numbered with a 1. The algorithm continues to Step 4, where it finds $S = \{5, 20\}$; S is not modified at Step 1, and at Step 2 the algorithm determines $Y = \{5, 20\}$, which becomes the second member of the partition.

At Step 4, the algorithm finds $S = \{7\}$, the only vertex in level 4 which is adjacent to 5 and 20. S is not modified at Step 1, since the stack is still empty; at Step 2 the algorithm determines $Y = \{14, 16, 1, 7\}$ and finds that Y has adjacent vertices in L_5 which have not yet been placed in any partition. Thus $S = \{7\}$ is pushed onto the stack and the algorithm branches to Step 5, where, picking $v_5 = 13$, it is found that the path cannot be prolonged any longer, so $t = 1$. Letting $S = \{13\}$, the algorithm continues with Step 1, where S is not modified, and with Step 2, where Y is determined to be $\{13, 15\}$, which becomes the third partition member.

Next, at Step 4, the algorithm finds $S = \{14\}$. Since this time the set $\{7\}$ is on top of the stack and $\{7\}$ and $\{14\}$ are on the same level, the set S is modified at Step 1, and becomes $S = \{14, 7\}$. At Step 2, $Y = \{14, 16, 1, 7\}$, which is the fourth partition member. The reader can continue the execution of the algorithm. The result is the quotient tree shown in Fig. 4.2(c), labelled in monotone order by the algorithm. The sets of vertices which belong to each composite vertex are indicated inside the circles; the labels, outside.

Figure 4.12(a) displays the structure of the sparse matrix which corresponds to the graph of Fig. 4.2(a). If Gauss elimination with diagonal pivoting were performed on it, abundant, scattered fill-in would be produced.

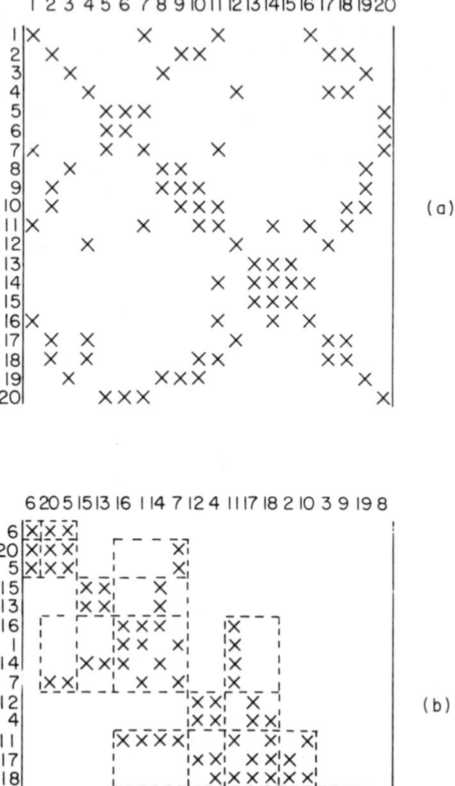

Figure 4.12 The Refined Quotient Tree algorithm. (a) Structure of the matrix corresponding to the graph of Fig. 4.2(a). (b) The permuted block matrix corresponding to the quotient tree of Fig. 4.2(c).

Figure 4.12(b) shows the permuted matrix in block form, corresponding to the quotient tree of Fig. 4.2(c) labelled by the algorithm. If Gauss elimination were performed on this matrix, the fill-in would be little and confined to the diagonal blocks. Numerical experiments with test problems were given by George (1977). The symbolic factorization of a block partitioned matrix deserves special consideration, because, unlike the scalar case where the product of two nonzero scalars is always nonzero, the product of two non-null sparse blocks may yield a zero block. Zero blocks cause no fill-in and should be excluded from the block structure of the triangular factors. An algorithm which takes this problem into account was presented by George and Rashwan (1981).

4.10. Nested dissection

Nested dissection is a method due to George (1973) for systematically partitioning the graph associated with a matrix using separators (see Section 4.2 for definitions). When a separator is found its vertices are labelled and removed from the graph, leaving the graph partitioned into two or more components. Separators are then found for each component, and the procedure is continued, forming smaller and smaller nests, until all vertices have been numbered. The matrix can then be permuted accordingly. The *nested dissection ordering* obtained in this way has several desired properties.

The idea is illustrated in Fig. 4.13. Let us assume that the set of vertices is represented by a rectangle R_0, Fig. 4.13(a). We choose a separator S_0, consisting of a set of vertices the removal of which leaves the graph disconnected into two (in this example) components, R_1^1 and R_1^2. The vertices in R_1^1 are numbered first, then those in R_1^2 and finally those in S_0. The zero–nonzero pattern induced in the matrix by this numbering is shown in Fig. 4.13(b), where the areas in which the nonzeros are confined are shaded. This arrangement of the matrix has the important property that the fill-in caused by Gauss elimination with diagonal pivoting is also confined to the shaded areas.

The procedure is repeated recursively. R_1^1 is partitioned by a separator S_1^1 into two disconnected components. R_2^1 and R_2^2. R_1^2 is partitioned by S_1^2 into R_2^3 and R_2^4. The sets are renumbered in the order R_2^1, R_2^2, S_1^1, R_2^3, R_2^4, S_1^2. As before S_0 is numbered last. The new arrangement of the matrix is shown in Fig. 4.13(c). Again, the fill-in will be confined to the shaded areas, which are now smaller. As the procedure progresses and the partitioning becomes finer, R-sets will eventually be found which have no separators. When one such R-set is found, the corresponding S-set is taken equal to the R-set and its vertices are numbered. The procedure terminates when no more R-sets exist. A one-to-one correspondence exists between each R_l^j and its separator S_l^j, and a *nested dissection tree* can be associated with the partitioning. Each S-set is a vertex of the tree, the tree is rooted at S_0, S_1^1 and S_1^2 are the sons of S_0, and so on. The *terminal members* of the dissection tree are the S-sets which were chosen equal to the corresponding R-sets, because they have no descendants. The *height* h of the nested dissection partitioning is the maximum l for which at least one R_l^j is not empty. Note that the dissection tree is not the quotient graph associated with the partitioning.

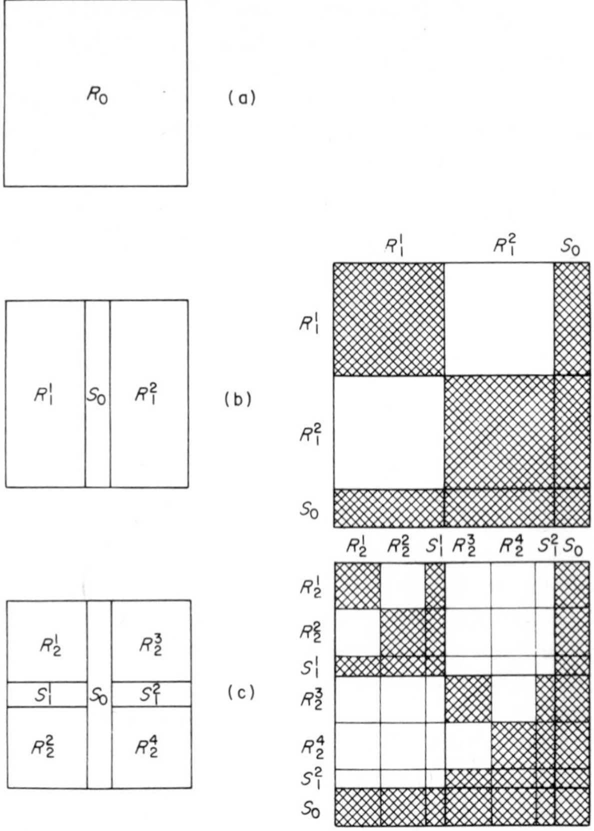

Figure 4.13 Illustration of nested dissection.

Several points must be made before a complete description of the algorithm can be given. Renumbering the vertices of the *R*-sets at each stage as suggested by the previous example would be inconvenient, and is avoided in practice by arranging the matrix as shown in Fig. 4.14, where the fill-in confinement property still holds. The vertices of each *S*-set are numbered in reverse order as soon as the *S*-set is constructed, while the *R*-sets remain unnumbered. Thus, the final numbering is directly obtained when the algorithm terminates.

A good nested dissection ordering is obtained when the separators are small, because small separators cause the shaded areas associated with the *S*-sets to be small. The algorithm uses minimal separators, i.e., each separator is such that no part of it is in turn a separator. A nested dissection partitioning

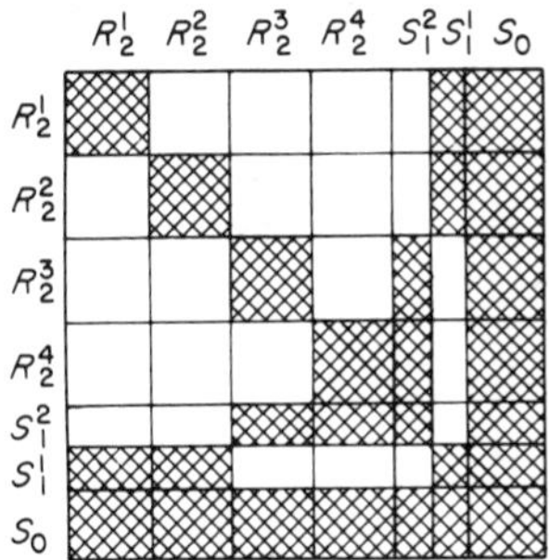

Figure 4.14 An improved version of nested dissection.

where every separator is minimal is called a *minimal nested dissection partitioning*. It is also convenient that the R-sets determined by each separator be of comparable size, because this will tend to produce a finer partitioning.

We have not discussed so far the order in which the vertices of each S-set should be numbered. For a minimal nested dissection partitioning, it has been proved (George and Liu, 1976) that any internal numbering of the S-sets will cause the same amount of fill and the same number of operations when Gauss elimination is performed on the matrix. When only the nonzeros are stored and operated upon, the S-sets can be numbered arbitrarily. If, however, a storage scheme is used where a fraction of zeros is stored, it may be convenient to number each S-set in some specific order. For example, if the diagonal blocks are stored according to Jennings' scheme (see Section 1.6), it is convenient to number the terminal S-sets using the reverse Cuthill–McKee algorithm (see Section 4.6), because this will produce a smaller envelope (George, 1977). The same idea cannot be applied to nonterminal members because the corresponding diagonal blocks will completely fill in, but in certain cases it may still be convenient to use the reverse Cuthill–McKee algorithm to number the nonterminal separators because the overhead storage will be minimized. When the matrix is associated with a Finite Element mesh (see Section 4.2), it may be advisable to number the nonterminal members using an improved version of the reverse Cuthill–McKee algorithm (Brown and Wait, 1981) because this will tend to reduce the oscillations in the ordering of the nodes of the mesh.

We can now discuss the *Automatic Nested Dissection algorithm* in detail. Given the undirected graph associated with the matrix, the algorithm generates a level structure rooted at some pseudoperipheral vertex. A level structure rooted at a pseudoperipheral vertex is likely to have many levels, and a finer partitioning is likely to be obtained. A minimal separator is then selected from the "middle" level and its vertices are numbered backwards in some convenient order. In order to state the algorithm explicitly, we drop the indices l and j, which were introduced for theoretical reasons. Thus, S_l^j and R_l^j are simply the current S and the current R in the algorithm. A set C is introduced, defined at each stage as the union of all separators found at or before that stage. We use bars to indicate the number of elements in a set, e.g. $|S|$ = number of vertices in S. The algorithm is as follows:

Step 1 Let a graph $G = (V, E)$ be given and let $N = |V|$ be the number of vertices of the graph. Let C be the empty set.

Step 2 If $N = 0$ stop. Otherwise, consider the section graph $G(V - C)$, obtained by removing from the original graph all vertices which belong to C together with their incident edges. Find a connected component of $G(V - C)$, say $G(R)$, and determine a pseudoperipheral vertex u in $G(R)$. Pseudoperipheral vertices can be found using the algorithm of Gibbs discussed in Section 4.4.

Step 3 In the subgraph $G(R)$, generate a level structure $L_0, L_1, \ldots, L_m$, rooted at u. If $m \leqslant 2$, set $S \leftarrow R$ and go to Step 5. Otherwise choose a "middle" level j = the largest integer smaller than or equal to $(m + 1)/2$.

Step 4 Choose $S \subseteq L_j$ such that S is a minimal separator of $G(R)$.

Step 5 S is a new partition member. Set $C \leftarrow C \cup S$ and label the vertices of S from $N - |S| + 1$ to N.

Step 6 Set $N \leftarrow N - |S|$ and go to Step 2.

In many practical cases, a good partitioning is obtained when the separators are small, even if some of them are not actually minimal. A small separator can be determined at Step 4 by taking only those vertices of L_j which are adjacent to some vertex in L_{j+1}. In other words, S is obtained by discarding from L_j all those vertices which are not adjacent to any vertex in L_{j+1}. Such a separator may be not minimal, however, as shown by the example below. The computer implementation of this algorithm was explicitly given by George and Liu (1981). Nested dissection can be combined with partial pivoting (Gilbert and Schreiber, 1982).

For the sake of an example, consider the graph of Fig. 4.2(a) and its level structure rooted at the peripheral vertex 8, shown in Fig. 4.2(b). Since $m = 6$, $j = 3$, and the first separator must be chosen from $L_3 = (17, 18, 11)$. But L_3 is not a minimal separator, since vertex 11 alone is a separator, and the set (17, 18) is also a separator. In order for the graph to be partitioned into components of comparable size we choose $S_0 = (11)$, and we label vertex 11 with the number 20, see Fig. 4.15(a). The removal of vertex 11 leaves the two connected components $R_1^1 = (12, 4, 17, 18, 2, 10, 9, 19, 8, 3)$ and $R_1^2 = (13, 15, 14, 16, 1, 7, 5, 20, 6)$.

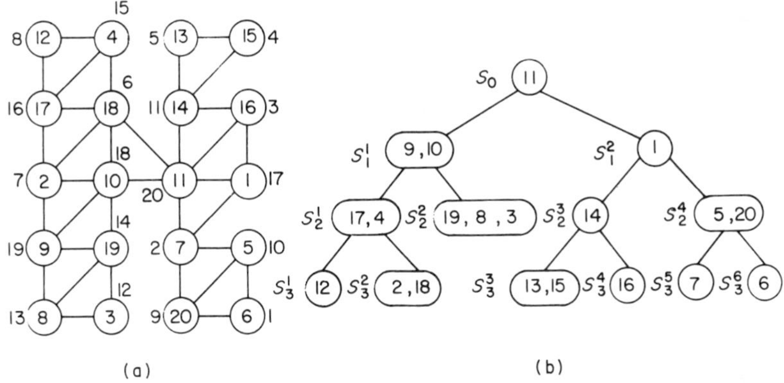

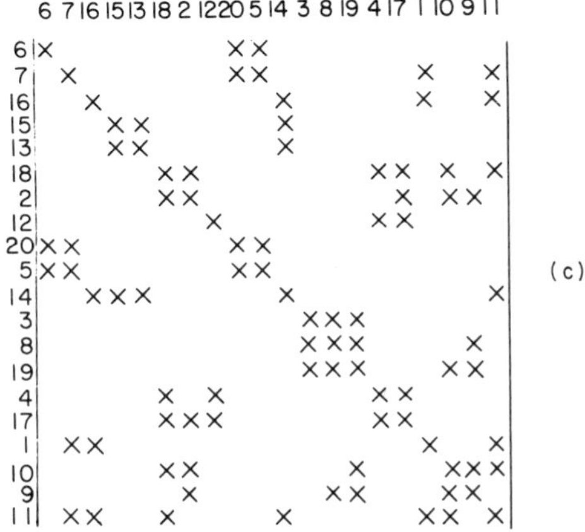

Figure 4.15 Application of nested dissection to the graph of Fig. 4.2(a). The relabelled graph is shown in (a), the dissection tree in (b), and the permuted matrix in (c).

Consider now R_1^1. The level structure rooted at 12 has $m = 5$, thus $j = 3$, and $S_1^1 = L_3 = (9, 10)$. Vertices 9 and 10 are labelled 19 and 18, respectively. For R_1^2, 13 is a peripheral vertex, $m = 6$ for the corresponding rooted level structure, and $j = 3$. Thus $S_1^2 = L_3 = (1)$. Vertex 1 is labelled 17.

At this point, C consists of the union of S_0, S_1^1 and S_1^2, and its removal leaves the following connected components: $R_2^1 = (12, 4, 17, 18, 2)$; $R_2^2 = (19, 8, 3)$; $R_2^3 = (13, 15, 14, 16)$ and $R_2^4 = (7, 5, 20, 6)$. The separator for R_2^1 is $S_2^1 = (17, 4)$. R_2^2 is a clique and has no separator, thus $S_2^2 = R_2^2$. The other two separators are $S_2^3 = (14)$ and $S_2^4 = (5, 20)$. The vertices of these new separators are labelled and removed from the graph. All the remaining R-sets have no separators. The final labelling is indicated in Fig. 4.15(a) by numbers outside the circles, and the dissection tree is shown in Fig. 4.15(b). The permuted matrix is given in Fig. 4.15(c). Should elimination be performed on it, the fill-in would be only 14 elements, which should be compared with 27 for the arbitrary ordering of Fig. 4.12(a) and 2 for the refined quotient tree ordering of Fig. 4.12(b). Of course, the results from this simple example should not be extrapolated. Numerical experiments with test problems are presented by George (1977).

4.11. Properties of nested dissection orderings

In this section we describe some properties of nested dissection orderings which were proved by George and Liu (1976) as theorems, and are important for a good understanding of the subject.

Consider a graph $G = (V, E)$ which has been partitioned by nested dissection, and consider a numbering of the vertices of the graph. The numbering is said to be *compatible* with the partitioning if the vertices of each partition are numbered consecutively. Figure 4.16(a) shows a graph with a nested dissection partitioning into three parts, as indicated. The numbering shown is compatible with the partitioning. Another possible compatible numbering is shown in Fig. 4.16(c), while Fig. 4.16(b) illustrates a numbering which is not compatible with the partitioning. The algorithm discussed in the preceding section generates a numbering which is compatible with the partitioning. Note that the order in which the vertices of each separator are numbered is irrelevant, the important point is that they are numbered consecutively.

Consider now any of the R-sets defined by a nested dissection partitioning, and the corresponding separator S. The numbering is said to be *consistent* with the partitioning when all vertices in S are numbered after all vertices in $R - S$, should $R - S$ be nonempty. When $S = R$, as is the case for terminal members, the vertices in S can be numbered arbitrarily. The numbering shown in Fig. 4.16(a) is consistent with the partitioning because the vertices in S_0 are numbered after those in $R_0 - S_0$. Another consistent numbering is given in Fig. 4.16(b); in both cases, (a) and (b), the vertices of the terminal members S_1^1 and S_1^2 are numbered arbitrarily. The numbering of Fig. 4.16(c) is not consistent. The numbering produced by the nested dissection algorithm of the preceding section is consistent with the partitioning.

A monotone ordering of a tree was defined in Section 4.2 as one in which each member of the tree is numbered before its father. A monotone ordering of the dissection tree induces a numbering of the vertices of the graph which is both compatible and consistent with the nested dissection partitioning, and

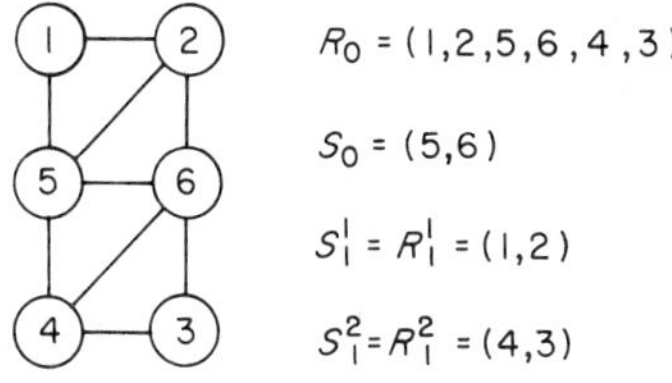

(a) COMPATIBLE AND CONSISTENT

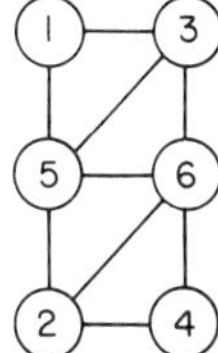

(b) CONSISTENT BUT NOT COMPATIBLE

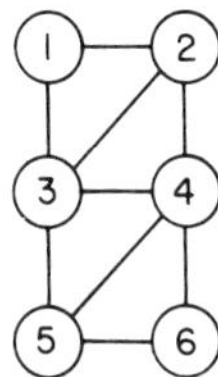

(c) COMPATIBLE BUT NOT CONSISTENT

Figure 4.16 Three possible numberings of the vertices of a graph with a nested dissection partitioning.

this is precisely what the algorithm of Section 4.10 does. Now, when the nested dissection partitioning is minimal (i.e., each separator is minimal), the following important property holds: all numberings which are consistent with the partitioning are equivalent, in the sense that the corresponding permuted matrices will suffer the same fill-in and will require the same number of operations during elimination. This is the reason why we can restrict our attention only to a particular class of numberings: those which are compatible, besides being consistent, with the partitioning. Since nothing would be gained by using more general numberings, the algorithm was designed to produce only consistent and compatible numberings.

Suppose now that a matrix **A** was given, its graph was partitioned by minimal nested dissection, and the resulting permuted matrix **A**′ was factorized as $\mathbf{A}' = \mathbf{U}^{\mathrm{T}}\mathbf{D}\mathbf{U}$. An important measure of the quality of the partitioning is the number of nonzeros Z in the upper factor $\mathbf{U}$ above the diagonal. Z is bounded by:

$$Z \leqslant \sum |S_l^j|[|\text{Adj}(R_l^j)| + (|S_l^j| - 1)/2] \qquad (4.18)$$

where the sum is extended to all separators and its corresponding R-sets, and bars are used to indicate the number of vertices in a set. The bound is attained when the condition

$$\text{Adj}(R_l^j) \subset \text{Adj}(R_l^j - S_l^j) \qquad (4.19)$$

is satisfied in all cases. This condition may be violated by the algorithm of Section 4.10, but this seldom happens in practice and the above bound for Z is sufficiently tight for most cases.

A planar graph has been defined in Section 4.2 as one which can be represented on a plane in such a way that no two edges intersect. A given graph may be tested for planarity; an algorithm which performs the test in a time proportional to the number of vertices was given by Tarjan (1971). Alternatively, a graph may be known to be planar by construction. An important source of sparse matrices with planar graphs is the finite element method. In its simplest version, a problem governed by a differential equation is solved by dividing the region of interest into finite elements which have nodes at the corners and may have additional nodes at the boundary or interior. A sparse matrix $\mathbf{A}$ is then constructed, in which a row and a column correspond to each node in the grid and $A_{ij} \neq 0$ if and only if nodes i and j belong to the same finite element. Consider now the graph associated with matrix $\mathbf{A}$. There is a one-to-one correspondence between vertices of the graph and nodes of the finite element grid. Two vertices are connected by an edge only if the corresponding nodes belong to the same finite element. If the problem to be solved is two-dimensional, the grid is two-dimensional and the graph is planar. This is the case we wish to discuss in more detail.

A 5×5 regular grid of three-noded triangles is shown in Fig. 4.17. The same drawing also represents the graph associated with the finite element

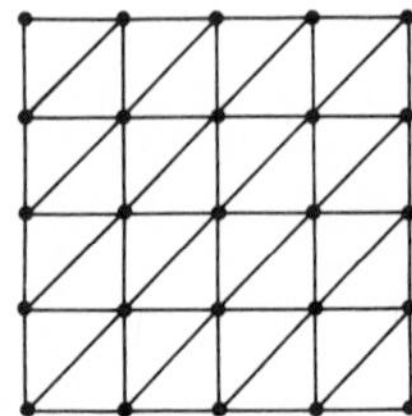

Figure 4.17 A regular grid of three-noded triangles. The same drawing also represents the corresponding planar graph.

grid. The graph is planar, but it turns out that the following results apply equally well for a regular grid of four-noded quadrilaterals, which has a nonplanar graph.

Consider nested dissection applied to a regular $k \times k$ finite element grid, as shown in Fig. 4.18. The vertices associated with nodes on a grid line are used as separators. The first separator S_0 is a vertical grid line. The next separators S_1^1 and S_1^2 are on a horizontal grid line. Grid lines are chosen in such a way that each rectangle is divided as nearly as possible into parts with comparable numbers of nodes. Each time a separator is found, its nodes are numbered in the reverse order, e.g. the n nodes of S_0 are numbered from $n = k^2$ (the total number of nodes in the grid) to $n - k + 1$. The process is continued until all nodes have been numbered. If now the matrix **A** is constructed and factorized into $\mathbf{U}^T\mathbf{D}\mathbf{U}$, the number Z of nonzeros above the diagonal of **U** and the number P of multiplicative operations required to compute **U** are (George and Liu, 1981):

$$Z = \frac{31}{8} n \log_2 n + O(n) \tag{4.20}$$

$$P = \frac{829}{84} n^{3/2} + O(n \log_2 n) \tag{4.21}$$

where O means "of the order of". Although in practice a grid will usually be irregular, estimates of storage and operation count can be obtained using these expressions.

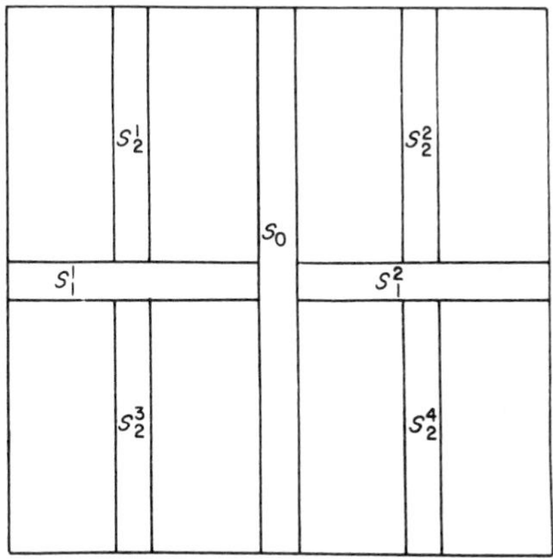

Figure 4.18 Nested dissection of a regular grid.

4.12. Generalized nested dissection

At this point it must be clear for the reader that the success of nested dissection in generating a good ordering depends on how small the separators of the graph are. There is a direct connection between the size of the separators and the efficiency of Gauss elimination (Lipton *et al.*, 1979): sparse Gauss elimination is efficient for any matrix having a graph with good separators. Conversely, the efficiency will be poor if good separators are absent. The quality of separators is stated quantitatively as follows. Consider a graph $G = (V, E)$ with $n = |V|$ vertices and consider also all possible subgraphs of G. We wish to define bounds to the size of separators of G or of any of its subgraphs in terms of three constants: α, β and σ. Suppose then that G or any subgraph of G has been partitioned by a separator S into R_1 and R_2, and define α, β and σ by:

$$\begin{aligned} |R_1|, |R_2| &\leqslant \alpha n \\ |S| &\leqslant \beta n^{\sigma} \end{aligned} \tag{4.22}$$

The constants must satisfy $1/2 \leqslant \alpha < 1$ and $\beta > 0$ (except if G itself has no separators, whence $S = G$ and $\beta = \sigma = 1$). The three constants are used to characterize classes of graphs and to calculate orders of magnitude of storage and execution time of sparse Gauss elimination. A summary of the main results follows.

All systems of equations of which the graphs satisfy Equation (4.22) with $\sigma = 1/2$ can be ordered in such a way that the resulting fill-in is at most $c_3 n \log_2 n + O(n)$ and the multiplication count is at most $c_7 n^{3/2} + O(n(\log n)^2)$ (Lipton *et al.*, 1977), where:

$$\begin{aligned} c_3 &= \beta^2 \left(\frac{1}{2} + \frac{2\sqrt{\alpha}}{1 - \sqrt{\alpha}}\right)\left[\log_2\left(\frac{1}{\alpha}\right)\right]^{-1} \\ c_7 &= \beta^2 \left[\frac{1}{6} + \frac{\beta\sqrt{\alpha}}{1 - \sqrt{\alpha}}\left(2 + \frac{\sqrt{\alpha}}{1 + \sqrt{\alpha}} + \frac{4\alpha}{1 - \alpha}\right)\right][1 - \alpha^{3/2} - (1 - \alpha)^{3/2}]^{-1} \end{aligned} \tag{4.23}$$

An algorithm for finding the ordering was proposed by Lipton *et al.* (1979). The algorithm dissects the graph recursively, as was done in Section 4.10, but in this case the running time depends on the difficulty in finding separators which satisfy (4.22) with $\sigma = 1/2$. If the required separators can be found in $O(m + n)$ time for a graph with n vertices and m edges, then the execution time of the ordering algorithm is $O[(m + n) \log n]$.

A particular class of graphs which satisfy Equation (4.22) with $\sigma = 1/2$ are planar graphs, which also have $\alpha = 2/3$ and $\beta = 2\sqrt{2}$ (Lipton and Tarjan,

1979). Any planar graph can be ordered in such a way that the fill-in produced by sparse elimination will be at most $c_3 n \log n + O(n)$ and the multiplication count is at most $c_7 n^{3/2} + O[n(\log n)^2]$, where $c_3 \leqslant 129$ and $c_7 \leqslant 4002$. Furthermore, the separators can be found in $O(n)$ time, whence the execution time of the ordering algorithm is $O(n \log n)$. The algorithm for finding the separators is explicitly given by Lipton and Tarjan (1979).

Two-dimensional finite element graphs are almost-planar graphs which satisfy Equation (4.22) with $\sigma = 1/2$ and $\alpha = 2/3$. If no element has more than k boundary nodes, then $\beta = 4\lfloor k/2 \rfloor$. Any two-dimensional finite element graph has an ordering which produces a fill-in of size $O(k^2 n \log n)$ and a multiplication count $O(k^3 n^{3/2})$. Since the separators can be found in $O(n)$ time, the execution time of the ordering algorithm is $O(n \log n)$. These figures can be reduced even further by using the fast matrix multiplication and factorization algorithm of Strassen (1969) and Bunch and Hopcroft (1974). When the equations are to be solved for just one right-hand side, the fill-in can be reduced to $O(n)$ by storing only part of $\mathbf{U}^{\mathrm{T}}$ and recomputing the rest when necessary. The procedure is described by Eisenstat *et al.* (1976) for ordinary nested dissection, but it can be generalized (Lipton *et al.*, 1979).

The results discussed in this section, those of the preceding section and a few others are presented for clarity in tabular form in Table 4.1.

4.13. One-way dissection for finite element problems

The heuristic method we discuss in this section was designed by A. George (1980) primarily for two-dimensional finite element problems. It combines the best of several ideas, such as Jennings' envelope method, tree partitioning and dissection, yet it is simple and admits a rather straightforward implementation. The extension to three-dimensional finite element problems is also straightforward. The algorithm, discussed below, can be used to minimize either storage, or number of operations performed during factorization, or number of operations performed during backsolution, at the user's convenience. It is even possible to minimize *total* cost by taking into account the computer charging algorithm and the number of right-hand sides for which the linear equations have to be solved, and to do all this *automatically*. When storage is minimized and the problem is not very large, less storage is needed than with any other method, a fact which is closely related to the low overhead storage required by one-way dissection. Of course, it is still necessary to compare one-way dissection further with the two methods extensively used: band matrices and Jennings' scheme. In our opinion, one-way dissection is a candidate for becoming the next industry standard in finite element computations.

Table 4.1

Class of graphs	Bound for fill-in	Bound for multiplication count	Observations and references
Any, such that $\sigma = \frac{1}{2}$	$c_3 n \log_2 n + O(n)$	$c_7 n^{3/2} + O[n(\log n)^2]$	Ordering time is $O[(m+n) \log n]$ if separators can be found in $O(m+n)$ time. c_3 and c_7 given by Equation (4.23) (Lipton *et al.*, 1977)
Planar graphs (in this case $\sigma = \frac{1}{2}$, $\alpha = \frac{2}{3}$, $\beta = 2\sqrt{2}$)	$c_3 n \log n + O(n)$	$c_7 n^{3/2} + O[n(\log n)^2]$	$c_3 \leqslant 129$, $c_7 \leqslant 4002$. Ordering time is $O(n \log n)$ (Lipton and Tarjan, 1979; Lipton *et al.*, 1979)
Two-dimensional finite element graphs (in this case $\sigma = \frac{1}{2}$, $\alpha = \frac{2}{3}$, $\beta = 4\lfloor k/2 \rfloor$)	$O(k^2 n \log n)$	$O(k^3 n^{3/2})$	k is the maximum number of boundary nodes of the elements. Ordering time is $O(n \log n)$ (Lipton *et al.*, 1979)
Regular planar grid	$\frac{31}{8} n \log_2 n + O(n)$	$\frac{829}{84} n^{3/2} + O(n \log_2 n)$	(George and Liu, 1981)
Any such that $\sigma > \frac{1}{2}$	$O(n^{2\sigma})$	$O(n^{3\sigma})$	(Lipton *et al.*, 1979)
Three-dimensional grid graphs (in this case $\sigma = \frac{2}{3}$)	$O(n^{4/3})$	$O(n^2)$	(Lipton *et al.*, 1979)
Any, such that $\frac{1}{3} < \sigma < \frac{1}{2}$	$O(n)$	$O(n^{3\sigma})$	(Lipton *et al.*, 1979)
Any, such that $\sigma = \frac{1}{3}$	$O(n)$	$O(n \log_2 n)$	(Lipton *et al.*, 1979)
Any, such that $\sigma < \frac{1}{3}$	$O(n)$	$O(n)$	(Lipton *et al.*, 1979)

The idea is illustrated in Fig. 4.19(a), where the rectangle represents the set of nodes of a two-dimensional finite element grid. Choose σ small separators ($\sigma = 3$ in the figure) which consists of grid lines and dissect the grid into $\sigma + 1$ blocks $R_1, R_2, \ldots$ of comparable size. If all separators are considered to form another single block, a tree partitioning is obtained as shown by the quotient tree of Fig. 4.19(b). The advantages of tree partitionings regarding the reduction of fill-in and operation count were discussed in Section 4.9. Now, let us number the nodes of each R-set sequentially, following lines from left to right as closely as possible, and starting at the bottom left as indicated by the arrows. When all R-sets have been numbered, the separators are also

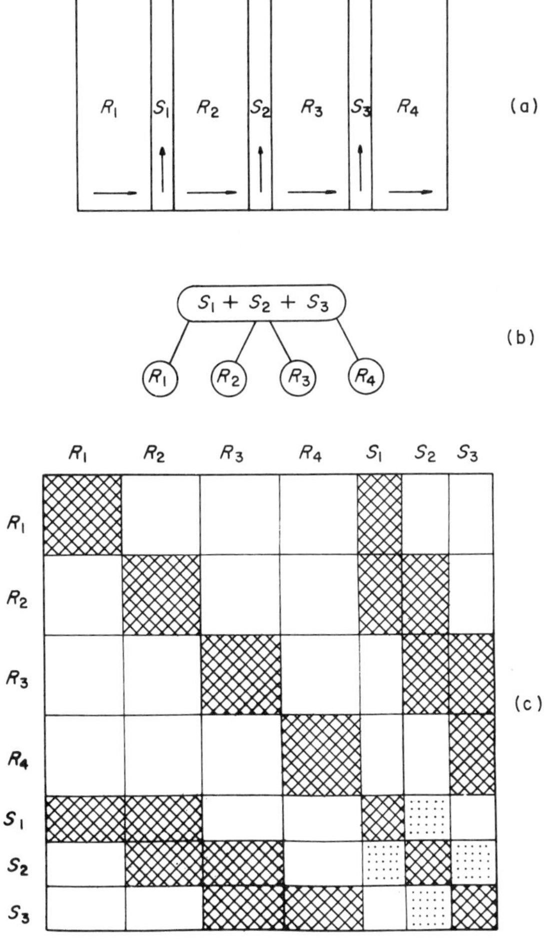

Figure 4.19 One-way dissection of a regular grid.

numbered sequentially, as the arrows show. This numbering corresponds to a monotone ordering of the tree. The matrix associated with the finite element grid is partitioned into blocks as shown in Fig. 4.19(c), where all nonzeros are confined to the cross-hatched areas. If Gauss elimination is performed on this matrix, fill-in will result only inside the cross-hatched areas and in the pointed areas. Besides, the hatched blocks are not completely full. For example, the four leading diagonal blocks are banded. Advantage is taken of this additional structure by using the implicit storage scheme for partitioned matrices discussed in Section 1.11.

The number of separators, σ, yet remains to be determined. σ is a central parameter for the method. In order to determine it, estimations of storage requirements and operations count will be given as explicit functions of σ. Any of these functions, or any combination of them such as the one dictated by the computer charging algorithm, can then be minimized by selecting the appropriate value of σ. Since the functions are only estimates and have flat minima, it will normally be sufficient to take for σ the integer closest to the resulting approximation. The analysis (George and Liu, 1981) is carried out for a regular $m \times l$ grid, with $m \leqslant l$, such as the one shown in Fig. 4.17. If the separators are grid lines, the partitions have approximately the same number of vertices, and the implicit storage scheme is used, the total storage requirement is, asymptotically:

$$S \cong \frac{ml^2}{\sigma} + \frac{3\sigma m^2}{2}. \tag{4.24}$$

This expression achieves its minimum value of $S_{\min} = \sqrt{6}m^{3/2}l + O(ml)$, when $\sigma = \sqrt{2}l/\sqrt{(3m)}$, although a more careful analysis and some experimentation suggest that a better value for σ at the minimum is $\sigma = \sqrt{2}l/\sqrt{(3m + 13)}$.

The total number of operations required by the factorization is asymptotically:

$$\Theta_F \cong \frac{ml^3}{2\sigma^2} + \frac{7\sigma m^3}{6} + \frac{2m^2l^2}{\sigma} \tag{4.25}$$

which is approximately minimized for large m and l when $\sigma = \sqrt{12}l/\sqrt{(7m)}$, yielding a value of $\Theta_{F,\min} = \sqrt{(28/3)}m^{5/2}l + O(m^2l)$.

The total number of operations required to solve the system of linear equations, once the factorization is available, is, asymptotically:

$$\Theta_S \cong \frac{4ml^2}{\sigma} + 3\sigma m^2. \tag{4.26}$$

Θ_S achieves its minimum value of $\Theta_{S,\min} = 4\sqrt{3}m^{3/2}l + O(ml)$ when $\sigma = 2l/\sqrt{(3m)}$.

Let us compare the approximate performance of one-way dissection with what one would expect if a band or envelope scheme were used with the grid numbered column by column. With a band or envelope scheme, the storage and operation count for factorization and solution would be, respectively, of the order of $m^2 l$, $m^3 l/2$ and $2m^2 l$. Thus, if one-way dissection with storage optimization is used, storage is less by a factor of $\sqrt{(m/6)}$. If one-way dissection with factorization optimization is used, the number of operations for factorization is less by a factor of $\sqrt{(m/37)}$. If one-way dissection with solution optimization is used, the number of operations for solution is less by a factor of $\sqrt{(m/12)}$. Of course, all three parameters cannot be optimized at the same time. Since in practice m is frequently in the range 20 to 100 (remember $l \geqslant m$), we conclude that the use of one-way dissection can produce important savings in storage or in solution cost in most practical cases, and that savings in factorization cost are worthwhile for large problems. The reader can estimate the possible savings in *total* cost for running his/her particular problem on his/her particular computer.

The above ideas can be carried through for irregular finite element grids using the concept of level structures, thus obtaining the basis for the design of the automatic algorithm. A level structure rooted at some pseudoperipheral node of the irregular grid is, hopefully, long and narrow. Thus, the number of levels can play the role of l, and the average width of the structure, that of m. A value of σ can then be calculated using either of the estimations given to optimize storage, factorization cost or solution cost, or any other desired parameter, as if the level structure were an approximately regular grid. The separators are then chosen from the levels of the structure and the nodes are numbered using the reverse Cuthill–McKee algorithm discussed in Section 4.6 for each connected component in order to reduce the profile of each diagonal block of the matrix. In detail, the algorithm is as follows (George and Liu, 1981):

Step 1 (Generate level structure). Given a two-dimensional finite element grid with N nodes, find a pseudoperipheral vertex of the associated graph $G(V, E)$ and generate the rooted level structure. Let the $l + 1$ levels be $L_0, L_1, \ldots, L_l$.

Step 2 (Estimate distance δ between separators). Calculate $m = N/(l + 1)$, estimate the number of separators σ so as to optimize the desired parameter, and estimate the distance between separators $\delta = (l + 1)/(\sigma + 1)$. Note that $l + 1$ now plays the role of l in the regular grid.

Step 3 (Limiting case). If $\delta < l/2$ and $N > 50$ go to Step 4. Otherwise, it is not worthwhile making use of one-way dissection. Set $p = 0$ and go to Step 6.

Step 4 (Find separators). Initialize $i = 1$ and $S = \emptyset$.

(4.1) Set $j = \lfloor i\delta + 0.5 \rfloor$ (the integer nearest $i\delta$). If $j \geqslant l$ go to Step 5. Otherwise continue.

(4.2) Let S_i be the set of all vertices of level L_j which are adjacent to any vertex of level L_{j+1}.

(4.3) Set $S \leftarrow S \cup S_i$.

(4.4) Set $i \leftarrow i + 1$ and go to (4.1).

Step 5 (Define blocks). Find the p connected components $R_1, R_2, \ldots, R_p$ formed when set S is removed. Note that p may be different from $\sigma + 1$ because σ is in general not an integer and because the graph may be partitioned into more blocks.

Step 6 (Internal numbering). Number each R_k, $k = 1, 2, \ldots, p$, using the reverse Cuthill–McKee algorithm on each section graph. Finally, number the nodes of S arbitrarily.

In Step 6, it may be advisable to use the improved version of the reverse Cuthill–McKee algorithm (Brown and Wait, 1981), because this will tend to reduce the oscillations in the numbering of the nodes of the grid.

For an example of one-way dissection consider the graph of Fig. 4.2(a) and the level structure rooted at the peripheral vertex 8, shown in (b). Since $N = 20$ and $l = 6$, we obtain $m = 20/7$. If we want to optimize storage we take $\sigma = \sqrt{2}(l + 1)/\sqrt{(3m + 13)} \cong 2.13$, and $\delta = (l + 1)/(\sigma + 1) \cong 2.23$. The levels from which the separators are chosen at Step 4 are 2 and 4. Thus:

$$S_1 = (2, 10)$$

$$S_2 = (14, 7).$$

Note that vertices 14 and 7 are the only vertices of level 4 which are adjacent to vertices in L_5. The blocks are:

$$R_1 = (8, 9, 19, 3)$$

$$R_2 = (17, 18, 11, 12, 4, 16, 1)$$

$$R_3 = (13, 15)$$

$$R_4 = (5, 20, 6).$$

Thus $p = 4$ in this example. Each of the four R-sets is locally numbered using the reverse Cuthill–McKee algorithm. The two S-sets are then numbered arbitrarily. The final numbering is shown in Fig. 4.20(a), and the corresponding permuted matrix in Fig. 4.20(b). The block partitioning and the envelope structure of the diagonal blocks can be clearly appreciated.

Fortran software for this algorithm is explicitly presented by George and Liu (1981).

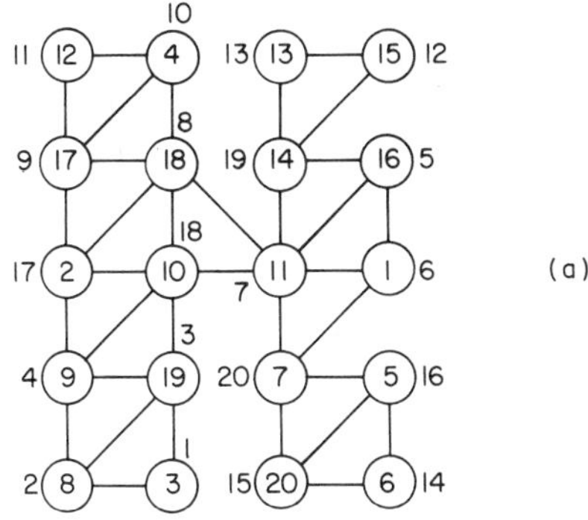

		R_1				R_2							R_3		R_4			S_1		S_2	
		3	8	19	9	16	1	11	18	17	4	12	15	13	6	20	5	2	10	14	7
R_1	3	×	×	×																	
	8	×	×	×	×																
	19	×	×	×	×														×		
	9		×	×	×													×	×		
R_2	16					×	×	×												×	
	1					×	×	×													×
	11					×	×	×	×										×	×	×
	18							×	×	×	×							×	×		
	17								×	×	×	×						×			
	4								×	×	×	×									
	12									×	×	×									
R_3	15												×	×						×	
	13												×	×						×	
R_4	6														×	×	×				
	20														×	×	×				×
	5														×	×	×				×
S_1	2				×				×	×								×	×		
	10			×	×			×	×									×	×		
S_2	14					×		×					×	×						×	
	7						×	×								×	×				×

(b)

Figure 4.20 One-way dissection of the graph of Fig. 4.2. The resulting numbering of the graph is shown in (a), and the block partitioned matrix, in (b).

4.14. Orderings for the finite element method

A brief description of the numerical aspects of the finite element method which are of interest to us follows. The method is used to solve a problem governed by a differential equation in a given region. The region is divided into subregions of simple form called *finite elements*, which share the inter-element boundaries but otherwise do not overlap. If the region is unbounded, *infinite elements* can be used equally well (Bettess, 1977; Pissanetzky, 1982). *Nodes* exist on the element boundaries, and additional nodes may exist in the interior of the elements. We say that a node which is on the boundary between two elements belongs to both, and a node on a corner or edge belongs to all the elements which share the corner or edge. Elements and nodes are numbered arbitrarily, and the assembled set of elements and nodes is called the *mesh*. Figure 4.17 shows a two-dimensional example in which the elements are triangles with nodes at the corners. To use the method, a sparse linear system of order n is constructed

$$\mathbf{A}\mathbf{x} = \mathbf{b}, \tag{4.27}$$

where n is the number of nodes in the mesh. Our discussion is limited to the case where there is just one unknown and one equation associated with each node, although in more general cases there may be more than one nodal unknown per node and n may thus be larger than the number of nodes.

If the mesh has m elements, $\mathbf{A}$ is calculated as the sum of m *element matrices* $\mathbf{A}^{(e)}$. Each $\mathbf{A}^{(e)}$ is square of order n, depends on the particular problem being solved, and has the important property that $A_{ij}^{(e)}$ can be different from zero only if nodes i and j belong to element e. Although cases exist where $A_{ij}^{(e)} = 0$ even when i and j belong to e, they are not frequent, and we will assume for simplicity that $A_{ij}^{(e)}$ is a nonzero if and only if nodes i and j belong to element e. Hence:

$$\mathbf{A} = \sum_{e=1}^{m} \mathbf{A}^{(e)} \tag{4.28}$$

and A_{ij} is a nonzero if and only if there exists a finite element to which nodes i and j belong (cancellations are neglected, as usual). More formally: let E be the set of finite elements, and let E_i be the set of elements to which node i belongs. We have $E_i \neq \emptyset$ because any node belongs to at least one element, and $E_i \subseteq E$, although E_i is properly contained in E in all practical cases. Then A_{ij} is a nonzero if and only if $E_i \cap E_j \neq \emptyset$.

It is frequently said that the matrices $\mathbf{A}^{(e)}$ in Equation (4.28) are *assembled* to form $\mathbf{A}$. We will also say for brevity that "a finite element e is assembled" when its element matrix $\mathbf{A}^{(e)}$ has been computed and added to the sum of Equation (4.28).

If β is the maximum absolute difference between the reference numbers of all pairs of nodes which belong to the same element in the mesh, i.e.

$$\beta = \max_{e,k,l} \{|k - l| \; | k \text{ and } l \text{ are nodes of } e\}, \tag{4.29}$$

then $A_{ij} = 0$ if $|i - j| > \beta$. This means that A_{ij} is a band matrix with half-bandwidth β. As a consequence, the use of band schemes for solving Equation (4.27) is very popular. A simple method for reducing the bandwidth is also very popular: it consists in numbering the nodes of the mesh in such a way that β is small. An example is given in Fig. 4.21, where three different numberings of the nodes of a simple mesh are shown. Also shown is the structure of the matrix corresponding to one of the numberings.

The Finite Element method is so important in practice and so widely used that, in addition to classical techniques such as band matrices, specific ordering procedures have been devised to solve (4.27) efficiently. Among such procedures are one-way dissection and nested dissection, although nested dissection was later generalized as explained in Section 4.12, and one-way dissection can be generalized as well. In both band and dissection methods, the assumption is made that the summation indicated by Equation (4.28) is complete and **A** is fully assembled before elimination on **A** starts. We will now discuss the *frontal method* (Irons, 1970), in which the converse assumption is made: elimination starts before the summation (4.28) is complete. Our discussion is restricted to the frequent case where **A** is symmetric and positive definite, although the method is not. Therefore, any elimination order meets the requirements for numerical stability discussed in Chapter 3, provided all pivots are chosen from the diagonal.

Assume that, at a certain stage, **A** is partially assembled, and let C be the set of assembled finite elements (i.e., of finite elements of which the element matrices have already been assembled), where $C \subset E$. Note that the summation in Equation (4.28) can be computed in any order, not necessarily

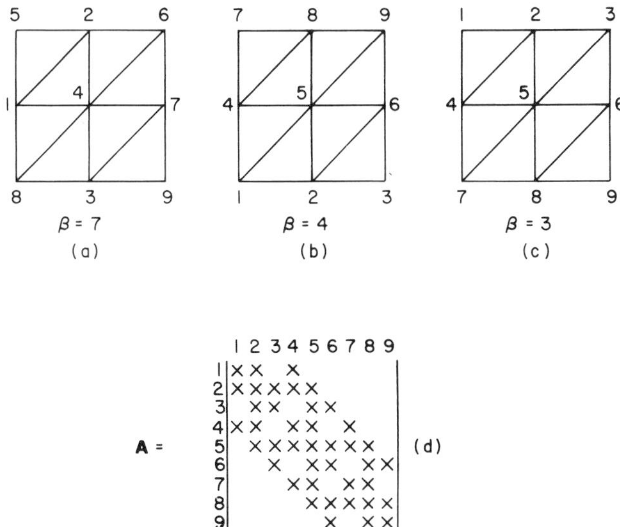

Figure 4.21 Three different numberings of the nodes of a simple mesh. The structure of the matrix shown in (d) has a half-bandwidth $\beta = 3$, and corresponds to the numbering shown in (c).

in the conventional order defined by the index e; thus, C may in general be any subset of E. At this stage, the n nodes of the mesh can be sorted into three sets:

$$G\text{– fully assembled: } G = \{i \mid E_i \subseteq C\}$$

$$F\text{– partially assembled or } \textit{front}\text{:}$$

$$F = \{i \mid E_i \cap C \neq \emptyset,\ E_i \cap (E - C) \neq \emptyset\}$$

$$H\text{– not assembled} \quad H = \{i \mid E_i \subseteq E - C\}$$

Clearly, if e is an element not in C, $A^{(e)}_{ij} = 0$ if either i or j, or both, are in G. This means that all rows and columns of $\mathbf{A}$ associated with nodes in G are fully assembled at this stage. Note also that $A_{ij} = 0$ if $i \in G$ and $j \in H$, because $E_i \cap E_j = \phi$. At this stage, the partially assembled matrix $\mathbf{A}$ looks as shown in Fig. 4.22, and it is clear that all unknowns associated with nodes in G can be eliminated and that fill-in will take place only in the area marked "partially assembled". After this has been done, new elements from $E - C$ are assembled, the sets G, F and H are redefined, and new variables are eliminated. The front moves across the mesh. The process is continued until $\mathbf{A}$ is fully assembled and factorized.

In practical implementations of the frontal method, the eliminations are performed as early as possible, and the order in which elements are assembled is selected in such a way that the front is kept small. All nodes in the front lie on the border between the region covered by the elements in set C and the rest. If this is a connected region at each stage, then the border is a continuous line and the approach is called *uni-frontal*. There is no conceptual

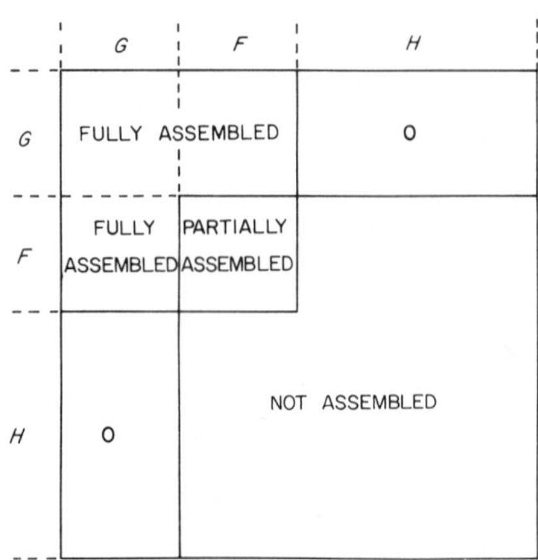

Figure 4.22 Illustration of the frontal method. The partially assembled matrix $\mathbf{A}$.

difficulty in generalizing the idea: the approach is said to be *multi-frontal* when the elements in C cover two or more separate regions with independent borders. Each such region is sometimes called a *generalized element* or *super-element* (Speelpenning, 1978). The selection of the regions can be dictated by engineering considerations, for example they may correspond to parts of a physical body. This technique is known as *substructuring*, and is particularly convenient when several such parts have identical structure and the same analysis holds for all of them, or when the parts are very complex and each must be designed by a different team of engineers. Substructures may be nested to any depth, and trees are suitable data structures for representing nested substructuring. For a very good discussion and other related references, see Reid (1981).

An alternative possibility which tries to keep the front small and lends itself for automatic operation on a general sparse matrix, is to generate a level structure on the graph associated with the matrix, rooted at a pseudoperipheral vertex, and then to use the levels as successive fronts. Since each level is a separator of the graph, a necessary condition for the front to be small is that the graph have good separators. From Section 4.12 we know that this condition is met by planar and almost-planar graphs.

The frontal method does not actually try to reduce fill-in; it minimizes the amount of information which must be kept in main memory at a time. If variables are eliminated as soon as possible, the corresponding lines of **A** can be immediately copied onto a peripheral device, and only the submatrix marked "partially assembled" in Fig. 4.22 must remain in main memory. If the front is small, this submatrix is also small, and it is common practice to treat it as a full matrix. The full matrix code which originates in this way is very convenient for parallel processing (Duff, 1980b), although pipeline processors can perform equally well with sparse code (Coleman and Kushner, 1982). The final factorized form of **A**, obtained in peripheral storage, may be larger than what would have been obtained if fill-in were truly reduced.

In Chapter 5, we will discuss the extension of the frontal method to the case where **A** is not symmetric and positive definite.

In some cases, an alternative formulation of the Finite Element method is possible. So far we have implicitly assumed that the mesh is assembled, and that a node may belong to several elements. We will now make the converse assumption: each element has its own set of nodes, but the set of elements is disassembled, so that a node belongs to a single element. As before, a nodal unknown and an equation are associated with each node, but a set of additional constraints is introduced to force unknowns associated with coincident nodes to have identical values. For any node i of the disassembled mesh, $E_i = \{e\}$, where e is the only element to which i belongs, so that A_{ij} is a nonzero only when both i and j are nodes of the same element. This means that, if the nodes of each element are numbered consecutively (a compatible numbering), then the nonzeros are clustered together into square diagonal blocks of size equal to the number of nodes per element. There results a block-diagonal matrix **A**, which can be conveniently represented in memory by storing a vector with pointers to the actual positions of the diagonal blocks. The blocks themselves are kept elsewhere in memory. Now, for linear finite element problems, it is frequently the case that many of the blocks are identical, because they correspond to identical elements. Only one copy of identical blocks has to be stored, and since even the largest problems usually require no more than 10 or 20 different sizes or types of elements, it turns out that **A** can be represented by a full vector of pointers of size equal to the number of elements in the mesh, plus a few full blocks each of size, say 3×3 or 8×8. Furthermore, since triangular factorization produces no fill-in outside the blocks, and identical blocks give identical results, each block can be factorized separately and replaced in memory by the corresponding triangular factor. In this way, savings in both storage and labour can be achieved.

The constraint equations take the form:

$$\mathbf{C}^{\mathrm{T}}\mathbf{x} = 0 \tag{4.30}$$

and the complete linear system is obtained using Lagrange multipliers (see, for example, Gallagher, 1975):

$$\begin{vmatrix} \mathbf{A} & \mathbf{C} \\ \mathbf{C}^{\mathrm{T}} & \mathbf{0} \end{vmatrix} \begin{vmatrix} \mathbf{x} \\ \boldsymbol{\lambda} \end{vmatrix} = \begin{vmatrix} \mathbf{b} \\ \mathbf{0} \end{vmatrix} \tag{4.31}$$

where $\boldsymbol{\lambda}$ is the vector of Lagrange multipliers. This is a *diakoptical* system. Its matrix is symmetric but indefinite. The methods discussed in Section 4.17 can be used to solve system (4.31). For illustration, consider the example of a disassembled mesh shown in Fig. 4.23. The constraints are $x_2 = x_4$, $x_2 = x_7$, $x_3 = x_6$ and $x_5 = x_9$, which can be written in the form of Equation (4.30) of $\mathbf{C}^{\mathrm{T}}$ is defined as in Fig. 4.23(b). The resulting linear system is given in (c). A good account on this subject and other useful references are presented by McDonald and Wexler (1980). *Augmented systems* of forms similar to (4.31) are used for a variety of applications, see for example (Duff, 1977, p. 520). A further approach is the sparse tableau (Hachtel, 1976).

4.15. Depth-first search of an undirected graph

In Section 4.3 we have described a search as a procedure by which we visit the vertices and edges of a graph in some sequence, labelling the vertices as they

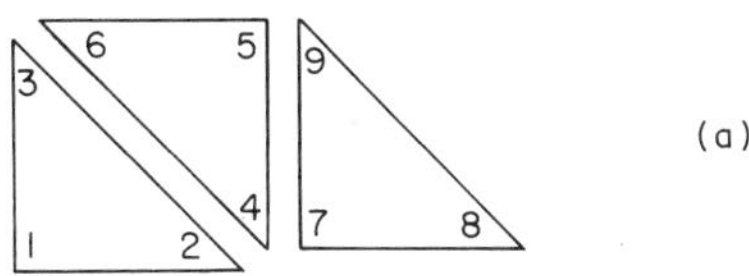

(a)

(b)

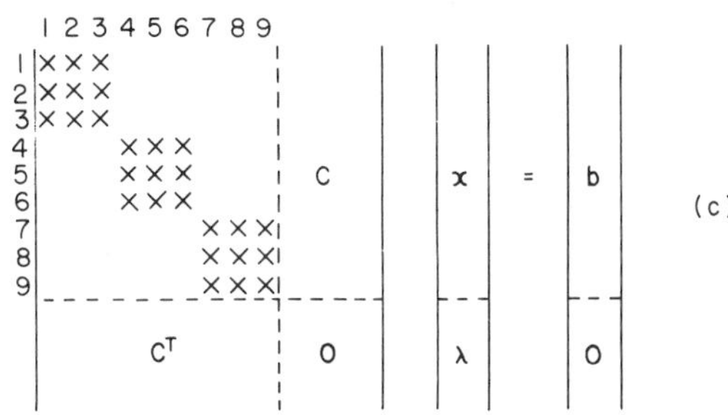

(c)

Figure 4.23 A disassembled finite element mesh, the constraint matrix and the diakoptical system.

are visited and sorting edges into classes. We have also mentioned that search is used by many sparse matrix algorithms, and that different rules are employed to determine, at each step, which vertex to visit next or which edge to explore next. In this section we consider *depth-first search*, in which we explore the graph trying to preserve the sequence vertex–edge–vertex–edge ... while possible. In more detail, consider an undirected connected graph $G = (V, E)$. At the beginning of the search, all edges are unexplored and all vertices are unvisited. We start at an arbitrarily selected vertex s and consider it to be the first current vertex and the first visited vertex. Let V_v and E_e be the sets of visited vertices and explored edges, respectively. Initially we set $E_e \leftarrow \emptyset$ and $V_v \leftarrow \{s\}$. Then, at each step, we consider the current vertex, say $v \in V_v$, and look for an unexplored edge leaving v, say $(v, w) \notin E_e$. The following possibilities exist:

(1) w has not been visited before, i.e. $w \notin V_v$. We add (v, w) to the set of explored edges, i.e. $E_e \leftarrow E_e \cup (v, w)$, and w to the set of visited vertices, i.e. $V_v \leftarrow V_v \cup w$. Vertex w is ordered next in the sequence and becomes the current vertex. The search is continued at w. The edge (v, w) is called a *tree arc*.

(2) w has been visited before. We just add (v, w) to E_e and continue the search at v, which is still the current vertex. The edge (v, w) is a *frond*.

(3) There are no unexplored edges leaving v. In this case we *backtrack*, i.e., we move to the preceding vertex in the ordering, which becomes the new current vertex, and resume the search.

The procedure is repeated until all vertices have been visited and all edges explored. At the end of the search, vertices are ordered and edges are sorted into tree arcs and fronds. The important property here is that, if we delete fronds, the subgraph we obtain is a tree T, and since T contains all the vertices of G, T is a spanning tree. Thus, if G has $|V|$ vertices and $|E|$ edges, there are $|V| - 1$ tree arcs and $|E| - |V| + 1$ fronds. Besides, the ordering performed by depth-first search is a reverse monotone ordering of the spanning tree T. An algorithm which performs depth-first search in $O(|V|, |E|)$ space and time was presented by Tarjan (1972).

For an example of the application of depth-first search to a connected undirected graph, consider Fig. 4.24(a). We choose 9 as the starting vertex, and find that one of the edges leaving 9 is (9, 11). Inspecting vertex 11, we find (say) vertex 10, then 1, and then 6. All the edges so far explored are tree arcs, as shown in Fig. 4.24(b) with full lines. Now 6 is the current vertex, and it

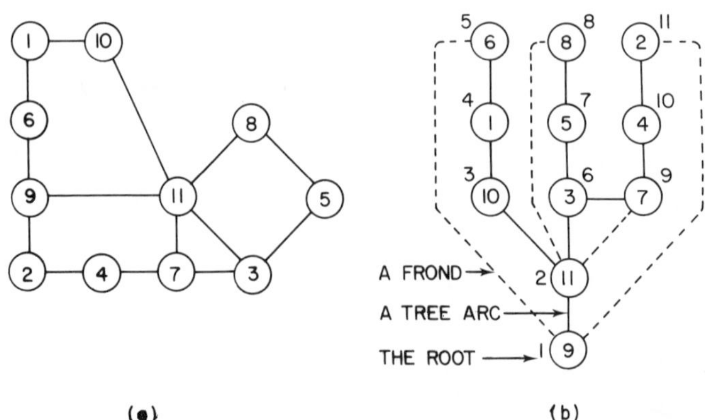

Figure 4.24 Depth-first search of the undirected connected graph of Fig. 4.1. In (b), edges of the spanning tree are shown with full lines, and fronds with dotted lines.

only has a connection to vertex 9, which has been visited before. Thus, the edge (6, 9) is a frond, shown by a dashed line, and 6 remains the current vertex. Since we have run out of edges leaving it, we backtrack to vertex 11, where we now find (say) edge (11, 3), then (3, 5) and finally (5, 8), which are all tree arcs. At vertex 8 we find the frond (8, 11), and we backtrack to vertex 3. Then we find the tree arcs (3, 7), (7, 4) and (4, 2), and the frond (2, 11). Backtracking to 7 we find the frond (7, 11). The result is shown in Fig. 4.24(b). The subgraph of which the edges are tree arcs, shown by full lines, is a spanning tree. The ordering of the vertices is shown by numbers near the circles. Of course, this result is not unique; the reader can obtain many other results as an exercise.

Let us examine the properties of depth-first search in more detail. It is easy to see that a frond always connects an ancestor with a descendant. For, assume (v, w) is an edge of G, which is a frond, and without loss of generality assume that v has been ordered before w by the search. Consider the subtree T_v of T of which v is the root. We enter T_v when we first visit vertex v. Before leaving T_v by backtracking we explore all edges incident to v. (v, w) is an edge incident to v, but it is not a tree arc and it was not found when we were at v. (v, w) was found when we were at w but before leaving T_v, which means that w belongs to T_v and is a descendant of v.

Thus, a frond always connects a vertex with one of its ancestors in the spanning tree. Tree arcs also connect a vertex with its ancestors in T. This means that any path between any two vertices v and w of G must necessarily contain at least one common ancestor of v and w, and that removing all common ancestors of v and w would disconnect v and w. In other words, the stem of the spanning tree is a separator of G. Removing it leaves T disconnected into two or more subtrees, of which the stems are in turn separators of the corresponding subgraphs. This observation leads to the *reverse depth-first ordering* for Gauss elimination. From the discussion given in Section 4.7 we know that numbering a separator last introduces an entire block of zeros in the upper factor **U**. The spanning tree obtained by depth-first search, and thus the size and number of the separators, depend on the choice of the starting vertex and on the strategy we use to decide which edge to explore among the edges which leave each vertex. We would like the tree and subtrees to have short stems and many branches of comparable size. Hopefully, this can be achieved as follows: start with a vertex of the maximum degree, and number it with $n = |V|$. Then carry on depth-first search and number vertices as they are visited but in the reverse order. At some step, let u be the current vertex and V_v the set of visited vertices. The *short frond* strategy is as follows: explore the edge which leads to a vertex w of maximum degree in the set $\text{Adj}(u) - V_v$. If several such vertices exist, select one for which $|\text{Adj}(w) \cap V_v|$ is maximum. By "short" we mean that, if the edge (x, y) is a frond, the distance between x and y in the spanning tree is short. This technique tends to produce many short fronds and to number adjacent vertices in sequence, producing a piecewise narrow band structure of the permuted matrix where fill-in is confined. The *long frond* strategy is as follows: explore the edge which leads to a vertex w in $\mathrm{Adj}(u) - V_v$ for which $|\mathrm{Adj}(w) - V_v|$ is maximum. If several such vertices exist, select one for which $|\mathrm{Adj}(w) \cap V_v|$ is minimum. This technique tends to produce long fronds and better separators.

For an example of application of these techniques consider the graph of Fig. 4.2(a), and let us apply the short frond strategy to it. We start at vertex 11, which is of degree 6. In Adj(11), vertices 10 and 18 both have the maximum degree, which is 5, and for both $|\mathrm{Adj}(w) \cap V_v| = 1$, since $V_v = \{11\}$. We arbitrarily select vertex 10 and explore the edge (11, 10). Now vertex 18 must be visited, because it is of degree 5. After visiting 18, we have as candidates vertices 2 and 17, both of degree 4; we select 2 because it is adjacent to the two visited vertices 10 and 18, while 17 is only adjacent to 18. Next we visit vertex 9, and the tie between vertices 8 and 19 is broken in favour of vertex 19, which is adjacent to two visited vertices: 9 and 10. The reader may continue the search and verify that the spanning tree and reverse depth-first ordering shown in Fig. 4.25(a) may be obtained. The separators (11), (10, 18, 2) and (14) can be immediately identified. The corresponding permuted matrix is shown in Fig. 4.25(b). No fill-in at all is produced by elimination on this matrix, a result obtained at a very low computational cost. The reason why an ordering with no fill-in exists for the graph of Fig. 4.2(a) is that this graph is triangulated (Rose, 1970), see Section 4.16.

Now consider the application of the long frond strategy to the same graph. Again 11 is the starting vertex. Vertices 10 and 18 are the next candidates, both of degree 5. We arbitrarily select vertex 10. At this point $V_v = \{11, 10\}$, and vertices 18, 2, 9 and 19 all have three edges leading to vertices not in V_v. Vertex 18 is discarded because it is adjacent to both visited vertices, while 2, 9 and 19 are adjacent to only one of the visited vertices. Let us choose vertex 2 to be the next vertex to visit.

At this point $V_v = \{11, 10, 2\}$, and $|\mathrm{Adj}(w) - V_v|$ is equal to 3, 2 and 2 for vertices 17, 18 and 9, respectively. Thus, we select vertex 17. Next is vertex 4, which introduces two new edges (while 12 or 18 would have introduced only one), and finally vertex 12, which is adjacent to only two visited vertices (while 18 is adjacent to five). On backtracking to vertex 4 we find the tree arc (4, 18). Figure 4.26(a) shows one possible ordering obtained in this way. The four separators (11), (10, 2), (17, 4) and (14) can be identified. As expected, this strategy has produced more separators than the short frond strategy. The corresponding permuted matrix is shown in Fig. 4.26(b). Elimination would produce 10 fill-ins in this matrix.

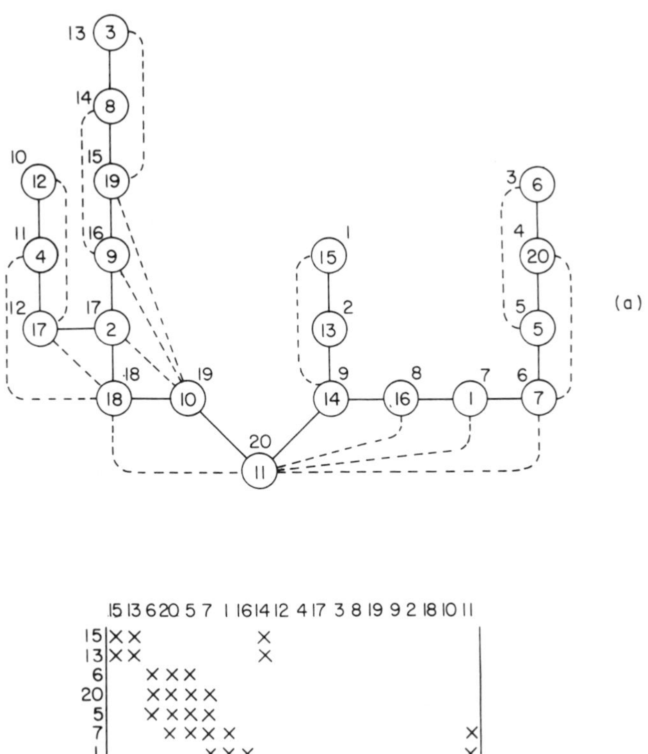

	15	13	6	20	5	7	1	16	14	12	4	17	3	8	19	9	2	18	10	11
15	×	×							×											
13	×	×							×											
6			×	×	×															
20			×	×	×	×														
5			×	×	×	×														
7				×	×	×	×													×
1						×	×	×												×
16							×	×	×											×
14	×	×						×	×											×
12										×	×	×								
4										×	×	×						×		
17										×	×	×					×	×		
3													×	×	×					
8													×	×	×	×				
19													×	×	×	×			×	
9														×	×	×	×		×	
2												×				×	×	×	×	
18											×	×					×	×	×	×
10															×	×	×	×	×	×
11						×	×	×	×									×	×	×

(b)

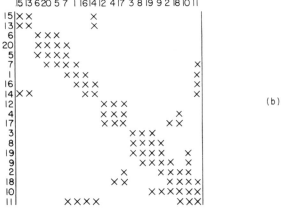

Figure 4.25 Reverse depth-first ordering, short frond strategy, for the graph of Fig. 4.2(a).

When the user is dealing with a large problem, a sophisticated ordering algorithm may be convenient, and may even determine whether the problem is tractable or not. For a medium-size problem, a simple ordering technique may often produce a large improvement as compared with no ordering at all, at a low programming cost.

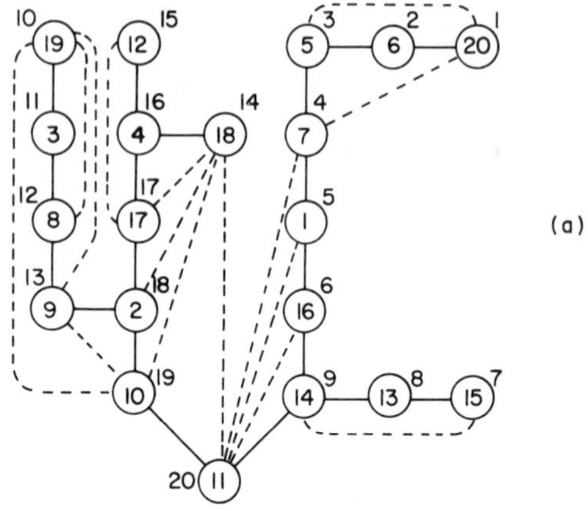

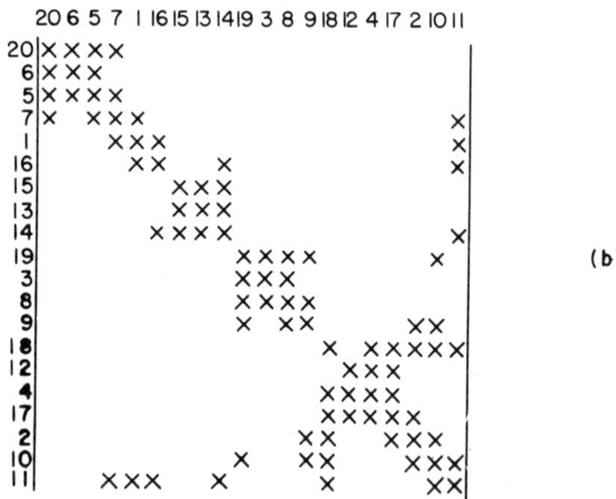

Figure 4.26 Reverse depth-first ordering, long frond strategy, for the graph of Fig. 4.2(a).

4.16. Lexicographic search

In this section we continue the analysis of low fill orderings for symmetric matrices, but now from a different point of view. We consider a special class of matrices which can be ordered in such a way that Gauss elimination would cause no fill-in. Then we take advantage of the properties of such matrices to give a procedure which finds a low fill ordering for any symmetric matrix. As usual, we discuss the ideas in terms of graph theory. Let $G^A = (V, E)$ be the undirected graph associated with a symmetric matrix **A**, and let

$G^F = (V, E \cup F)$ be the corresponding filled graph associated with $\mathbf{U} + \mathbf{U}^T$, where $\mathbf{A} = \mathbf{U}^T\mathbf{D}\mathbf{U}$ is the factorization of $\mathbf{A}$ and F is the set of new edges (or nonzeros of $\mathbf{U}$) introduced during factorization. If the graph G^A has an elimination ordering for which $F = \emptyset$, i.e., no fill-in is produced if elimination is carried out in that order, we say that G^A is a *perfect elimination graph*. The ordering itself is called a *perfect elimination ordering*. Note that fill-in may result if we eliminate in a different order, even when G^A is a perfect elimination graph. Note also that every elimination graph G^F is a perfect elimination graph since no fill-in would result if elimination were performed again in the same order.

A graph is said to be *triangulated* if, for any cycle of length 4 or more, there exists at least one edge joining some pair of nonconsecutive vertices of the cycle. Note the difference between a clique and a triangulated graph. Every clique is triangulated, but a triangulated graph need not be a clique. The graph of Fig. 4.1(b) is not triangulated; for example, the path (1, 6, 9, 11, 10, 1) is a cycle of length 5 which has no edge joining a pair of nonconsecutive vertices. The graph of Fig. 4.2(a) is triangulated, because it is impossible to find any cycle of length 4 or more which is not divided by at least one edge. The reader can verify as an exercise that the graph of Fig. 4.17 is not triangulated. Any tree is a triangulated graph, because it has no cycles. Other important classes of graphs, such as k-trees (Rose, 1974) and interval graphs (Fulkerson and Gross, 1965; Gilmore and Hoffmann, 1964) are also triangulated.

The fundamental property which relates triangulated graphs and perfect elimination graphs is given by the following theorem (Rose, 1970; Rose *et al.*, 1976): a graph G is a perfect elimination graph if and only if it is triangulated.

Keeping this basic property in mind, consider the following approaches to the problem of reducing the fill-in. If we are given a matrix of which the graph is known to be triangulated, we may wish to find a perfect elimination ordering, for which no fill-in would be generated. If we do not know whether the graph is triangulated or not, we must first face a recognition problem. A third problem, frequently encountered in practice, arises when the graph $G^A = (V, E)$ is not triangulated and we ask about a good ordering. Since we know that the corresponding elimination graph $G^F = (V, E \cup F)$ is a perfect elimination graph, and is therefore triangulated, we may regard the addition of the set F of edges to G^A as a *triangulation* of G^A. We may then ask how G^A can be triangulated by adding a small number of edges. These problems will be discussed after we describe lexicographic search.

As any search, *lexicographic search* (Rose *et al.*, 1976) is a systematic procedure for visiting the vertices and exploring the edges of a graph $G = (V, E)$. The vertices are visited in some sequence and numbered in the reverse order from $n = |V|$ to 1. During the search a label is associated with each vertex. The label consists of a set of distinct numbers selected from the set $\{n, n-1, \ldots, 1\}$, given in decreasing order. An order relation is established between labels as follows. Given two labels:

$$L_1 = (p_1, p_2, \ldots, p_k)$$

$$L_2 = (q_1, q_2, \ldots, q_l) \tag{4.32}$$

we define, $L_1 > L_2$ if, for some j:

$$p_i = q_i, \qquad i = 1, 2, \ldots, j-1$$

$$\text{and } p_j > q_j$$

or if

$$p_i = q_i, \qquad i = 1, 2, \ldots, l$$

$$\text{and } k > l$$

The two labels are equal if $k = l$ and $p_i = q_i$ for $i = 1, 2, \ldots, k$. Thus, for example:

$$(7, 3) > (6, 4, 3, 2)$$

$$(7, 5, 2) > (7, 4, 3)$$

$$(7, 3, 1) > (7, 3)$$

$$(7, 3) = (7, 3)$$

Explicitly, the algorithm for lexicographic search is as follows:

Step 1 (Initialization). Assign an empty label to all vertices. Set $i \leftarrow n$.
Step 2 (Select next vertex). Pick any unnumbered vertex v with largest label and number v with i. Label (v) is in final form at this point and may be stored if required. If not required, it may be destroyed because it will not be used any more by the algorithm.
Step 3 (Find set S). Find the set S of vertices such that $w \in S$ if w is unnumbered and w is either adjacent to v or there is a path $(v = v_1, v_2, \ldots, v_k, v_{k+1} = w)$ such that label $(w) >$ label (v_j) for $j = 2, 3, \ldots, k$.
Step 4 (Update labels). For each $w \in S$, add i to label (w).
Step 5 (Loop or stop). Set $i \leftarrow i - 1$. If $i > 0$ go to Step 2. Otherwise stop.

This algorithm selects the vertex with the largest label as the next to be visited. This means that, at Step 3, w is either adjacent to v or w will be numbered higher than any of the intermediate vertices v_j in the path. In both cases, and since w will be numbered lower than v, we have that in the ordered graph v will necessarily be reachable from w through the set of vertices numbered lower than w (see Section 4.2 for definition of reachable vertex).

This means that (v, w) is an edge of G^F. In other words, the label of each vertex, obtained in final form at Step 2, is precisely the set of nonzeros in the corresponding row of the upper triangular factor **U**.

If F_α is the set of new nonzeros introduced by elimination in a certain order α, we say that α is a *minimal elimination ordering* if no other order β satisfies $F_\beta \subset F_\alpha$, where the containment is proper. If no other ordering β satisfies $|F_\beta| < |F_\alpha|$, i.e., there is no other ordering β introducing less fill-in, then α is a *minimum elimination ordering*. There are no known efficient algorithms for producing minimum orderings, but the main property of lexicographic search is that it produces a minimal ordering of any graph.

Lexicographic search requires $O(|V||E|)$ time for execution. Its output is not only the minimal ordering but also, if so desired, the complete structure of the upper triangular factor **U**. Besides, the list of column indices of the nonzeros of each row, which is the final label of the corresponding vertex, is obtained, ordered in decreasing order. If the given graph is a perfect elimination graph, then lexicographic search finds a perfect elimination ordering, which is minimum. Thus, if we do not know whether the graph is a perfect elimination one, we can find out in $O(|V||E|)$ time, and obtain in addition a perfect ordering. However, if we do know that the graph is a perfect elimination graph, we can modify Step 3 as follows:

Step 3′ (Find partial triangulation set). Find the set S of unnumbered vertices adjacent to v.

With this modification the algorithm executes in $O(|V| + |E|)$ time. Of course, if the graph is not a perfect elimination one, then the resulting ordering may not be minimal.

In the implementation of this algorithm, the authors do not actually calculate the labels of the vertices. Instead, for each label value, they keep a set of all vertices which have that label. The sets are kept in a queue ordered lexicographically, highest to lowest. This idea combines very well with Sherman's compressed storage scheme discussed in Section 1.10. A different algorithm for finding minimal orderings was developed by Ohtsuki (1976). The time required for execution of this algorithm is also $O(|V||E|)$, but it does not calculate the fill-in produced by the ordering. Minimal orderings are not necessarily close to minimum orderings; for instance, for a square grid graph with n by n vertices, the fill-in produced by lexicographic ordering is $O(n^3)$, while nested dissection gives a fill-in of $O(n^2 \log n)$, which is minimum within a constant factor.

For an example of lexicographic search consider the graph shown in Fig. 4.27(a), which is the same graph as Fig. 4.1(b) but with vertices identified by alphabetic symbols to avoid confusion. Let us start the search at vertex A. Vertex A is numbered 11. Since all vertices have empty labels at this point,

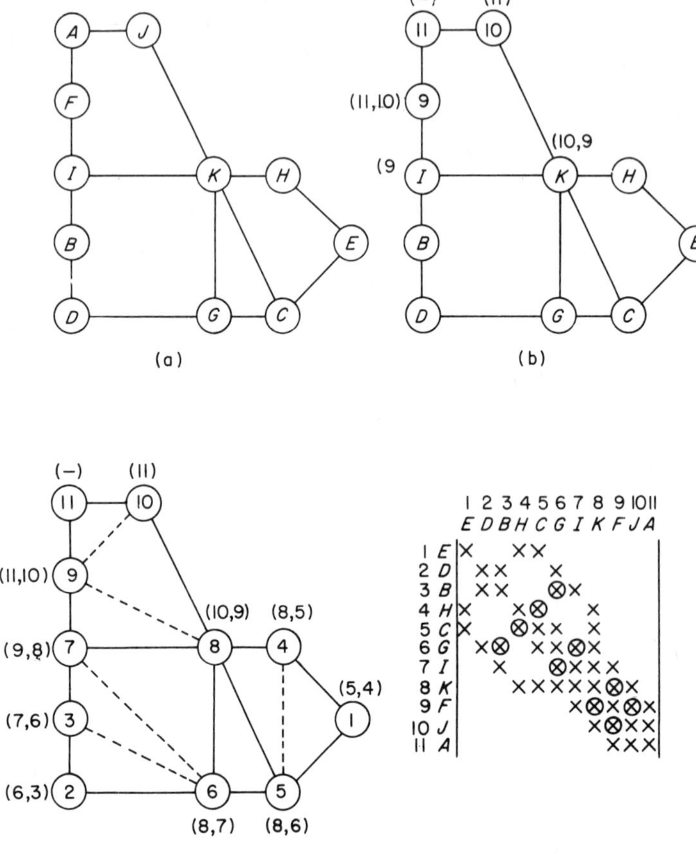

Figure 4.27 Lexicographic search of the graph of Fig. 4.1(b), starting at vertex A.

the set S contains only vertices J and F. We add 11 to the labels of vertices J and F. In the next execution of the loop we find a tie, since vertices J and F both have identical labels. Breaking this tie arbitrarily we select vertex J and number it 10. Now $S = \{K, F\}$, since K is adjacent to J and F is connected with J by the path (J, K, I, F), where the intermediate vertices K and I have smaller labels than F, and K, I and F are unnumbered. Thus, we add 10 to the labels of K and F. Note that this result is independent of the order in which labels are updated. We could equally well have updated the label of K first, and we would still have label(K) < label(F).

Now F has the largest label, which is (11, 10). Thus we number F with 9, and add 9 to the labels of vertices I and K, which belong to the new S set. The situation at this point is depicted in Fig. 4.27(b). The reader can finish the exercise. The result is given in Fig. 4.27(c), where the minimal ordering and the final labels of the vertices are shown. The corresponding permuted matrix is given in Fig. 4.27(d). Elimination causes five fill-ins as shown by encircled crosses in (d), which correspond to the five edges shown with dashed lines in (c), and the nonzeros in each row have the column indices given by the labels. The original graph is not triangulated and does not have a perfect elimination ordering. Note however that the filled graph of Fig. 4.27(c) is triangulated, and that the triangulation is minimal since none of the extra edges can be removed without losing that property.

Another useful example is obtained applying lexicographic search to the graph of Fig. 4.2(a). This graph is triangulated, and starting at vertex 12 the following order can be obtained: (6, 5, 20, 15, 13, 3, 8, 7, 1, 16, 14, 19, 9, 11, 10, 2, 18, 17, 4, 12), which is a perfect elimination ordering because elimination causes no fill-in, as the reader can verify. Compare with Fig. 4.25, where another perfect elimination ordering of the same matrix is shown.

4.17. Symmetric indefinite matrices

When elimination is performed on a symmetric positive definite matrix and pivots are taken from the diagonal in any order, numerical stability is guaranteed. This rule does not hold for an indefinite matrix, where some of the methods for pivot selection of Section 3.6 must be used if good results are expected.

When the given matrix $\mathbf{A}$ is symmetric and indefinite, we may ignore symmetry and use any of the methods discussed in Chapter 5 for general indefinite matrices. Duff and Reid (1976) have found that this idea may even be better than trying to preserve symmetry, at least in some cases.

If $\mathbf{A}$ is symmetric and nearly positive definite, and we wish to preserve symmetry, Duff (1980b) suggests splitting $\mathbf{A}$ as follows:

$$\mathbf{A} = \mathbf{M} - \mathbf{N} \tag{4.33}$$

where $\mathbf{M}$ is symmetric positive definite and $\mathbf{N}$ is symmetric, and then solving $\mathbf{Ax} = \mathbf{b}$ by the iteration:

$$\mathbf{Mx}^{(k+1)} = \mathbf{Nx}^{(k)} + \mathbf{b}. \tag{4.34}$$

The linear system in Equation (4.34) must be solved at each iteration, using any of the powerful methods for positive definite matrices, or some iterative method like conjugate gradients (Concus *et al.*, 1976).

More generally, when **A** is symmetric and indefinite, and symmetry is to be preserved, then block diagonal pivoting is recommended. The method was briefly described in Section 3.6. It was extended by Duff *et al.* (1977) to the sparse case and a code was developed by Munksgaard (1977). Further discussion of this method and other ideas can be found in (Duff, 1978) and (Duff, 1981a). The other methods mentioned at the end of Section 3.6 can also be used, but they use congruence transformations rather than Gauss elimination and tend to destroy sparsity.

CHAPTER 5

Ordering for Gauss Elimination: General Matrices

5.1. Introduction: Statement of the problem

In this chapter we examine how sparsity is affected when Gauss elimination is performed on a general sparse matrix **B**, and the triangular factorization of **B** is obtained either in the form

$$\mathbf{B} = \mathbf{LDU} \tag{5.1}$$

or

$$\mathbf{B} = \mathbf{L'U} \tag{5.2}$$

where **U** is upper triangular with unit diagonal, **D** is diagonal, **L** is lower triangular with unit diagonal, $\mathbf{L'} = \mathbf{LD}$ is lower triangular, **L** and **L'** have the same nonzero pattern, and $\mathbf{L} \neq \mathbf{U}^{\mathrm{T}}$ if **B** is unsymmetric.

As usual, we disregard accidental cancellations which may occur in the course of elimination. Cancellations are rare and trying to take advantage of them is generally unrewarding. Thus, the nonzero patterns of **L** and **U** contain all nonzero locations of the lower and the upper triangles of **B**, respectively, plus the fill-in, which is the set of positions of the additional nonzeros introduced in both **L** and **U** by the elimination. When we speak in terms of reducing the fill-in, we mean the total fill-in introduced in $\mathbf{L} + \mathbf{U}$. Here we are concerned with the positions of the nonzeros, not with their values.

To state our problem explicitly, let

$$\mathbf{Ax} = \mathbf{b} \tag{5.3}$$

be the system of linear equations we wish to solve, with **A** a general sparse matrix. If **P** and **Q** are any permutation matrices, and thus $\mathbf{QQ}^{\mathrm{T}} = \mathbf{I}$, Equation (5.3) can be written:

$$\mathbf{PAQQ}^{\mathrm{T}}\mathbf{x} = \mathbf{Pb} \tag{5.4}$$

or

$$\mathbf{By} = \mathbf{c} \tag{5.5}$$

where $\mathbf{y} = \mathbf{Q}^{\mathrm{T}}\mathbf{x}$, $\mathbf{c} = \mathbf{Pb}$, and $\mathbf{B} = \mathbf{PAQ}$ is the permuted form of **A**. In general $\mathbf{Q} \neq \mathbf{P}^{\mathrm{T}}$, so that **B** is obtained by performing unsymmetric permutations of the rows and columns of **A**. We wish to find **P** and **Q** such that the factorization of **B** in the form (5.1) or (5.2) be numerically stable and the fill-in be small.

Even if no properties of **A** are known, elimination can start immediately, using for example the standard combination of threshold pivoting to ensure stability (Section 3.6) with the Markowitz technique to preserve sparsity (Section 5.11). Pivoting will automatically generate **P** and **Q**. If **A** is singular, this fact will be discovered during factorization, because at some stage zero or very small pivots will be encountered. The system $\mathbf{Ax} = \mathbf{b}$ with **A** singular may have no solution, for example:

$$\begin{vmatrix} 1 & 1 \\ 1 & 1 \end{vmatrix} \begin{vmatrix} x_1 \\ x_2 \end{vmatrix} = \begin{vmatrix} 1 \\ 2 \end{vmatrix} \tag{5.6}$$

or, if it has one solution, then it has infinitely many, for example:

$$\begin{vmatrix} 1 & 1 \\ 1 & 1 \end{vmatrix} \begin{vmatrix} x_1 \\ x_2 \end{vmatrix} = \begin{vmatrix} 1 \\ 1 \end{vmatrix}. \tag{5.7}$$

The reader who would like to proceed directly with the factorization may omit Sections 5.2 to 5.10, and go to Section 5.11, where pivoting techniques are described.

However, when **A** has no known properties, it may be worthwhile trying to permute it to block lower triangular form before initiating elimination. A linear system with a block lower triangular matrix of order N has the following form:

$$\begin{vmatrix} \mathbf{A}_{1\,1} & & & \\ \mathbf{A}_{2\,1} & \mathbf{A}_{2\,2} & & \\ \vdots & & \ddots & \\ \mathbf{A}_{N\,1} & & & \mathbf{A}_{NN} \end{vmatrix} \begin{vmatrix} \mathbf{x}_1 \\ \mathbf{x}_2 \\ \vdots \\ \mathbf{x}_N \end{vmatrix} = \begin{vmatrix} \mathbf{b}_1 \\ \mathbf{b}_2 \\ \vdots \\ \mathbf{b}_N \end{vmatrix} \tag{5.8}$$

where the elements are matrices, each diagonal block $\mathbf{A}_{i\,i}$ is square of order n_i and

$$\sum_{i=1}^{N} n_i = n.$$

The system (5.8) can be solved as a sequence of N smaller problems. Problem i is of order n_i and the matrix of coefficients is $\mathbf{A}_{i\,i}$, $i = 1, 2, \ldots, N$. In this way fil-in will occur only in the diagonal blocks, even if unsymmetric interchanges between the rows and columns of each block were forced by pivoting. The procedure is as follows:

(i) Solve the first subsystem, with $\mathbf{A}_{1\,1}$ as the matrix of coefficients, for the first n_1 unknowns. Compute the vector $\mathbf{x}_1$ of order n_1.
(ii) Subtract the products $\mathbf{A}_{j\,1}\mathbf{x}_1$ from the right-hand side for $j = 2, \ldots, N$. A block lower triangular matrix of order $N - 1$ is obtained, and the procedure is repeated until the complete solution is obtained.

Obviously, the assumption must be made that the diagonal blocks in Equation (5.8) are nonsingular.

We say that a matrix has a full *transversal* when the diagonal is free from zeros. The transversal is, precisely, the set of nonzero diagonal elements. Any nonsingular matrix $\mathbf{A}$ can be permuted unsymmetrically, using suitable permutation matrices $\mathbf{P}$ and $\mathbf{Q}$, in such a way that $\mathbf{PAQ}$ has a full transversal. The converse is not true, however; for example, the singular matrix of Equation (5.6) has a full transversal.

When the matrix $\mathbf{A}$ of the given linear system, Equation (5.3), has a full transversal, then the block lower triangular form (5.8) can be obtained by means of symmetric permutations of the form $\mathbf{PAP}^{\mathrm{T}}$. If the block form exists we say that $\mathbf{A}$ is *reducible*. Some matrices may not be reducible to (nontrivial) block lower triangular form. This is almost always the case for systems obtained from the discretization of partial differential equations. In other cases it may be known by construction that the matrix is reducible. Procedures for reducing a matrix are discussed in Sections 5.9 and 5.10.

When $\mathbf{A}$ has zeros on its diagonal, then it is necessary to find a full transversal before permutation to block form can be attempted. Finding a full transversal requires unsymmetric permutations. A matrix which can be unsymmetrically permuted to a form with a full transversal, which in turn can be symmetrically permuted to block lower triangular form, is called *bireducible*. Procedures for bireducing a matrix are discussed in Sections 5.7 and 5.8.

Graph theory plays an important role in the analysis of sparse unsymmetric matrices. A *digraph* or directed graph can be associated with any unsymmetric matrix which has a transversal. The digraph is invariant under symmetric permutations of the rows and columns of the matrix, only its labelling changes. The digraph can be partitioned into *strong components*, which correspond to the diagonal blocks of the block lower triangular form (5.8) of the matrix. It can be shown that a matrix is reducible if and only if its digraph can be partitioned into strong components (Harary, 1959). Both tasks, reducing a sparse matrix and partitioning a digraph, are equivalent, and the same algorithms are used.

When the matrix has no transversal, then a *bigraph* or bipartite graph can be associated with it. The bigraph is invariant under unsymmetric permutations of the matrix, and finding a transversal is equivalent to finding a matching in the bigraph. This variety of important applications of graph theory to the analysis of sparse unsymmetric matrices has motivated Section 1.2, where definitions are given and properties are discussed. Graph theory is then used throughout the chapter.

5.2. Graph theory for unsymmetric matrices

In Section 4.2 it was shown that an undirected graph can be associated with any symmetric matrix with a zero-free diagonal. Many definitions and properties of undirected graphs were discussed, in particular that the graph remains the same if a symmetric permutation is performed with the rows and the columns of the matrix.

In this section we will consider other types of graphs which are used in connection with general matrices. A graph $G = (V, E)$ is a *directed graph* or a *digraph* (Harary *et al.*, 1965) when the pairs of vertices which represent edges are ordered. We will frequently use the notation $(u \to v)$ for a directed edge.

A digraph can be associated with any general square matrix $\mathbf{A}$ (Rose and Bunch, 1972). If $\mathbf{A}$ is of order n and A_{ij} are its elements, the digraph has n vertices $v_1, v_2, \ldots, v_n$, and $(v_i \to v_j)$ is an edge if and only if $A_{ij} \neq 0$. Each diagonal nonzero A_{ii} corresponds to a loop or selfedge $(v_i \to v_i)$. In cases where the diagonal of $\mathbf{A}$ is free from zeros all selfedges are present and it will usually not be necessary to take them explicitly into account. The set of diagonal nonzeros is called a *transversal*. The digraph associated with $\mathbf{A}$

remains the same if the rows and columns are symmetrically permuted. A symmetric permutation leaves all diagonal elements on the diagonal. Explicitly, if $\mathbf{B} = \mathbf{PAP}^{\mathrm{T}}$, where $\mathbf{P}$ is a permutation matrix, and G_A and G_B are the digraphs corresponding to $\mathbf{A}$ and $\mathbf{B}$, then G_A and G_B are identical except for the labelling. Figure 5.1 shows an unsymmetric sparse matrix with a full transversal and its corresponding digraph.

A directed edge $(u \to v)$ is said to *leave* vertex u or to *start* at vertex u, and to *enter* vertex v or to *terminate* at vertex v. We also say that edge $(u \to v)$ *leads* from u to v. The *indegree* of vertex v is the number of edges that enter v. The *outdegree* is the number of edges that leave v. A *transmitter* or *source* is a vertex of indegree zero and positive outdegree, a *receiver* or *sink* is a vertex of outdegree zero and positive indegree.

If $(u \to v)$ is a directed edge, we say that v is *adjacent* to u. If W is a subset of the vertices of G, the *adjacent set* of W, denoted by $\mathrm{Adj}(W)$, is the set of all vertices not in W which are adjacent to vertices in W. Namely, given $G = (V, E)$ and $W \subset V$:

$$\mathrm{Adj}(W) = \{v \in V - W \mid \exists u \in W \ni . (u \to v) \in E\}. \tag{5.9}$$

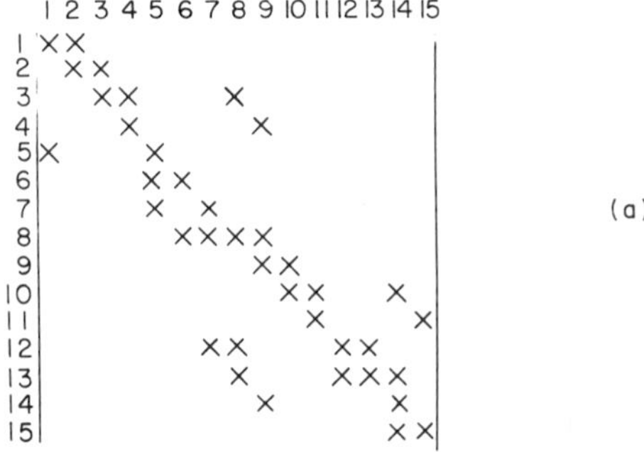

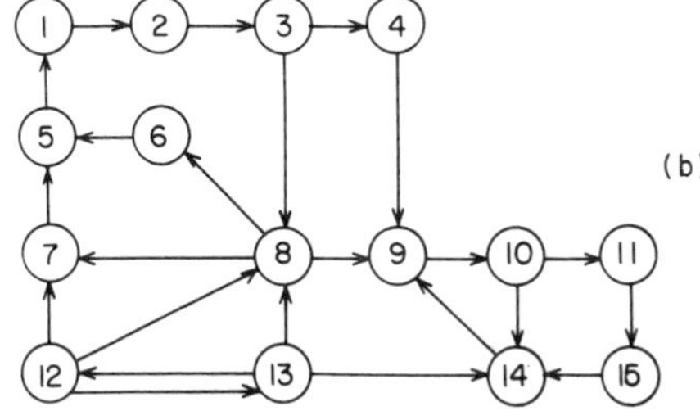

Figure 5.1 Unsymmetric matrix and its directed graph.

If a path exists from a vertex u to a vertex v in the digraph, we say that v is *reachable* from u. The *reachability matrix* $\mathbf{R}$ of a digraph is a Boolean matrix defined as follows: $R_{ij} = 1$ if v_j is reachable from v_i in the digraph, $R_{ij} = 0$ otherwise. A *directed cycle* is a path with at least two vertices which begins and ends at the same vertex. If v is reachable from u in G, the *distance* from u to v is the length of the shortest path from u to v; note that the distance from v to u may be undefined or different from the distance from u to v.

The kth *elimination digraph* is the digraph associated with the active submatrix corresponding to the kth step of Gauss elimination on the matrix $\mathbf{A}$. Each elimination digraph is obtained from the preceding one by deleting the vertex corresponding to the variable eliminated at that step, say vertex v, together with all edges entering or leaving v, and adding a directed edge $(u \to w)$ whenever there exists a directed path (u, v, w). As an exercise, the reader can construct the first few elimination digraphs for the matrix of Fig. 5.1. The *filled digraph* is the digraph of $\mathbf{L} + \mathbf{U}$. Many of the results given in the preceding chapters in connection with undirected graphs can be extended to the directed case. See, for example, Rose *et al.* (1976, p. 281).

A digraph is said to be *connected* when the corresponding undirected graph, obtained by removing the direction from every edge, is connected. The digraph of Fig. 5.1 is connected. Vertices 6, 7 and 9 are adjacent to vertex 8. If $W = (8, 13)$, then $\text{Adj}(W) = (6, 7, 9, 12, 14)$. Vertex 5 has indegree 2 and outdegree 1. Vertex 4 is reachable from vertex 8, and there are no sources or sinks in the digraph.

A connected digraph may be partitioned by sorting the vertices into disjoint subsets. Partitioning into strong components will be considered in Section 5.3, where connectivity level structures will also be introduced. Adjacency level substructures, which are employed for finding a transversal of a sparse matrix, are discussed in Section 5.5.

When dealing with general matrices we will also be interested in unsymmetric permutations of the rows and columns of $\mathbf{A}$, i.e. in permutations of the form $\mathbf{B} = \mathbf{PAQ}$ where $\mathbf{Q} \neq \mathbf{P}^{\mathrm{T}}$. The digraph of $\mathbf{A}$ is not invariant under unsymmetric permutations. This has motivated the use of *bipartite graphs* or *bigraphs* (Dulmage and Mendelsohn, 1959, 1967). A bigraph consists of two distinct sets R and C of n vertices each and undirected edges which join the vertices in R to those in C. The set R is associated with the rows of the matrix, and the set C with the columns. Vertices in R are called *boys*, and those in C, *girls*. Edge (r_i, c_j) is present in the bigraph if and only if $r_i \in R$, $c_j \in C$ and $A_{ij} \neq 0$. Selfedges (r_i, c_i) are always included, since one of the important applications of bigraphs is to find permutations such that the transversal of $\mathbf{A}$ is maximized, which is equivalent to maximizing the number of selfedges. It is shown in Section 5.8 that this is also equivalent to finding a *maximum assignment* or *matching* between boys and girls. The application of different row and column permutations to **A** leaves its bigraph unchanged except for the labelling. Explicitly, **A** and $\mathbf{B} = \mathbf{PAQ}$ have the same bigraph, except for the labelling, even if $\mathbf{Q} \neq \mathbf{P}^{\mathrm{T}}$. A matrix and its bigraph are shown in Fig. 5.11.

There exist other types of graphs used in connection with sparse matrices, for example *row graphs* and *column graphs* (Mayoh, 1965; Tewarson, 1967a). The row graph of a matrix **A** is the undirected graph of the symmetric matrix $\mathbf{B} = \mathbf{A} * \mathbf{A}^{\mathrm{T}}$, where $*$ denotes matrix multiplication without taking cancellations into account; in other words, if some element of **B** is zero as a result of numerical cancellation, it is considered as a nonzero and the corresponding edge is included in the row graph. Row permutations on **A** only lead to a relabelling of the vertices of the row graph, while column permutations leave the row graph completely unaffected. The column graph of **A** is the undirected graph of the symmetric matrix $\mathbf{C} = \mathbf{A}^{\mathrm{T}} * \mathbf{A}$. The column graph of **A** is not affected by row permutations, but its labelling is modified by column permutations.

Additional material on this subject can be found, for example, in Tewarson (1973), Harary (1971) and Tarjan (1976).

5.3. The strong components of a digraph

Consider a directed graph $G = (V, E)$ which is connected. The digraph G is said to be *strongly connected* if, for any pair of vertices $v, w \in V$, there exists a path from v to w and a path from w to v, i.e., if v and w are mutually reachable. Since a path from v to w followed by a path from w to v is a cycle, we may equally well define a strongly connected digraph as one in which, for any given pair of vertices, there exists a cycle to which both vertices belong. The reachability matrix of a strongly connected digraph is full. The digraph shown in Fig. 5.1 is not strongly connected: if we take 12 and 9 as test vertices, we find the path (12, 8, 9) from 12 to 9, but there is no path from 9 to 12.

A general digraph G may not be strongly connected. A *strongly connected component* or *strong component* of G is a section subgraph of G which is strongly connected and cannot be enlarged without losing this property. We recall from Section 4.2 that a section subgraph is a subgraph of G which contains all edges (v, w) such that both vertices v and w belong to the subgraph. The definition of strong component implies that a cycle exists to which any given pair of vertices of the component belongs. It also implies that any cycle in G must be either entirely composed of vertices of the strong component, or otherwise be entirely composed of vertices of G which do not belong to the strong component. For, if a cycle existed which contained a vertex v of the strong component and a vertex w which was not in the strong component, then we could enlarge the strong component by adding w to it without losing the strong connectivity, in contradiction with the definition. This property is used to find a strong component: a cycle is first found in G, and then enlarged as much as possible by exploring other cycles. In the graph of Fig. 5.1, for example, examination reveals the cycles (1, 2, 3, 8, 7, 5, 1) and (1, 2, 3, 8, 6, 5, 1), which share vertices 1, 2, 3, 8 and 5. The set of vertices {1, 2, 3, 5, 6, 7, 8} and the corresponding edges are a strong component, because no other cycle of the graph contains any of the vertices in this set.

The properties we have just discussed mean that a connected digraph $G = (V, E)$ can be partitioned into a set of strong components $C_1, C_2, \ldots, C_s$, which are disjoint. If G is itself strongly connected, then $s = 1$ and there is a single strong component. Otherwise G is partitionable and $s > 1$. We say that an edge $(v \rightarrow w)$ is an *exit* or *leaves* a strong component $C = (V_c, E_c)$ when $v \in V_c$ and $w \notin V_c$. The edge $(v \rightarrow w)$ is an *entrance* or *enters* C when $v \notin V_c$ and $w \in V_c$. Since a strong component is a section subgraph, exits and entrances do not belong to any strong component.

When G is partitionable, it is easy to see that at least one strong component must exist with no exit. For, if every component had an exit, then we would be able to trace a path from one component to another, then to another, and continue in this way until we eventually reach one of the components which we have visited before; the cycle obtained in this way contradicts the definition of strong components. In general, there may be more than one strong component with no exit. We say that all strong components with no exit belong to *level 1*.

Following a similar reasoning, we can conclude that among the remaining strong components of G one at least must exist such that every edge leaving it enters some component in level 1. In general, there may be several such components and we say that they all belong to *level 2*. Among the components of G which are neither in level 1 nor in level 2, one at least must exist with all exits leading to levels 1 and 2; at least one of such exits must enter level 2, because otherwise the component would be in level 2 and we have assumed that this is not so; this component, and any other with the same property which might exist, form *level 3*. Note that components in level 3 may lack exits leading to level 1. If the procedure is continued, a *connectivity level structure* is obtained, which is rigorously defined as follows:

$$L_1 = \{C_i \mid C_i \text{ has no exit}\}$$

$$L_l = \{C_i \mid \text{if } (u \rightarrow v) \text{ is an exit from } C_i \text{ and } v \in C_j, \text{ then } C_j \in L_{l'} \text{ with } l' < l\}, \; l = 2, 3, \ldots, m.$$

The definition implies that any strong component in level $l > 1$ must have at least one exit leading into a component in level $l - 1$. m is called the *length* of the partitioning. Unlike adjacency level structures, the connectivity level structure of a digraph is unique. We also say that a vertex v of G is in level l, or that Level(v) $= l$, when v belongs to a strong component which is in level l. If $(v \to w)$ is an edge of the digraph, then Level(w) $=$ Level(v) if and only if v and w are in the same strong component, otherwise Level(w) $<$ Level(v). A strong component which is in level l may be reached only by edges coming from levels $l + 1, \ldots, m$; however, it may happen that a strong component has no entrance even if it is in a level $l < m$.

A different connectivity level structure can be defined by placing in level 1 all components with no entrance and repeating the definition with the words exit and entrance interchanged. The two level structures are said to be *dual*. We will restrict our attention to the first type of level structure.

Acyclic digraphs deserve a special mention. A digraph is acyclic when it has no cycles: if a path is started at any vertex v, then the path will never reach v again. This means that every vertex of an acyclic digraph is a strong component. Therefore, an acyclic digraph has as many strong components as vertices, at least one of the vertices has outdegree zero, and at least one of the vertices has indegree zero. An application of acyclic digraphs to sparse matrix technology is considered before the end of this section. Another application will be considered in Section 5.6 in connection with the algorithm of Hopcroft and Karp.

The partitioning of a general digraph into strong components can be conveniently represented by the corresponding quotient digraph or *condensation*, which has the strong components as its vertices (Harary *et al.*, 1965). The condensation of any digraph is an acyclic digraph, and like any acyclic digraph it has at least one vertex of outdegree zero, i.e., at least one strong component with no exit. Figure 5.2 shows an example of condensation and

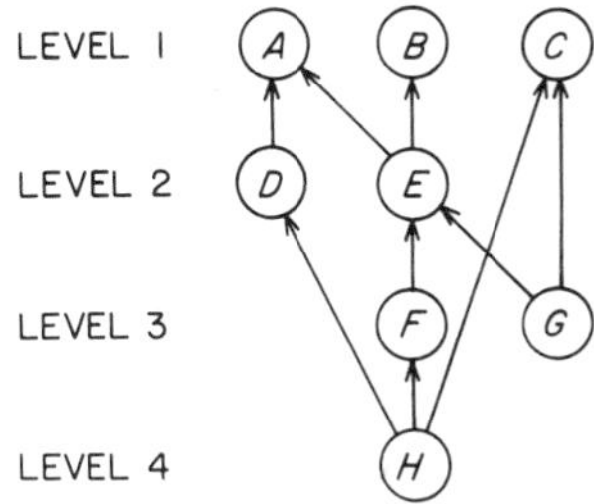

Figure 5.2 Condensation and connectivity level structure of a digraph with eight strong components.

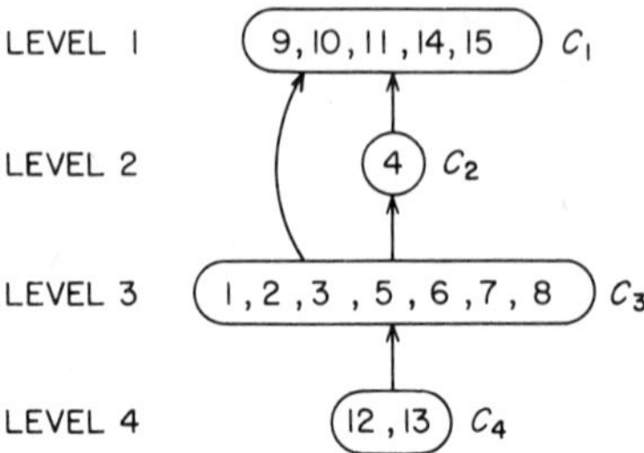

Figure 5.3 Condensation and connectivity level structure of the digraph of Fig. 5.1(b).

connectivity level structure for a digraph with 8 strong components. Figure 5.3 shows the condensation and level structure corresponding to the digraph of Fig. 5.1.

Let now G be the digraph associated with an unsymmetric matrix **A**. Let G be partitioned into strong components and the level structure be constructed as before. Let the vertices of G be ordered and the ordering be compatible with the component partitioning and monotone with respect to the levels, i.e., all vertices in each component are numbered sequentially and all components of each level l, $l = 1, 2, \ldots, m$, are numbered before any component in level $l' > l$. Then, the corresponding symmetrically permuted matrix is block lower triangular, with one square diagonal block of size $n_i \times n_i$ corresponding to each strong component with n_i vertices, and with off-diagonal blocks corresponding to connections between strong components. These ideas were stated by Harary (1969, p. 205). Figure 5.4 illustrates the point for the matrix and graph given in Fig. 5.1.

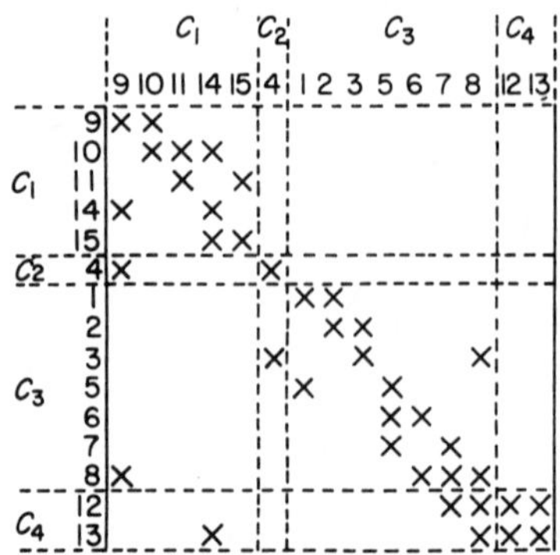

Figure 5.4 Block lower diagonal matrix, obtained by reduction of the matrix of Fig. 5.1(a).

5.4. Depth-first search of a digraph

Depth-first search was described in Section 4.15 as a procedure by which all vertices and edges of a graph are visited, starting at an arbitrary vertex s_1 and trying to follow the sequence vertex–edge–vertex–edge ... while possible, or *backtracking* to the preceding vertex when the current one lacks unexplored edges. In this section we describe the structures which are obtained when depth-first search is performed on a digraph, where the direction in which each edge can be explored is fixed (Tarjan, 1972). We assume that all selfedges are present. As before, each time an edge $(v \to w)$ is explored, where the current vertex v is either the last visited vertex or has been reached by backtracking and w has not been visited before, w becomes the current vertex and the edge $(v \to w)$ is a *tree arc*. If only tree arcs were retained and all other edges were neglected, a tree rooted at the starting vertex s_1 would be obtained. Now, since edges are directed, it may become impossible to continue the search before all vertices of the graph have been visited. This will certainly happen if, for example, s_1 is in a strong component C which has no exit (see preceding section): both edge exploration and backtracking will always lead to vertices in C, and the tree rooted at s_1 will span C exactly. More generally, when s_1 is arbitrarily chosen, a tree rooted at s_1 is obtained which spans only some of the strong components of the graph. The search is then restarted from a new starting vertex s_2, which is unvisited for the moment and thus does not belong to any of the strong components spanned by the first tree. Neglecting again every edge which is not a tree arc, a second tree is obtained, rooted at s_2 and spanning a new set of strong components. The procedure is continued until all vertices are visited. The result is a set of disjoint trees, called a *spanning forest*, which contain all the vertices of the digraph and those edges which are tree arcs. Also, the vertices are numbered by the search in the order in which they are visited and we call Number(v) the number of a vertex v assigned by the search. In sparse matrix technology, the ordering and the correspondence between trees in the forest and strong components are employed by the algorithms which reduce a matrix to block lower triangular form.

For an example of a forest, consider the digraph shown in Fig. 5.1. Choosing 2 as the starting vertex, the path (2, 3, 4, 9, 10, 11, 15, 14) can be followed. All the edges encountered are tree arcs, as shown in Fig. 5.5 by full arrows. Restricting our attention for the moment to edges which are tree arcs, we notice that no tree arcs leave vertex 14. We have to backtrack to vertex 3, where $(3 \to 8)$ is a tree arc. The path (3, 8, 7, 5, 1) is then found, and backtracking again to vertex 8, the tree arc $(8 \to 6)$ is found. The first tree is now complete, and comparing with Fig. 5.3 we notice that this tree spans components C_1, C_2 and C_3 of the digraph. Since some vertices still remain

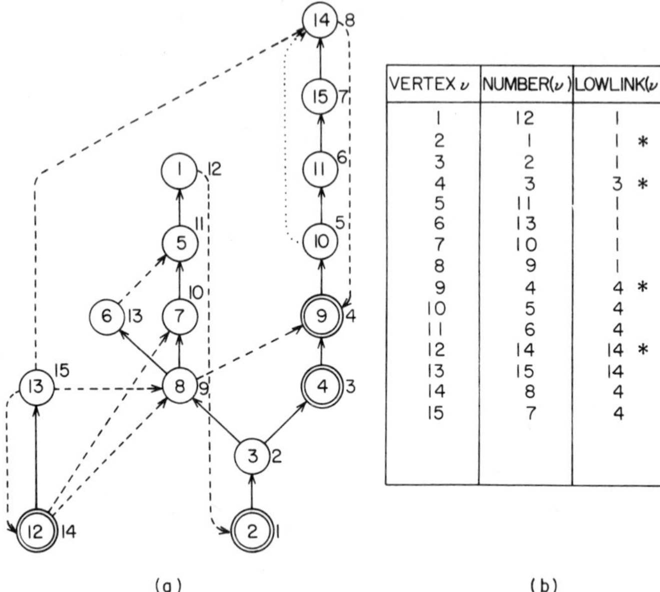

VERTEX v	NUMBER(v)	LOWLINK(v)
1	12	1
2	1	1 *
3	2	1
4	3	3 *
5	11	1
6	13	1
7	10	1
8	9	1
9	4	4 *
10	5	4
11	6	4
12	14	14 *
13	15	14
14	8	4
15	7	4

Figure 5.5 A jungle, obtained when the algorithm of Tarjan is applied to the digraph of Fig. 5.1(b). The order of search is indicated by the numbers near the circles. Roots of strong components are indicated by double circles.

unvisited, we have to choose a new starting vertex, say 12. Tree arc $(12 \rightarrow 13)$ is found, and this completes the search. The second tree spans the strong component C_4. The spanning forest consists of two trees in this example, which span all four strong components of the digraph.

Let us now examine in more detail the relationship between each tree and the set of strong components it spans. Let s be a starting vertex and let T be the tree rooted at s constructed by depth-first search. We will first show that T can be partitioned into disjoint subtrees, each of which spans exactly one strong component. Let $C = (V_c, E_c)$ be one of the strong components spanned by T, and let T_c be the *smallest* subtree of T which contains *all* vertices of C. Let $v \in V_c$ be the root of T_c. We can easily prove that T_c contains *only* vertices of C. For, assume that $w \notin V_c$ is a vertex of T_c. Vertex w is not the root of T_c; neither can it be a terminal member since we have assumed that T_c is the smallest subtree containing all vertices of C. Then v is an ancestor of w, and w must have a descendant, say x, which belongs to C. A path exists in T_c from v *to* x, which contains w; and a path exists in C from x to v because C is a strong component. Both paths form a cycle to which w belongs; then w must belong to C, in contradiction with the assumption that w does not belong to C. □

Thus, T can be partitioned into disjoint subtrees each of which spans exactly one strong component. The root of a subtree is the first vertex of the corresponding component to be visited during the search and is called the *root of the strong component*. In particular, the starting vertex s is the root of the strong component to which it belongs. These results were proved as theorems by Tarjan (1972). Thus, the problem of finding the strong components of a digraph reduces to the problem of finding the roots of the subtrees. We say that a subtree belongs to level l when the corresponding strong component is in that level in the connectivity level structure of the digraph (see Section 5.3). For examples of subtrees, compare Fig. 5.5 with Fig. 5.3. Vertex 12 is the root of the subtree (12, 13), which is in level 4. Vertex 2 is the root of the subtree (2, 3, 8, 7, 5, 1, 6), which belongs to level 3. Vertex 4 alone is a subtree, which is in level 2; and 9 is the root of (9, 10, 11, 15, 14), in level 1. Each of the subtrees spans exactly one strong component of the graph shown in Fig. 5.1. Note that the subtree in level 1 has no exit.

Let us finally examine the behaviour of edges which are not tree arcs, in relation to the trees of the forest and the strong components of the digraph. This will be done in the light of the following essential properties of depth-first search. Let T be one of the trees in the forest, let v be any vertex of T, and let T_v be the subtree rooted at v which contains v and all its descendants in T. Then, v is the first vertex in T_v to be visited during the search, and is thus the smallest numbered vertex in T_v: if w is a descendant of v, then Number(v) $<$ Number(w). Furthermore, all vertices in T_v are visited before backtracking through v takes place. In particular, if v is the root of a strong component, then v is numbered with a smaller number than any other vertex in the component, and all vertices in the component are visited before the component is abandoned by backtracking through v.

Consider now some stage during the search, let v be the current vertex and let $(v \to w)$ be an edge which is not a tree arc. $(v \to w)$ is not a tree arc because w has been visited before v became the current vertex. Thus both Number(v) and Number(w) are defined at this point. Furthermore, if v is in some level l, we know that the level l' of w must satisfy $l' \leqslant l$, where the equal sign holds only when v and w are in the same strong component. When an edge $(v \to w)$ is found, and $(v \to w)$ is not a tree arc, the following possibilities exist:

(1) w is an ancestor of v. The edge $(v \to w)$ is a *frond* and Number(w) $<$ Number(v). Since a path from w to v already exists, formed by the tree arcs which connect w with its descendant v, the effect of the frond is to close a cycle. Thus, v and the pedigree of v up to and including w belong to the same strong component. In Fig. 5.5, edge $(14 \to 9)$ is a frond because 9 is an ancestor of 14, and vertices 9, 10, 11, 15 and 14 all belong to the same strong component C_1.

(2) w is a descendant of v. The edge $(v \to w)$ is called a *redundant tree arc* (Gustavson, 1976b) and Number(w) > Number(v). A redundant tree arc connects two vertices which are already connected by a path of tree arcs. Thus, it does not affect the strong components and may be neglected if our purpose is to find the strong components. In Fig. 5.5, edge $(10 \to 14)$ is a redundant tree arc.

(3) w is neither an ancestor nor a descendant of v. The edge $(v \to w)$ is called a *cross-link*. Consider the subtree T_v rooted at v which consists of v and its offspring. During the search, after v is found, all vertices of T_v and only vertices in T_v are visited, and numbered, until T_v is abandoned by backtracking through v. w does not belong to T_v but was numbered before v became the current vertex. This means that w was numbered before v was found for the first time, or Number(w) < Number(v). Vertices v and w may belong to the same or to different strong components; in the first case Level(w) = Level(v), while Level(w) < Level(v) when v and w belong to different components. In Fig. 5.5, $(8 \to 9)$ and $(6 \to 5)$ are cross-links. Vertices 6 and 5 belong to the same strong component C_3 and are in level 3. Vertices 8 and 9 belong to C_3 and C_1, respectively, and Level(9) = 1 < Level(8) = 3.

A structure composed of a spanning forest and additional edges which are fronds, redundant tree arcs and cross-links, is called a *jungle*.

If depth-first search is performed on an acyclic digraph, where each vertex is a strong component, a simpler structure is obtained. Each vertex in the spanning forest is the root of its own strong component. There are no fronds nor active cross-links. All edges are either tree arcs or sterile cross-links. Depth-first search of acyclic digraphs was employed by Hopcroft and Karp (1973) in connection with the problem of finding maximum matchings in bipartite graphs.

5.5. Breadth-first search of a digraph and directed adjacency level structures

In this section we consider a class of partitionings of a connected digraph $G = (V, E)$ which can be constructed by breadth-first search. A *directed adjacency level substructure* $L_0, L_1, \ldots, L_m$ is obtained when $L_0 \subset V$ is a given subset of the vertices of G and each of the remaining levels is the adjacent of the union of the preceding levels:

$$L_i = \text{Adj}\left(\bigcup_{j=0}^{i-1} L_j\right), \qquad i = 1, 2, \ldots, m. \tag{5.10}$$

m is the *length* of the level substructure and the *width* is defined as the maximum number of vertices in any level. The substructure is *rooted* at L_0. If L_0 is a single vertex u, i.e., $L_0 = \{u\}$, we say that the substructure is rooted at vertex u. The set of vertices

$$V_s = \bigcup_{i=0}^{m} L_i \tag{5.11}$$

spanned by the substructure contains all vertices in L_0 and those which are reachable from vertices in L_0. V_s may not contain all vertices of G. If this is the case, then the remaining subset $V - V_s$ may be recursively partitioned in an analogous way until a *directed adjacency level structure* is obtained which spans all vertices in G. Levels in the structure, however, are independently defined for each substructure.

Adjacency level structures are constructed using depth-first search. The procedure is similar to that described in Section 4.15 for undirected graphs, but some important differences exist. The search sorts vertices into levels and marks directed edges as either *tree arcs* or *cross-links*. Consider for simplicity that the search is started at some arbitrary starting vertex s. Then level L_0 is vertex s alone and a level substructure rooted at s will be obtained. At a certain stage during the search we have identified all vertices in a certain level L_i. All vertices in level L_i and in preceding levels have been marked as visited. Then, for some $v \in L_i$, we explore the edges leading from v to other vertices. If an edge $(v \to w)$ is found where w is unvisited, the edge is a tree arc and w belongs to level L_{i+1}. If edge $(v \to x)$ is found and x is a visited vertex, then this edge is a cross-link. Since visited vertices exist only in levels L_j where $j \leqslant i + 1$, we reach the conclusion that a cross-link which starts at a vertex in level L_i can only lead to a vertex in level L_j with $j \leqslant i + 1$. More generally, if other substructures have been previously constructed, a cross-link may also lead to any vertex of those substructures. A tree arc can only connect a vertex in some level L_i with a vertex in level L_{i+1}, and there may be no connection between a vertex in level L_i and a vertex in level L_j if $j > i + 1$. The graph $G_s = (V_s, E_s)$, where E_s is the set of tree arcs, is a tree rooted at s which spans the substructure. If the search is continued until all vertices in G are visited, starting at a new unvisited vertex each time a tree is completed, a jungle and a spanning forest are obtained (see Section 5.4). The algorithm of Rose *et al.* (1976) described in Section 4.3 can be used to perform the search, with only minor modifications.

The following property holds for an adjacency substructure rooted at vertex s: if $v \in L_i$, the distance from s to v in G, i.e. the length of a shortest path from s to v in G, is equal to i. Besides, exactly one shortest path of length i is contained in the spanning tree and consists entirely of tree arcs. This property will be used in Section 5.6 for finding a transversal of a sparse matrix.

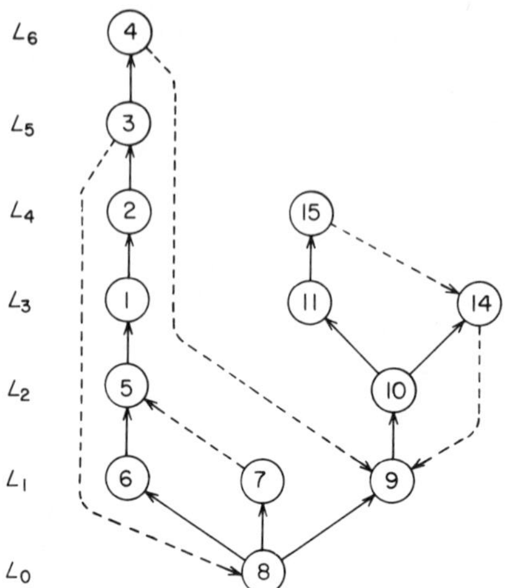

Figure 5.6 Directed adjacency level substructure rooted at vertex 8, for the digraph of Fig. 5.1(b).

As an example, consider the digraph shown in Fig. 5.1(b). The directed adjacency level substructure rooted at vertex 8 is shown in Fig. 5.6. Tree arcs are shown with full lines, and cross-links with dotted lines. The distance from vertex 8 to vertex 10 is 2 because vertex 10 belongs to L_2. The shortest path from 8 to 10 is (8, 9, 10), which is contained in the tree. The other two paths from 8 to 10, namely (8, 6, 5, 1, 2, 3, 4, 9, 10) and (8, 7, 5, 1, 2, 3, 4, 9, 10), are both longer. All vertices reachable from vertex 8 in the graph are contained in the substructure.

5.6. Finding a maximal set of vertex disjoint paths in an acyclic digraph

Depth-first search has several applications in sparse matrix technology. The one we consider in this section is connected with the reduction of a general sparse matrix to block lower triangular form by means of unsymmetric permutations, as will be discussed in Section 5.8. The problem is as follows: given an acyclic digraph $G = (V, E)$ and two of its vertices $s \in V$ and $t \in V$, find a maximal set of paths from s to t such that no vertex except s and t belongs to more than one path. We recall that a set is *maximal* with respect to a given property if its elements have the property and the set is not properly contained in any other set of elements having the property. On the other hand, a *maximum* set is a set having maximum cardinality. Figure 5.7 shows

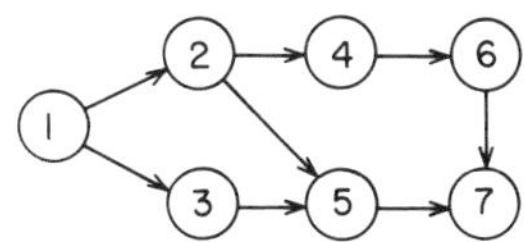

Figure 5.7 Paths in an acyclic digraph.

an example. A maximum set of disjoint paths from vertex 1 to vertex 7 consists of paths 1, 2, 4, 6, 7 and 1, 3, 5, 7. The cardinality of this set is 2. The set which consits of path 1, 2, 5, 7 alone is maximal, despite its cardinality being only 1, because no set of disjoint paths can be found which properly contains path 1, 2, 5, 7.

Using depth-first search to solve this problem was suggested by Hopcroft and Karp (1973). If the search is started at vertex s and at least one path exists from s to t, then t belongs to the tree rooted at s. Therefore it is only necessary to examine this tree. The algorithm employs a stack (see Section 1.2 for definition and terminology) where the vertex sequence from s to the current vertex is stored. Each edge is explored just once and then either becomes part of the path being constructed, or else there is no s to t path using that edge. Only edges leading to unvisited vertices are considered because we are looking for paths which are vertex-disjoint, except for the endpoints s and t. Since the algorithm may have to examine more than one edge leading to t, the convention is made that t never becomes a visited vertex. When t is found in the course of search, it is pushed onto the stack, which then contains a complete s, t path. All vertices are popped from the stack and printed, and s is pushed onto the stack again to start the search for a new path. The algorithm terminates when s is popped from the stack after all exits from s have been explored. Let V_v be the set of visited vertices and E_e the set of explored edges. Let the graph be represented by its adjacency structure (see Section 1.4). Then, explicitly, the algorithm is as follows:

Step 0 (Initialization). Set $V_v \leftarrow \emptyset$ and $E_e \leftarrow \emptyset$.
Step 1 (Start path). Push s onto stack.
Step 2 (Visit a vertex). Set $v \leftarrow$ vertex on top of stack.
Step 3 (Explore an edge). Look in the adjacency list of v for an edge $(v \to w) \notin E_e$ where $w \notin V_v$. Then:

(3*a*) If such an edge was found and $w \neq t$, set $V_v \leftarrow V_v \cup \{w\}$, $E_e \leftarrow E_e \cup (v \to w)$, push w onto stack and go to Step 2 to continue search.

(3*b*) If such an edge was found where $w = t$, set $E_e \leftarrow E_e \cup (v \to w)$, push w onto stack and go to Step 5 to gather path.

(3*c*) If v has no unexplored exits leading to unvisited vertices, go to next step for backtracking.

Step 4 (Backtracking). Pop stack. If stack is empty, stop. Otherwise go to Step 2.

Step 5 (Form path). Pop stack until empty, print path, and then go to Step 1 to start new path.

This algorithm was given by Hopcroft and Karp (1973; note that the operation DELETE is missing on page 230 of their paper; it must be included immediately after the line FIRST = first element of LIST(TOP)). The algorithm requires $O(|V|, |E|)$ space and time.

For an example of application of this algorithm, consider finding a set of disjoint paths from $s = 1$ to $t = 7$ in the acyclic digraph of Fig. 5.7. Vertex 1 is pushed onto the stack, and successive executions of Steps 2, 3 and 3a also push, say, vertices 2, 4 and 6. Then, again at Step 2, $v = 6$, and at Step 3 $w = t = 7$. Vertex 7 is pushed and the algorithm branches from Step 3b to Step 5, where the stack is emptied and path 1, 2, 4, 6, 7 is printed in the reverse order. Vertex 1 is pushed, and this time the path 1, 3, 5, 7 is found. The algorithm terminates because the adjacency list of vertex 1 is now exhausted.

Assume now that the algorithm finds path 1, 2, 5, 7 in the first attempt. Then, at Step 1, vertex $s = 1$ is pushed, $v = 1$ at Step 2, and $w = 3$ is found at Step 3 and pushed on top of the stack at Step 3a. Now $v = 3$ at Step 2, but Step 3 fails to find an exit from vertex 3 leading to an unvisited vertex because vertex 5 was visited before. The algorithm continues to Step 4, where vertex 3 is popped. Finally, at Step 2, $v = 1$, Step 3 finds no unexplored exits, vertex 1 is popped at Step 4 and the algorithm terminates. Note that this time a maximal set composed of just one path was found, and that vertices 4 and 6 were never visited: the search is incomplete because, as discussed above, it is sufficient to examine the tree rooted at $s = 1$.

5.7. Finding a transversal: the algorithm of Hall

If the given n by n matrix **A** has all its diagonal elements different from zero, the digraph can be constructed as explained in Section 5.2. However, when zeros exist on the main diagonal, then a previous step is to perform row and column interchanges in such a way that a zero-free diagonal results. The set of nonzeros obtained in this way is called a *transversal*. We will show below that a full transversal always exists if **A** is nonsingular. However, a singular matrix may also have a full transversal. A matrix of order n which cannot be permuted in such a way that a full transversal results, is said to be *symbolically singular*. If the maximum possible transversal has length $k < n$, then k is the *symbolic rank* and $n - k$ the *symbolic nullity*.

A maximum transversal of a matrix **A** can be found using the algorithm of

Hall (1956). We describe here a version with row interchanges, which is convenient for sparse matrices stored in row-wise format. The version with column interchanges was discussed by Duff (1976) and by Reid (1977), and a depth-first version was presented by Gustavson (1976b). The algorithm requires n steps: the purpose of the kth step is to place a nonzero on the kth position of the diagonal. After k steps have been performed, the diagonal contains nonzeros in its k initial positions. Then, at step $k + 1$:

(a) either $A_{k+1,k+1} \neq 0$, in which case step $k + 1$ is complete; or
(b) a nonzero can be found with row and column indices in the range $k + 1$ to n. In this case, a row and/or a column interchange will bring this nonzero to position $k + 1$ on the diagonal. The square submatrix situated in rows and columns 1 through k is not modified by such interchanges, and the nonzeros in positions 1 to k of the diagonal remain there.
(c) When only zeros exist in the square submatrix situated in rows and columns $k + 1$ to n, we can still hope to find a combination of row interchanges such that a nonzero is brought to the $(k + 1)$th diagonal position. In order to find the required interchanges we trace an *augmenting path* through the matrix. The path starts at position $(k + 1, k + 1)$, goes along row $k + 1$ up to a nonzero, say on column l (one such nonzero must exist, otherwise row $k + 1$ consists entirely of zeros and **A** is singular), then to position (l, l) along column l, next to an off-diagonal nonzero on row l, say on column m, etc. In other words, the path goes alternatively through a diagonal element and on off-diagonal nonzero. The path can not traverse any row or column more than once, and ends at a nonzero in the submatrix situated in rows 1 through k and columns $k + 1$ through n. The path can be described in the computer memory by recording the indices of the diagonal positions in the order in which they are visited; thus: $k + 1, l, m, \ldots$. Since some diagonal positions may have been visited and then deleted from the path, we must keep another record of the visited positions in order to avoid visiting them again. An example will be given below.

In order to construct such a path, we start at position $(k + 1, k + 1)$ and look for a nonzero on row $k + 1$. One must exist if **A** is nonsingular, because otherwise row $k + 1$ would be entirely composed of zeros. If the nonzero has been found on column l, then we go to row l and look for a nonzero on columns $k + 1$ to n. If one exists, the path is finished; otherwise, we look for a nonzero on row l, columns 1 to k, which must fall on a column which was not visited previously, say m. Then we go to row m and repeat the operations until the path is complete. If for some row we cannot find an off-diagonal nonzero on an unvisited column, then we delete that row from the path (but not from the list of visited positions) and go back to the previous row. If at some stage, after having visited r positions in the range 1 to k, our path becomes empty (that is, we are back at the starting point), this means that **A** is singular: in fact, we have found that the $r + 1$ rows (the r visited rows plus row $k + 1$) have nonzeros in only r columns.

Once a path is known, say $k + 1, l_1, l_2, \ldots, l_r$ where $l_r > k$, we interchange $r + 1$ rows and two columns in order to bring the last nonzero found to position $(k + 1, k + 1)$. The row interchanges required are:

row $k + 1$ becomes row l_1

row l_1 becomes row l_2

....

row l_{r-1} becomes row $k + 1$.

Since the rows have been selected in such a way that row l_i has a nonzero at position l_{i+1}, this nonzero will be brought to the diagonal position (l_{i+1}, l_{i+1}) when row l_i replaces row l_{i+1}. Thus, the nonzero structure of the diagonal in positions 1 to k will not be affected by the row interchanges. Further, the last nonzero of the path will be brought to position $(k + 1, l_r)$, and an exchange of columns $k + 1$ and l_r will bring that nonzero to position $(k + 1, k + 1)$, thus completing step k. Of course, if $l_r = k + 1$ this last column exchange is not necessary.

An example is useful to clarify this algorithm. Consider the matrix shown in Fig. 5.8, on which $k = 8$ steps have already been performed.

We start at (9, 9) and proceed as follows: row 9, column 5, row 5, column 2, row 2, column 4, row 4, column 7, row 7. At this point we have visited positions 9, 5, 2, 4 and 7, but the only off-diagonal nonzero of row 7 is on column 5, which has already been visited. This forces us to delete 7 and 4 from the current path (but not from the list of visited positions) and to continue from 2 to 6, 1 and finally 12. Thus, the path is:

9, 5, 2, 6, 1, 12.

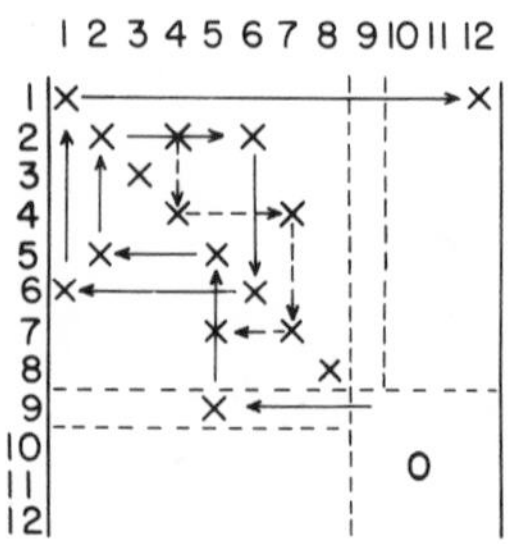

Figure 5.8 The algorithm of Hall for finding a transversal.

Now that the path has been found we must perform the following interchanges:

row 9 becomes row 5
row 5 becomes row 2
row 2 becomes row 6
row 6 becomes row 1
row 1 becomes row 12
row 12 becomes row 9.

This preserves the diagonal of nonzeros and brings the nonzero from position (1, 12) to (9, 12). Finally, we exchange columns 9 and 12; so we bring this nonzero to position (9, 9) and step 9 is complete.

Let us now examine what would happen if the element (6, 1) were zero. In such a case we would have found that rows 9, 5, 2, 4, 7 and 6 have nonzeros only on columns 5, 2, 4, 7 and 6, which would mean that **A** was singular.

Concerning the efficiency of this algorithm, note that, at each step, we scan each row at most twice, once when looking for a nonzero beyond column k, and a second time if we have to search a nonzero belonging to an unvisited column in the range 1 to k. Thus, if the matrix has z nonzeros in total, then $O(z)$ operations are performed at step k, and $O(nz)$ in total. This bound has been achieved by examples specifically designed for that purpose (Duff, 1976), but in practice the operation count is usually a small multiple of z.

5.8. Finding a transversal: the algorithm of Hopcroft and Karp

The algorithm of Hopcroft and Karp (1973) finds a maximum transversal of a sparse matrix. The central idea is the same as in Hall's algorithm: augmenting paths are traced and assignments are improved step by step. However, a careful analysis of augmenting paths is carried out, and their properties are used to break the sequence of assignments into a small number of phases. Within each phase, many short augmenting paths are simultaneously found, all of the same minimum length, and used to improve the current assignment. In this way, the efficiency of the algorithm is improved.

We start the analysis by considering an undirected graph $G = (V, E)$ and a subset $M \subseteq E$ of its edges. The subset M is a *matching* or an *assignment* if no vertex of G is incident with more than one edge. A *maximum matching* is a matching of maximum cardinality $m = |M|$. A vertex is *free* if it is incident with no edge in M. A path without repeated vertices in the graph G is an *augmenting path* relative to the matching M if its endpoints are both free vertices and its edges are alternatively in $E - M$ and in M. Augmenting paths serve to augment the cardinality of a matching. If an augmenting path relative to a matching M is known, then another matching M' with one edge more than M, i.e. $|M'| = |M| + 1$, can be obtained by taking all edges of the path which are not in the original matching M, plus all edges of M which are not in the augmenting path. This property holds for any augmenting path no matter what its length may be. In particular, we will be interested in *shortest augmenting paths* relative to M, which are of least cardinality among all augmenting paths relative to M. To make these statements more precise we first recall the notation used in set theory. Consider two sets S and T. Then $S - T$ denotes the set of elements in S which are not in T. Thus

$$S - T = S - S \cap T. \tag{5.12}$$

$S \oplus T$ denotes the symmetric difference between S and T. An element belongs to $S \oplus T$ if it is either in S or in T, but elements which are in $S \cap T$ do not belong to $S \oplus T$. Thus:

$$S \oplus T = S \cup T - S \cap T. \tag{5.13}$$

Now let P denote the set of edges in an augmenting path relative to a matching M in a graph G. Then $M \oplus P$ is also a matching and $|M \oplus P| = |M| + 1$. As an example, consider the graph of Fig. 4.1(b) of Chapter 4, which is reproduced for convenience in Fig. 5.9(a). A matching M with $|M| = 3$ edges is shown with full lines in Fig. 5.9(b). Vertices 9 and 7 are free, and the path 9, 6, 1, 10, 11, 7 is an augmenting path because its endpoints are both free, edges (6, 1) and (10, 11) are in M, and edges (9, 6), (1, 10) and (11, 7) are in E but not in M. The augmented matching $M \oplus P$ is shown in Fig. 5.9(c); it has $3 + 1 = 4$ edges. We could equally well have used a shortest augmenting path, such as 2, 9 or 4, 7 in Fig. 5.9(b), to obtain an augmented matching with 4 edges.

Let us now resume the analysis. We are seeking a maximum matching in a graph $G = (V, E)$. Starting from an empty matching $M_0 = \emptyset$ we compute a sequence of matchings $M_0, M_1, M_2, \ldots$, with increasing cardinality until a maximum matching is obtained. Each matching M_{i+1} is obtained from the preceding one M_i by constructing an augmenting path P_i relative to M_i. Thus $M_{i+1} = M_i \oplus P_i$ for $i = 0, 1, 2, \ldots$. If G is the bipartite graph associated with a sparse matrix, this is exactly the procedure employed by the algorithm of Hall, discussed in Section 5.7, which requires $O(nz)$ operations for a matrix of order n with z nonzeros.

On the other hand, the algorithm of Hopcroft and Karp employs only shortest augmenting paths. If P_i is a shortest augmenting path relative to M_i and $M_{i+1} = M_i \oplus P_i$ for $i = 0, 1, 2, \ldots$, then the following properties hold:

(i) $|P_{i+1}| \geqslant |P_i|$; i.e., a shortest augmenting path relative to M_{i+1} cannot have fewer edges than a shortest augmenting path relative to M_i.

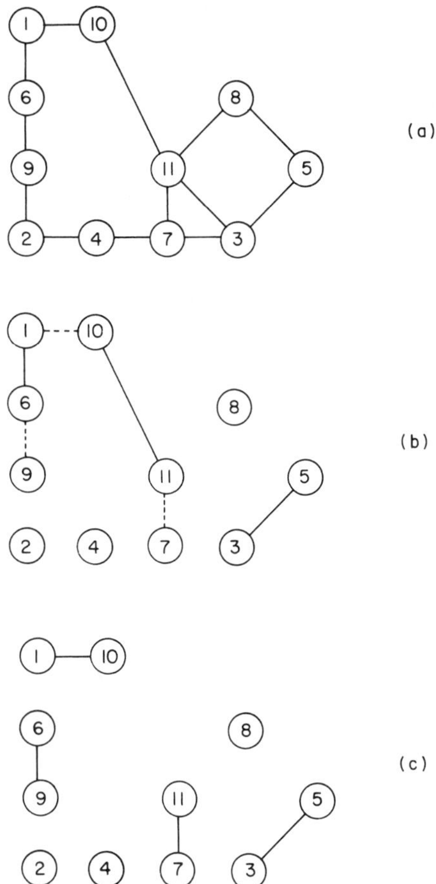

Figure 5.9 (a) A graph $G = (V, E)$. (b) A matching M and an augmenting path P. (c) The augmented matching $M \oplus P$.

(ii) For all j and k such that $|P_j| = |P_k|$, P_j and P_k are vertex disjoint.

(iii) For all j and k, $j < k$, such that $|P_j| = |P_k|$, P_k is a shortest augmenting path relative to matching M_j.

(iv) If m is the cardinality of a maximum matching, the number of distinct integers in the sequence $|P_0|, |P_1|, |P_2|, \ldots,$ cannot exceed $2m^{1/2} + 2$.

Furthermore, if m is the cardinality of a maximum matching and M is any matching with cardinality $|M| < m$, then the following property holds:

(v) There exists an augmenting path of length not exceeding $2|M|/(m - |M|) + 1$.

In view of these properties, the computation of the sequence of matchings breaks into no more than $2m^{1/2} + 2$ phases. Within each phase all the augmenting paths found are vertex-disjoint and of the same length. Furthermore, they are all shortest augmenting paths relative to the matching with which the phase is started. Therefore, instead of computing the entire sequence of matchings, Hopcroft and Karp have suggested the use of the following algorithm:

Step 0 (Initialization). Set $M \leftarrow \emptyset$.
Step 1 (Find paths). Find a maximal set $\{P_1, P_2, \ldots, P_t\}$ of vertex-disjoint shortest augmenting paths relative to M. Stop if no such paths exist.
Step 3 (Augment matching). Set $M \leftarrow M \oplus P_1 \oplus P_2 \oplus \ldots \oplus P_t$ and go to Step 1.

An example of application of this algorithm to the graph of Fig. 5.9(a) is given in Fig. 5.10. Let $M = \emptyset$ be the empty matching. A maximal set of vertex-disjoint shortest augmenting paths, all of length 1, consists of the 5 paths shown in Fig. 5.10 by dotted lines. When M is correspondingly augmented, a maximum matching is directly obtained. Vertex 3 can not be matched and remains free. In this example, the computation of just one phase is sufficient to produce a maximum matching.

It remains to be shown how the algorithm is applied to a sparse matrix. Let **A** be a square sparse matrix of order n. The procedure for finding a transversal is the following:

(1) Construct the bipartite graph $G = (V, E)$ associated with **A**, as discussed in Section 5.2. Graph G is undirected and has two sets, R and C, of n vertices each. The vertices in R are called boys and are associated with the rows of **A**; the vertices in C are girls, and are associated with the columns of **A**. Edge (r_i, c_j) is present when $A_{ij} \neq 0$.
(2) Let M be a matching in G. Initially M is empty, but during execution of the algorithm M becomes nonempty. Then, given G and the current M,

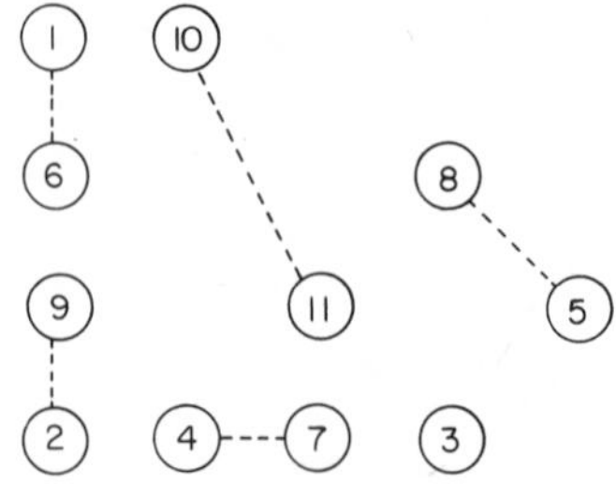

Figure 5.10 Matchings in the undirected graph of Fig. 5.9(a). A maximal set of vertex-disjoint augmenting paths is shown with dotted lines.

we assign directions to the edges of G: each edge in M runs from a boy to a girl, and each one of the remaining edges of G runs from a girl to a boy. Let $\bar{G} = (V, \bar{E})$ be the directed graph obtained in this way. The construction of $\bar{G}$ is motivated by the following property: the edges of any directed path in $\bar{G}$ are alternatively in $\bar{E} - M$ and in M. Therefore, if a path is found in $\bar{G}$ which connects a free girl with a free boy (relative to M) this path is necessarily an augmenting path relative to M.

(3) Let L_0 be the set of free girls. Then, using breadth-first search, construct the directed adjacency level substructure rooted at L_0, as discussed in Section 5.5. It is not necessary to construct the entire substructure. Only edges which run from any level L_i to level L_{i+1} are retained, and only levels $L_0, L_1, \ldots, L_p$ are necessary, where $p = \min\{i | L_i \cap \{\text{free boys}\} \neq \emptyset\}$. The substructure is an acyclic digraph with girls in even levels and boys in odd levels. Every path from a free girl to a free boy is a shortest augmenting path in G relative to M, and has length p. In order to find a maximal set of vertex-disjoint paths, the direction of every edge is reversed and a depth-first search is performed on the substructure, starting at free boys in level L_p, as explained in Section 5.6. Note that if edge direction were not reversed and search were started at free girls in level L_0, many edges leading to boys in level L_p which are not free might have to be inspected, requiring a much larger computational effort. Finally, if $\{P_1, P_2, \ldots, P_t\}$ is the set of paths just obtained, the current matching M can be augmented, and the new matching has cardinality $|M| + t$.

For an example of application of the algorithm to a sparse matrix, consider the sparse matrix shown in Fig. 5.11(a), and its corresponding bipartite graph shown in Fig. 5.11(b). Initially, all boys and girls are free, the matching is empty, and every edge runs from a girl to a boy. The root for the level substructure is the whole set of free girls. The substructure has just two levels. In this particular example the maximum matching (12, 24, 35, 46, 58, 61, 83) of cardinality 7, where the first digit in each pair refers to a row and the second to a column, might be found in just one phase. However, we assume that we were not so lucky and that only five tree arcs were found, yielding the matching (11, 22, 33, 44, 55) of cardinality 5. The computation of the second phase now begins. Edges representing matchings are directed from boys to girls, and the remaining edges from girls to boys, with the result shown in Fig. 5.11(c). The free girls $C6$, $C7$ and $C8$ are taken as the root, and the level substructure is constructed, retaining only those edges which run from a level L_i to level L_{i+1}. Figure 5.11(d) shows the result. Edges which belong to the substructure are indicated with full lines, and edges which belong both to the substructure and to the matching are shown with double lines. The remaining

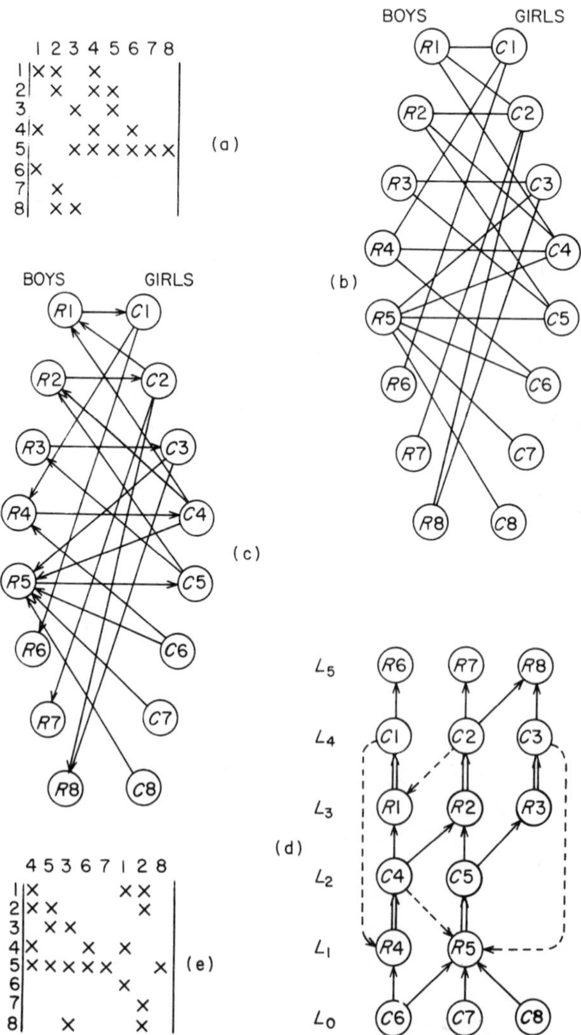

Figure 5.11 The algorithm of Hopcroft and Karp for finding a transversal: (a) structure of a sparse matrix; (b) bipartite graph; (c) directed matching; (d) level substructure; (e) permuted matrix.

edges of the bigraph are shown with dotted lines for the sake of illustration, but they are of no interest now. Finally, the direction of every edge is reversed and depth-first search is performed, starting at $R6$, $R7$ and $R8$. Assuming that we are lucky this time, the result of the search might be the following maximal set of disjoint paths: ($R6$, $C1$, $R1$, $C4$, $R4$, $C6$) and ($R7$, $C2$, $R2$, $C5$, $R5$, $C7$), both of length 5. The new matching of cardinality 7 is thus (14, 25, 33, 46, 57, 61, 72), where the first digit in each pair identifies a row, and the second digit identifies a column. The resulting permuted matrix is shown in Fig. 5.11(e). This is a maximum matching since no more augmenting paths can be found.

If the sparse matrix of order n has z nonzeros, the algorithm which finds the maximal set of paths in each phase requires $O(n, z)$ space and time. Since the cardinality of a maximum matching is not larger than n, there are no more than $2n^{1/2} + 2$ phases. Thus, the entire maximum matching algorithm requires at most $O(n^{3/2}, zn^{1/2})$ time and $O(n, z)$ space. If $z \sim n$, as frequently happens for sparse matrices, the bounds are $O(n^{3/2})$ for time and $O(n)$ for space.

The present algorithm, developed for bipartite graphs, was extended by Even and Kariv (1975) to directed graphs and a slightly better and simpler algorithm for the same problem, with running time $O(|V|^{1/2}|E|)$, was developed by Micali and Vazirani (1979). The algorithm of Hall, despite its higher asymptotic bound, has been found to perform better than the algorithm of Hopcroft and Karp on many practical matrices.

5.9. The algorithm of Sargent and Westerberg for finding the strong components of a digraph

It was mentioned in Section 5.1 that an unsymmetric sparse matrix which has a full transversal (a diagonal with no zeros) can be symmetrically permuted to block lower triangular form if the strong components of the corresponding digraph are known. Sargent and Westerberg (1964) proposed a simple algorithm for finding the strong components of any digraph. The algorithm is based on depth-first search because a path is traced following the sequence vertex–edge–vertex–edge ... while possible. The path is started at some arbitrarily chosen vertex and continued until either

(i) a cycle is found; or
(ii) a vertex with no exit is found.

A cycle is identified when the path reaches a vertex which has been visited before. All vertices in the cycle are known to belong to the same strong component. The procedure known as *vertex collapsing* is employed in this case: all vertices in the cycle are collapsed into a single *composite vertex*, all edges in the cycle are ignored, and edges connecting vertices in the cycle with other vertices of the graph are regarded as connecting the composite vertex with the other vertices. The composite vertex becomes the last vertex of the current path, and the search is resumed from that point in the modified graph.

When a vertex, or composite vertex, with no exit is found, this vertex or composite vertex is a strong component of level 1. The vertex or all the vertices which belong to the composite vertex are removed from the graph together with all their incident edges. The search then continues in the remaining subgraph, starting from the last vertex of the remaining path or from a new starting vertex if the path is empty. The procedure continues until all vertices in the original graph have been visited and all edges explored.

In this algorithm, each edge of the graph is explored just once. However, frequent modifications of the original graph are required and cause a serious overhead. Vertex collapsing is equivalent to forming a new quotient graph each time a cycle is found, and removal of a strong component amounts to the generation of a section subgraph. Records must be kept describing which vertex belongs to each composite vertex and to which composite vertex each vertex belongs. An inferior implementation may result in $O(|V|^2)$ vertex relabellings for a digraph $G = (V, E)$. Munro (1971a) suggested that vertex collapsing should be performed by relabelling only the composite vertex with fewer constituent vertices, and showed (Munro, 1971b) that the resulting algorithm requires $O(|V| \log |V|, |E|)$ time. If Tarjan's ideas (Tarjan, 1975) for the Union and Find operations in disjoint sets, mentioned in Section 1.13, are used in the algorithm of Sargent and Westerberg, the combination has a time bound of $O(|V| \log^* |V|, |E|)$, where

$$\log^* a = \min \{ i \mid \overbrace{\log \log \ldots \log}^{i\ times} (a) \leqslant 1 \}. \tag{5.14}$$

The function $\log^* a$ increases very slowly with a, for example $\log^* a < 4$ if $a < 3 \times 10^6$, which means that in practice the algorithm is linear with $|V|$ and $|E|$. The algorithm of Sargent and Westerberg was explained by Reid (1977) and by Duff and Reid (1978a), where a clear flow chart is included.

As an example of application of this algorithm consider the graph shown in Fig. 5.1(b). Starting arbitrarily at vertex 2, the path 2, 3, 4, 9, 10, 11, 15, 14, 9 may be traced. A cycle has been detected because vertex 9 was found twice. Vertices 9, 10, 11, 15 and 14, which belong to the cycle, are collapsed and a composite vertex, say A, is formed. When the search is resumed, it is found that the vertex at the end of the path, which is precisely vertex A, has no exit and is therefore a strong component of level 1. Vertices 9, 10, 11, 15 and 14 are removed from the graph and placed in the first component, say C_1.

Searching is resumed at vertex 4, which again has no exit and becomes component C_2. The remaining path is 2, 3. The search from vertex 3 finds the cycle 2, 3, 8, 7, 5, 1, 2, which becomes composite vertex B. Then searching from vertex B finds the cycle B, 6, B, which has no exit and is component C_3. Finally, since the path is now empty, vertex 12 is chosen as a new starting vertex, cycle 12, 13, 12 is found and component C_4 is identified.

5.10. The algorithm of Tarjan for finding the strong components of a digraph

Depth-first search of a digraph $G = (V, E)$ generates a spanning forest (see Section 5.4), composed of one or more trees. The vertices of each strong component C of the digraph define a subtree of a tree in the forest. The subtree contains all vertices of C and only vertices of C, and its root is the first vertex of C which is visited during the search. The problem of finding the strong components is thus reduced to finding the roots of the subtrees in the spanning forest generated by depth-first search.

The algorithm of Tarjan (1972) is designed in such a way that backtracking through the root of a component C into another component of higher level will never take place until all vertices of C are visited and identified as members of C. This means, in particular, that when v is the current vertex during the search, and an edge $(v \to w)$ is found where w is numbered but not yet assigned to some component, then v and w are in the same component. The proof is simple: let Level$(w) = l$; since w has not yet been assigned, the current vertex v must be in level $l' \leqslant l$. However, since $(v \to w)$ is an edge of G, $l' \geqslant l$; thus $l' = l$, which is possible only if v and w belong to the same component.

In the algorithm of Tarjan, the search is performed and a label is associated with each vertex v. The label consists of two numbers, called Number(v) and Lowlink(v). Number(v) is calculated during the search simply by numbering the vertices in the order in which they are visited from 1 to $n = |V|$. For any vertex v which is not the root of a strong component, Lowlink(v) is the number of some vertex w which is in the same strong component as v but is numbered lower, i.e. Lowlink$(v) =$ Number$(w) <$ Number(v); for the root r of any strong component we define Lowlink$(r) =$ Number(r). This property is used to recognize roots of strong components: if Lowlink(v) has been correctly calculated, then v is the root of a strong component if and only if Lowlink$(v) =$ Number(v). The calculation of Lowlink is done in three steps in the course of searching:

Step 1 (Initialization). When a vertex v is found for the first time, set Lowlink(v) = Number(v).

Step 2 (Updating). When v is the current vertex and an edge $(v \rightarrow w)$ is found where w is numbered before v but not yet assigned to a component, set Lowlink(v) = min[Lowlink(v), Lowlink(w)].

Step 3 (Backtracking). When $(v \rightarrow w)$ is a tree arc with v and w in the same component, and backtracking takes place from w to v, set Lowlink(v) = min[Lowlink(v), Lowlink(w)].

In Step 1, Lowlink is initialized for each vertex to the maximum possible value. In Step 2, Lowlink(v) is set to a smaller value when a connection from v to some suitable vertex w is found. Because of the requirement Number(w) < Number(v), only fronds and cross-links are taken into account. Besides, when w is numbered but not yet assigned we know that v and w are in the same component; this discards "sterile" cross-links, which are cross-links with v and w in different components (Gustavson, 1976b). Furthermore, Lowlink(w) is the number of some vertex which is in the same component as w and v and which, hopefully, might be numbered lower than w. The strategy of Step 2 is to adjust Lowlink(v) to point to the smallest vertex in the same component to which a connection is currently known to exist.

Finally, in Step 3, the minimum value of Lowlink is carried down the path by backtracking. The strategy of this step is the same as that used in Step 2: we know that v is connected to w and that w is connected to x = Lowlink(w), so that v is connected to x; if x is lower than the current value of Lowlink(v), then Lowlink(v) is adjusted. It is worth noting that relaxing the requirement of v and w being in the same component, as done for example in the implementation by Gustavson (1976b), causes no harm. For, if $(v \rightarrow w)$ is a tree arc where v and w are in different components, then w is the root of its component. When backtracking takes place, Lowlink(w) = Number(w) > Number(v). Since Lowlink(v) $\leqslant$ Number(v), Step 3 will not be executed in this case. Of course, it would be convenient to take advantage of the knowledge we have to avoid unnecessary testing.

We must now prove that Lowlink is correctly calculated. Let v be some vertex which belongs to the strong component C, and let T_v be the subtree rooted at v which contains the offspring of v in C. If v is not the root of T_v, T_v must have an exit into the component: there must be an edge $(w \rightarrow x)$ where w is in T_v, x in C, and $(w \rightarrow x)$ is not a tree arc. Thus, x must have been numbered before w. Furthermore, x must have been numbered before v for $(w \rightarrow x)$ to be an exit from T_v, so that Number(x) < Number(v). Edge $(w \rightarrow x)$ was discovered during the search, so that Lowlink(w) $\leqslant$ Number(x); later, this value was carried down to v by backtracking, so that Lowlink(v) $\leqslant$ Number(x) < Number(v). This is the test needed to determine that v is not the root of C. Note that the result remains valid either if we set Lowlink(w) = Number(x) or if we set Lowlink(w) = Lowlink(x) at the time edge ($w \to x$) is found. The first strategy is the original one used by Tarjan and Gustavson. The second strategy, used by Duff and Reid (1978a), implies taking advantage of the knowledge we may have that x is connected even lower in C to set Lowlink(w) to the lowest value we currently can. Since Lowlink(x) $\leqslant$ Number(x), the last strategy may avoid some assignments to Lowlink.

If v is the root of the strong component, then T_v has no exit and Lowlink(v) = Number(v). For examples of Lowlink consider the jungle shown in Fig. 5.5(a), where vertices which are roots of strong components are indicated by double circles, and a table of values of Number and Lowlink is given in Fig. 5.5(b).

The algorithm of Tarjan is basically identical to the algorithm of Sargent and Westerberg. The main difference is the use of the concept of Lowlink in Tarjan's algorithm to record composite vertices in the stack, in place of the concept of vertex collapsing used by Sargent and Westerberg. In fact, if Lowlink(v) = w, all vertices which are in the stack between the position of w and the position of v, both included, form a composite vertex.

We will now give the algorithm of Tarjan explicitly. The complete algorithm is a combination of depth-first search and the calculation of Lowlink just discussed. Two stacks are employed (see Section 1.2 for definition of stack); we will adhere to Tarjan's nomenclature and call the two stacks "the stack" and "the path", respectively. The path contains a list of the vertices which form a path from the starting vertex to the current vertex. Each new vertex found during the search is pushed onto the path, and each time backtracking is performed the corresponding vertex is popped from the top of the path; in this way the list of vertices stored in the path is in fact the desired path in the graph-theoretical sense.

The stack holds a list of vertices which belong to partially formed strong components. Each new vertex found during the search is pushed onto the stack. Vertices are not individually removed from the stack. Instead, when the strong component on top of the stack becomes complete, the entire component is removed.

The algorithm also needs the arrays Number and Lowlink, a Boolean array for testing in a fixed time if a vertex is on the stack or not, and specification of the sets V_v of visited vertices and E_e of explored edges. Explicitly, the algorithm is as follows:

Step 0 (Initialization). Set $E_e \leftarrow \emptyset$
$V_v \leftarrow \emptyset$
$i \leftarrow 0$.

Step 1 (Select starting vertex). Select any $v \notin V_v$. If none is available, stop.

Step 2 (Visit a vertex). Push v onto stack and path.

$$\text{Set:}\quad V_v \leftarrow V_v \cup \{v\}$$
$$i \leftarrow i + 1$$
$$\text{Number}(v) \leftarrow i$$
$$\text{Lowlink}(v) \leftarrow i.$$

Step 3 (Explore an edge). Look in the adjacency list of v for an edge $(v \to w) \notin E_e$. Then:

(3*a*) If edge $(v \to w)$ was found and $w \notin V_v$, set $E_e \leftarrow E_e \cup (v \to w)$ and $v \leftarrow w$, and go to Step 2 because $(v \to w)$ is a tree arc.

(3*b*) If edge $(v \to w)$ was found and $w \in V_v$, set $E_e \leftarrow E_e \cup (v \to w)$ and go to Step 4 to adjust Lowlink(v).

(3*c*) If v has no unexplored exits and Lowlink(v) < Number(v), go to Step 5 for backtracking.

(3d) If v has no unexplored exits and Lowlink(v) = Number(v), go to Step 6 to gather strong component.

Step 4 (Adjust Lowlink). If Number(w) < Number(v) and w is on the stack, set Lowlink$(v) \leftarrow \min[\text{Lowlink}(v), \text{Lowlink}(w)]$, and then go to Step 3.
Otherwise, go directly to Step 3.

Step 5 (Backtrack). Pop v from path.
Set: $u \leftarrow$ vertex on top of path.
Lowlink$(u) \leftarrow \min[\text{Lowlink}(u), \text{Lowlink}(v)]$.
$v \leftarrow u$
Go to Step 3.

Step 6 (Form strong component). Pop v and all vertices above v from stack and place them in current strong component. Pop v from path.
If path is empty go to Step 1.
Otherwise set $v \leftarrow$ vertex on top of path and go to Step 3.

This algorithm requires $O(|V|, |E|)$ space and time. An implementation with a remarkable economy of storage was presented by Gustavson (1976b) where a detailed analysis of operation counts is also given (his sentence 8c on page 287 is wrong due to a misprint; the correct sentence must be $V \leftarrow W$). Gustavson's program works directly on the unordered row-wise representation of the sparse matrix, which in Section 1.8 was shown to be equivalent to the adjacency structure of the corresponding digraph. The program requires that all selfedges, i.e., edges of the form $(v \to v)$, be explicitly present, as is the case with a complete row-wise representation of a matrix. This is equivalent to assuming that a full transversal is known and the matrix is (or can be) permuted in such a way that all diagonal elements are nonzero. This assumption is implicit in all our discussions of depth-first search.

Another excellent implementation was presented by Duff and Reid

(1978b), which incorporates the improvement of the calculation of Lowlink discussed above. A complexity analysis and a comparison with the algorithm of Sargent and Westerberg are also given.

For an example of the application of the algorithm of Tarjan consider the graph of Fig. 5.1(b) and the corresponding jungle shown in Fig. 5.5(a). Vertex 2 is chosen to start and the path 2, 3, 4, 9, 10, 11, 15, 14 is found. The vertices are numbered as indicated by the numbers near the circles. Initially, for each vertex Lowlink is set equal to Number. Then frond (14 → 9) is found and Lowlink(14) is adjusted to Lowlink(9) = 4. Since 14 has no other exits, backtracking takes place to vertex 10, where edge (10 → 14) is discarded, and then to vertex 9. On doing this, Lowlink is set equal to 4 for vertices 15, 11 and 10, which means that none of them is the root of any component. However, when vertex 9 becomes the current vertex, we find that Lowlink(9) = Number(9) = 4, thus 9 is the root of a component. The component consists of vertices 9, 10, 11, 15 and 14, which are currently on top of the stack. This set is removed from the stack to form the component.

Backtracking to vertex 4, we find that Lowlink(4) = Number(4) = 3, thus 4 is the root of another strong component. Vertex 4 is removed from the top of the stack, and backtracking continues to vertex 3, where the path of tree arcs 8, 7, 5, 1 is found. These vertices are numbered and Lowlink is initialized. Then edge (1 → 2) is found and Lowlink(1) is adjusted to 1. This value is carried down to vertex 8 when backtracking takes place. When 8 is the current vertex, the current path is 2, 3, 8, but the current stack is 2, 3, 8, 7, 5, 1. Edge (8 → 9) is discarded because 9 is visited but is not on the stack, edge (8 → 6) is found and Lowlink(6) and Number(6) are both set equal to 13. Then the cross-link (6 → 5) is found, which is known to be active because 5 is visited and is on the stack. Thus, Lowlink(6) is adjusted to Lowlink(5) = 1. Backtracking to vertex 2, the strong component 2, 3, 8, 7, 5, 1, 6 is gathered from the top of the stack.

Now, the first tree is complete, the path and the stack are empty, but not all vertices have been visited. If 12 is chosen to be the next starting vertex, the second tree is obtained, as the reader can easily verify.

5.11. Pivoting strategies for unsymmetric matrices

In this section we consider pivoting strategies for the local minimization of fill-in and number of operations produced by Gauss elimination on a general sparse matrix. The methods are suitable for any matrix **A**, but if **A** is large and known or suspected to be reducible, then it is almost certainly convenient to reduce it to block lower triangular form and then use the methods of this section for each block. All methods are variants of the original strategy proposed by Markowitz (1957). Markowitz's proposition was to take as pivot, at each step, that nonzero for which the product of the number of other nonzeros in the same row and number of other nonzeros in the same column of the active submatrix, is a minimum. This simple heuristic algorithm, combined with some good stability criterion, gives excellent results which outperform other much more sophisticated schemes.

The algorithm of Markowitz is local in the sense that it minimizes fill-in and number of operations at each step, without taking into account the possibility that a different sequence of previous pivots might have produced an even lower overall fill-in and operation count.

The idea of Markowitz and its variants, as well as the principles underlying other related methods, can best be understood with the help of the following picture of Gauss elimination by columns. At the beginning of the kth step we take $A_{kk}^{(k)}$ as pivot and normalize row k of the active submatrix by dividing all its elements by $A_{kk}^{(k)}$. The active submatrix is, as usual, the submatrix situated in rows and columns k through n. The situation at this point is illustrated in Fig. 5.12 for the case $n = 7$, $k = 3$. The vectors $\mathbf{r}$ and $\mathbf{c}$ are of order $n - k$. Consider the matrix $\mathbf{cr}^{\mathrm{T}}$, which is square of order $n - k$ and rank 1 (see Section 2.2). Then, the kth step of Gauss elimination consists of subtracting $\mathbf{cr}^{\mathrm{T}}$ from the submatrix situated in rows and columns $k + 1$ through n. Vector $\mathbf{c}$ becomes the kth subcolumn of $\mathbf{L}$, and $(1, \mathbf{r}^{\mathrm{T}})$ becomes the kth row of $\mathbf{U}$. Let $n(\mathbf{v})$ be the number of nonzeros in a vector $\mathbf{v}$. Markowitz's strategy can now be rephrased as follows: select a nonzero of the active submatrix and bring it to position (k, k) by means of the necessary row and column interchanges, in such a way that $n(\mathbf{c})n(\mathbf{r})$ is a minimum. Since $n(\mathbf{c})n(\mathbf{r})$ is the number of nonzeros in the matrix $\mathbf{cr}^{\mathrm{T}}$, it is now clear in what sense the strategy of Markowitz tends to minimize fill-in locally.

Three remarks must be made. It might be though that the product $n(\mathbf{c})n(\mathbf{r})$ is a minimum when each of the factors is a minimum, so that it would be sufficient to select for pivot the element in the row and the column with the least number of nonzeros. Such an element, however, may be zero, and thus not eligible for pivot. In fact, all chances are that such an element will be zero in many cases because it belongs to a row and to a column with many zeros.

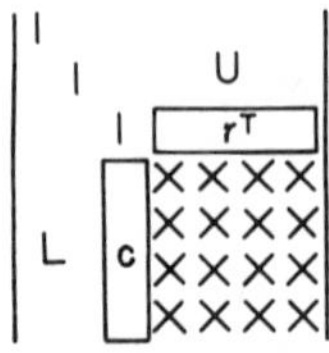

Figure 5.12 Step $k = 3$ of Gauss elimination on a general matrix of order $n = 7$.

The situation becomes worse when numerical stability is taken into account because not only zeros but even nonzeros which are too small are rejected. However, it still remains true that the acceptable nonzero which minimizes the product $n(\mathbf{c})n(\mathbf{r})$ will frequently correspond to *small* $n(\mathbf{c})$ and $n(\mathbf{r})$. Now, $n(\mathbf{c})$ and $n(\mathbf{r})$ are, precisely, the number of off-diagonal nonzeros in column k of $\mathbf{L}$ and row k of $\mathbf{U}$. This makes clear the fact that Markowitz's strategy directly tries to preserve the sparsity of $\mathbf{L}$ and $\mathbf{U}$.

Let C be the set of positions of the nonzeros of the matrix $\mathbf{cr}^{\mathrm{T}}$, and let D be the same set for the submatrix situated in rows and columns $k + 1$ through n of $\mathbf{A}^{(k)}$ (see Fig. 5.12). Usually $C \cap D \neq \emptyset$, so that the set F of fill-ins introduced in $\mathbf{A}^{(k+1)}$ at step k is given by

$$F = C - C \cap D. \tag{5.15}$$

Our second remark is that Markowitz's strategy minimizes $|C| = n(\mathbf{c})n(\mathbf{r})$. $|F|$ is not minimized, but the minimization of $|C|$ tends to reduce $|F|$. It has been suggested to minimize $|F|$ over all eligible nonzeros (Berry, 1971), but such an idea is computationally expensive because $|F|$ has to be computed for each of the candidates, and besides it does not give better results than the plain Markowitz's strategy (Duff and Reid, 1974). On the other hand, $|C| = n(\mathbf{c})n(\mathbf{r})$ is equal to the number of multiplications and additions performed at step k, if a fill-in is counted as an addition. Therefore, the method of Markowitz locally minimizes the number of multiplications and additions. The number of divisions per step is $n(\mathbf{r})$, which is usually small, as we have just explained.

Our third remark concerns the question of stability. Markowitz's strategy alone does not guarantee numerical stability. The following standard statement combines Markowitz's strategy with some of the stability criteria discussed in Section 3.6: at each stage, select for pivot, from all nonzeros of the active submatrix which satisfy the desired stability criterion, the one which minimizes $n(\mathbf{c})n(\mathbf{r})$. The standard stability criterion is threshold pivoting. In terms of the sets defined in Section 3.6: S_{pc} contains all nonzeros of the active submatrix; S_{st} contains those elements of S_{pc} which meet the desired stability condition; S_{sp} is a subset of S_{st}, determined by Markowitz's condition, and may in general contain more than one nonzero. Finally, the pivot is any element of $S_{\mathrm{piv}} \equiv S_{\mathrm{sp}}$.

As pointed out by Duff (1981a), one of the strengths of Markowitz's ordering lies on its symmetry, where symmetry means that the same ordering is obtained for either $\mathbf{A}$ or $\mathbf{A}^{\mathrm{T}}$ disregarding the effect of ties and the stability criterion. The cost of Markowitz's algorithm depends strongly on the size of S_{st} at each step, since $n(\mathbf{c})n(\mathbf{r})$ must be computed for each element in S_{st}. Duff has proposed a cheaper strategy, called r_i *in* c_j or *minrow-within-mincolumn*. This strategy, however, lacks symmetry. It is as follows: at each step, select the column with the least number of nonzeros. Then among the nonzeros of that column which satisfy the desired stability condition, select the one in the row with the least number of nonzeros. Here, S_{pc} contains all nonzeros of the active submatrix, S_{sp} is the column with fewest nonzeros, S_{st} is a subset of S_{sp} determined by the stability condition, and $S_{piv} \equiv S_{st}$. The final pivot is chosen from S_{piv} using further sparsity considerations. This criterion can do much worse than Markowitz's in some cases, as shown by Duff (1981a, p. 9). It can be symmetrized if some price is paid: at each step, do r_i in c_j, and then independently c_k in r_l (i.e., select the row with fewest nonzeros, say l; select the nonzeros in row l which meet the stability condition, and select the nonzero in the row k with fewest nonzeros). Finally, from the two resulting pivots take that one which minimizes $n(\mathbf{c})n(\mathbf{r})$.

A few other pivoting strategies exist, but none seems to be significantly better. The different methods were tested numerically by a number of authors. A survey of this material was published by Duff (1977, p. 505). An interesting generalization of Markowitz's strategy is Zlatev's strategy, discussed in Section 3.6.

The method of Markowitz requires for its implementation the use of two integer arrays, say NR and NC, initialized with the number of off-diagonal nonzeros in each row and column of **A**, respectively. NR and NC are updated when fill-ins and eliminations occur; the procedure is similar to that employed for the minimum degree algorithm (Section 4.8). The method is difficult to implement when the active submatrix is in backing store and only part of it can be brought to main memory. An alternative (Duff and Reid, 1974; Reid, 1977) is to order the columns of **A** initially and to process them in that order, without performing any column interchanges. From a number of possible strategies for choosing the initial order, it was found that ordering the columns by increasing number of nonzeros is as satisfactory as any other possibility. At each step, row interchanges are performed, selecting for pivot the nonzero in the pivotal column which satisfies the desired stability condition and has the least number of nonzeros in its *original* row in the matrix **A**. This selection is necessary because the number of nonzeros in the rows of the active submatrix is not being updated, but it was found that it gives satisfactory results. Other *a priori* orderings were surveyed by Duff (1977).

5.12. Other methods and availabe software

The method of Martin and Wilkinson (1967) for unsymmetric band matrices preserves the original ordering of the columns and selects pivots from the pivotal column by means of row interchanges. The lower semiband remains the same and the upper can at worst double. This method is related with the *a priori* ordering of Duff and Reid discussed at the end of Section 5.11.

A brief description of the finite element method and of the frontal ordering scheme in the symmetric positive definite case was given in Section 4.14. The frontal method was extended to the general case by Hood (1976). We make reference to Fig. 4.22 of Chapter 4. Hood's idea is to delay elimination until the partially assembled submatrix reaches its maximum permitted size, and then to use complete pivoting in the fully assembled submatrix. The idea was generalized by Cliffe *et al.* (1978), who suggested using threshold pivoting in the fully assembled submatrix and performing an elimination step as soon as an acceptable pivot becomes available. Since the nonzero selected for pivot belongs to the fully assembled submatrix ($G - G$ in Fig. 4.22), the corresponding row and column also are fully assembled, and the necessary interchanges can be performed. The eliminations are only slightly delayed, and the front grows only slightly beyond the size it would have if eliminations were performed as soon as a row and column become fully assembled, without any pivoting. A subroutine employing this method is available under the name MA32AD (Hopper, 1980). Duff (1980b) and Reid (1981) suggest using block diagonal pivoting (Section 3.6) in the same way when the frontal method is used for the symmetric indefinite case.

The reader who is interested in obtaining software for solving sparse unsymmetric or symmetric indefinite linear equations, can consult the Software Catalog (Heath, 1982), or the Harwell Catalogue (Hopper, 1980), or particularly Duff (1980a), where the existence of a version of the package for complex equations is announced.

CHAPTER 6

Sparse Eigenanalysis

6.1. Introduction

The standard eigenvalue problem is defined by

$$\mathbf{A}\mathbf{x} = \lambda\mathbf{x} \tag{6.1}$$

where **A** is the given n by n matrix. It is desired to find the *eigenpairs* $(\lambda, \mathbf{x})$ of **A**, where λ is an *eigenvalue* and **x** is the corresponding *eigenvector*. The generalized eigenvalue problem is

$$\mathbf{A}\mathbf{x} = \lambda\mathbf{B}\mathbf{x} \tag{6.2}$$

where **A** and **B** are given n by n matrices and again we wish to determine λ and **x**. For historical reasons the pair **A**, **B** is called a *pencil* (Gantmacher, 1959). When $\mathbf{B} = \mathbf{I}$ the generalized problem reduces to the standard one.

Both for simplicity and to follow the general trend imposed by most of the literature and existing software, we restrict the analysis to the case where **A** is real symmetric and **B** is real symmetric and positive definite, except when stated otherwise. Almost all the results become valid for hermitian matrices when the conjugate transpose superscript H is written in place of the transpose superscript T. On the other hand, an eigenvalue problem where **A** or **A** and **B**, are hermitian, can be solved using software for real matrices (Section 6.15).

Equation (6.1) has a nonzero solution **x** when

$$\operatorname{Det}(\mathbf{A} - \lambda \mathbf{I}) = 0. \tag{6.3}$$

This is a polynomial equation of the nth degree in λ, which has n roots λ_1, $\lambda_2, \ldots, \lambda_n$. The roots are the eigenvalues of **A**, and they may be either all different or there may be multiple roots with any *multiplicity*. When **A** is real symmetric, the eigenvalues are all real. The simplest example is the identity matrix **I**, which has an eigenvalue equal to 1 with multiplicity n. To each eigenvalue λ_i of **A**, there corresponds a nonzero real solution $\mathbf{x}_i$ of Equation (6.1). The n linearly independent solutions are the eigenvectors of **A**. If $\mathbf{x}_i$ is an eigenvector, clearly $\alpha\mathbf{x}_i$ is also an eigenvector for any real number α, so that we may always assume that the eigenvectors are normalized. Eigenvectors which belong to different eigenvalues are orthogonal to each other. An eigenvalue of multiplicity m has m eigenvectors which are not unique but which can be *chosen* as mutually orthogonal. If **X** is the n by n matrix of which the columns are the n eigenvectors defined in this way, we reach the conclusion that **X** is orthogonal, or

$$\mathbf{X}^{\mathrm{T}} = \mathbf{X}^{-1}. \tag{6.4}$$

Equation (6.1) can now be written $\mathbf{AX} = \mathbf{X\Lambda}$, where $\mathbf{\Lambda}$ is the diagonal n by n matrix of which the elements are the eigenvalues of **A** in ordered correspondence with the columns of **X**. Using (6.4), the unique *spectral factorization* of **A** is obtained:

$$\mathbf{A} = \mathbf{X\Lambda X}^{\mathrm{T}} \tag{6.5}$$

Clearly, also $\mathbf{X}^{\mathrm{T}}\mathbf{AX} = \mathbf{\Lambda}$; this is an *orthogonal similarity* or *congruence* transformation of **A** into the diagonal matrix $\mathbf{\Lambda}$. Other transformations of **A** are possible, which preserve the eigenvalues. If **G** is any n by n orthogonal matrix, i.e. $\mathbf{G}^{\mathrm{T}} = \mathbf{G}^{-1}$, the standard eigenproblem, Equation (6.1), can be written

$$(\mathbf{GAG}^{\mathrm{T}})(\mathbf{Gx}) = \lambda(\mathbf{Gx}). \tag{6.6}$$

Defining $\mathbf{A}' = \mathbf{GAG}^{\mathrm{T}}$, this shows that if $(\lambda, \mathbf{x})$ is an eigenpair of **A**, then $(\lambda, \mathbf{Gx})$ is an eigenpair of $\mathbf{A}'$.

Similar results hold for the generalized eigenproblem, Equation (6.2). Equation (6.2) has a nonzero solution $\mathbf{x}$ when λ satisfies

$$\text{Det}\,(\mathbf{A} - \lambda\mathbf{B}) = 0. \tag{6.7}$$

When $\mathbf{A}$ and $\mathbf{B}$ are real symmetric and $\mathbf{B}$ is positive definite, Equation (6.7) has n real solutions λ_i, $i = 1, 2, \ldots, n$, either simple or multiple, to each of which there corresponds a real eigenvector $\mathbf{x}_i$. The pairs $(\lambda_i, \mathbf{x}_i)$ are the eigenpairs of the pencil $\mathbf{A}, \mathbf{B}$. The n eigenvectors are linearly independent and can be $\mathbf{B}$-normalized, i.e., multiplied by a constant such that $\mathbf{x}_i^{\mathrm{T}}\mathbf{B}\mathbf{x}_i = 1$. Eigenvectors which belong to different eigenvalues are $\mathbf{B}$-orthogonal: $\mathbf{x}_i^{\mathrm{T}}\mathbf{B}\mathbf{x}_j = 0$ if $\lambda_i \neq \lambda_j$, and eigenvectors which belong to a multiple eigenvalue may be chosen to be $\mathbf{B}$-orthogonal. The matrix $\mathbf{X}$ of which the columns are the eigenvectors chosen in this way satisfies

$$\mathbf{X}^{\mathrm{T}}\mathbf{B}\mathbf{X} = \mathbf{I}, \tag{6.8}$$

and the generalized eigenproblem can be written $\mathbf{AX} = \mathbf{BX\Lambda}$, where $\mathbf{\Lambda}$ is the diagonal matrix of eigenvalues.

Let $\mathbf{G}$ be any invertible n by n matrix. $\mathbf{G}$ need not be orthogonal or $\mathbf{B}$-orthogonal. Let $\mathbf{A}' = \mathbf{G}^{\mathrm{T}}\mathbf{A}\mathbf{G}$ and $\mathbf{B}' = \mathbf{G}^{\mathrm{T}}\mathbf{B}\mathbf{G}$. The generalized eigenproblem, Equation (6.2), can be written:

$$(\mathbf{G}^{\mathrm{T}}\mathbf{A}\mathbf{G})(\mathbf{G}^{-1}\mathbf{x}) = \lambda(\mathbf{G}^{\mathrm{T}}\mathbf{B}\mathbf{G})(\mathbf{G}^{-1}\mathbf{x}) \tag{6.9}$$

which shows that, if $(\lambda, \mathbf{x})$ is an eigenpair of $\mathbf{A}, \mathbf{B}$, then $(\lambda, \mathbf{G}^{-1}\mathbf{x})$ is an eigenpair of $\mathbf{A}', \mathbf{B}'$. $\mathbf{A}, \mathbf{B}$ and $\mathbf{A}', \mathbf{B}'$ are *congruent pencils*. There exist many matrices $\mathbf{G}$ such that $\mathbf{A}', \mathbf{B}'$ are both diagonal; in particular, with $\mathbf{G} = \mathbf{X}$ and using Equation (6.8), the generalized eigenproblem reduces to $\mathbf{X}^{\mathrm{T}}\mathbf{A}\mathbf{X} = \mathbf{\Lambda}$.

The generalized eigenproblem can be converted to standard form. The simplest way is to write Equation (6.2) as follows:

$$\mathbf{B}^{-1}\mathbf{A}\mathbf{x} = \lambda\mathbf{x}, \tag{6.10}$$

where $\mathbf{B}^{-1}$ exists because we have assumed that $\mathbf{B}$ is positive definite. $\mathbf{B}^{-1}\mathbf{A}$ is neither symmetric nor sparse, and the form (6.10) is not recommended for large sparse $\mathbf{A}$ and $\mathbf{B}$ if $\mathbf{B}^{-1}\mathbf{A}$ is to be formed explicitly. Equation (6.10) is convenient when it is used implicitly, in combination with a method which only requires the ability to multiply a matrix by a vector efficiently: if $\mathbf{u}$ is any vector and we need $\mathbf{w} = \mathbf{B}^{-1}\mathbf{A}\mathbf{u}$, we form $\mathbf{v} = \mathbf{A}\mathbf{u}$ and then solve $\mathbf{B}\mathbf{w} = \mathbf{v}$ for $\mathbf{w}$. When the Cholesky factorization $\mathbf{B} = \mathbf{U}_B^{\mathrm{T}}\mathbf{U}_B$ can be computed, Equation (6.2) can be written as follows:

$$(\mathbf{U}_B^{-\mathrm{T}}\mathbf{A}\mathbf{U}_B^{-1})(\mathbf{U}_B\mathbf{x}) = \lambda(\mathbf{U}_B\mathbf{x}). \tag{6.11}$$

Alternatively, when $\mathbf{A}$ is positive definite and the factorization $\mathbf{A} = \mathbf{U}_A^{\mathrm{T}}\mathbf{U}_A$

can be obtained, Equation (6.2) takes the form:

$$(\mathbf{U}_A^{-T}\mathbf{B}\mathbf{U}_A^{-1})(\mathbf{U}_A\mathbf{x}) = \frac{1}{\lambda}(\mathbf{U}_A\mathbf{x}). \tag{6.12}$$

Both Equations (6.11) and (6.12) preserve symmetry, but this property is not very important for large sparse matrices because both forms are usually implicitly used.

It is well known that equations like (6.3) or (6.7) cannot be solved algebraically when $n > 4$. As a consequence, eigenvalue problems with $n > 4$ can be solved exclusively by iterative procedures. Before the iterations start, the given eigenproblem can be modified or reduced to a simpler form for which the iterations require less work per step, converge faster, and are numerically more stable. The reduction itself usually takes an appreciable amount of computation, a fact which must be considered by the user. As a general criterion, reduction may be worthwhile for large sparse matrices only in some cases where many eigenpairs are required. It is important to establish a clear distinction between methods which modify the given eigenproblem and methods which actually solve the eigenproblem by performing the iterations.

Among the iterative methods employed to solve an eigenproblem there are some which use the given matrices only for computing products with the vectors of a sequence. These methods are, generally speaking, the best choice for large sparse matrices. It is very unlikely that the complete eigensystem of a large matrix be needed. The set of eigenvectors is the full n by n matrix $\mathbf{X}$. The usual requirements are: (i) to compute some eigenvalues in an interval or at the extremes of the spectrum, or (ii) to compute some eigenpairs, or (iii) to compute many or all eigenvalues and no eigenvectors. The properties of each method determine its field of application.

All the methods are well established and extensively documented in the literature. The acknowledged leading treatise is Wilkinson's "The Algebraic Eigenvalue Problem" (1965). An excellent and modern book is "The Symmetric Eigenvalue Problem" by Parlett (1980). Anyone involved in eigenanalysis should read Parlett's book. Also recommended is the review by Stewart (1976a), although it is already partially out of date. The eigenanalysis of small dense matrices is an essentially solved problem because very efficient programs exist, which are automatic in the sense that no user specified parameters are required and the programs can be used as a black box. The basic algorithms are given in the Handbook (Wilkinson and Reinsch, 1971), and the most renowned and carefully tested Fortran versions were published in the two EISPACK guides (Smith *et al.*, 1976; Garbow *et al.*, 1977).

Evidence shows that a comparable degree of sophistication will soon be achieved for large sparse matrices. EISPACK programs cannot be applied in this field, except for large band and tridiagonal matrices, which are particular classes of sparse matrices. Sparse eigenanalysis has motivated a considerable theoretical effort. [See for example the article by Ruhe (1977), the survey of eigenvalue methods for structural vibration by Jennings (1981), and Section 5 of the survey of sparse matrix software by Duff (1982).] The book by Cullum and Willoughby (1983) is devoted to the Lanczos algorithm, considered as the most promising method for large matrices. The first good programs, however, have become available only recently. The Catalog (Heath, 1982) lists 123 general purpose sparse matrix programs, only ten of which are devoted to solving large eigenvalue problems. In this chapter we cover those aspects and methods of solution of large eigenproblems which take advantage of sparseness. Some available software is listed at the end of each section.

Before the eigenproblem is solved numerically, it may be convenient to balance the given matrix **A** to improve the accuracy of the computed eigenvalues and/or eigenvectors. A usual procedure is to apply a similarity transformation

$$\mathbf{A}' = \mathbf{D}^{-1}\mathbf{A}\mathbf{D},$$

where **D** is a diagonal matrix such that the absolute sums of the magnitudes of the elements in corresponding rows and columns of **A**′ are nearly equal. **D** can be determined iteratively with the additional restriction that its diagonal elements be powers of the radix of the floating point arithmetic of the machine in order to prevent the introduction of round-off errors. The procedure was discussed by Parlett and Reinsch (1969) and is implemented in EISPACK.

6.2. The Rayleigh quotient

Numerical methods only provide approximate results. If an approximation **x** for an eigenvector of **A** is available, is it possible to compute an approximation to the corresponding eigenvalue? First, we quote the following result: for any nonzero vector **x** and any real number σ define $s = |\mathbf{Ax} - \sigma\mathbf{x}|/|\mathbf{x}|$; then there exists an eigenvalue λ of **A** in the interval $[\sigma - s, \sigma + s]$, or:

$$\sigma - s \leqslant \lambda \leqslant \sigma + s. \tag{6.13}$$

The width of the interval is $2s$, and it depends on σ. The width is minimized when σ is chosen in such a way that the *residual vector* $\mathbf{r} = \mathbf{Ax} - \sigma\mathbf{x}$ is perpendicular to **x**, as the two-dimensional example of Fig. 6.1 shows. This

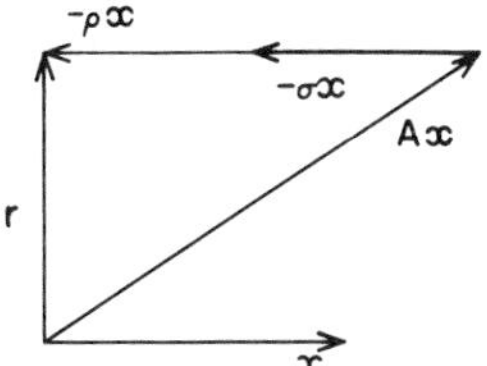

Figure 6.1 Two-dimensional example of a minimized residual vector.

particular value of σ is the *Rayleigh quotient* $\rho(\mathbf{x})$. From $\mathbf{x}^T\mathbf{r} = 0$ is obtained:

$$\rho(\mathbf{x}) = \frac{\mathbf{x}^T\mathbf{A}\mathbf{x}}{\mathbf{x}^T\mathbf{x}}. \tag{6.14}$$

The Rayleigh quotient is the best approximation to an eigenvalue of $\mathbf{A}$ which can be obtained from the available information.

For any nonzero $\mathbf{x}$, $\rho(\mathbf{x})$ has the following property:

$$\lambda_{\min} \leqslant \rho(\mathbf{x}) \leqslant \lambda_{\max}, \tag{6.15}$$

where $\lambda_{\min}$ and $\lambda_{\max}$ are the minimum and the maximum eigenvalues of $\mathbf{A}$, respectively. Equation (6.15) is the basis of a method for finding extreme eigenvalues by maximizing or minimizing the Rayleigh quotient $\rho(\mathbf{x})$ over all normalized $\mathbf{x}$. The conjugate gradient algorithm can be used for this purpose, see for example Geradin (1971) or Longsine and McCormick (1981), who simultaneously minimize several Rayleigh quotients. *Coordinate relaxation* is one of the methods most commonly used to minimize a Rayleigh quotient. If $\mathbf{x}_k$ is the current approximation to an eigenvector, the new iterate is $\mathbf{x}_{k+1} = \mathbf{x}_k + \alpha\mathbf{e}_j$, obtained from $\mathbf{x}_k$ by simply adding α to its jth component. The value of α is chosen in such a way that $\rho(\mathbf{x}_{k+1})$ is minimized. In practice, convergence is made faster using *coordinate over-relaxation*, where $\mathbf{x}_{k+1} = \mathbf{x}_k + \beta\alpha\mathbf{e}_j$, α is such that $\rho(\mathbf{x}_k + \alpha\mathbf{e}_j)$ is minimum, and β is the *over-relaxation parameter*, usually in the range $1 \leqslant \beta \leqslant 2$. A survey of relaxation methods is found in Ruhe (1977). Schwartz (1977) iterates several vectors simultaneously.

The extension to the generalized eigenproblem, Equation (6.2), is performed as follows. Let $|\mathbf{u}|_{\mathbf{B}^{-1}} = (\mathbf{u}^T\mathbf{B}^{-1}\mathbf{u})^{1/2}$ for any vector $\mathbf{u}$. For any nonzero vector $\mathbf{x}$ and any real number σ define $s = |\mathbf{A}\mathbf{x} - \sigma\mathbf{B}\mathbf{x}|_{\mathbf{B}^{-1}}/|\mathbf{B}\mathbf{x}|_{\mathbf{B}^{-1}}$; then there exists an eigenvalue λ of the pencil $\mathbf{A}$, $\mathbf{B}$ in the interval $[\sigma - s, \sigma + s]$, or:

$$\sigma - s \leqslant \lambda \leqslant \sigma + s. \tag{6.16}$$

For any nonzero $\mathbf{x}$ the Rayleigh quotient is:

$$\rho(\mathbf{x}) = \frac{\mathbf{x}^T\mathbf{A}\mathbf{x}}{\mathbf{x}^T\mathbf{B}\mathbf{x}} \tag{6.17}$$

and has the property that

$$\lambda_{min} \leqslant \rho(\mathbf{x}) \leqslant \lambda_{max}, \tag{6.18}$$

where λ_{min}, λ_{max} are the extreme eigenvalues of **A**, **B**. For **x** and σ given, the residual vector is $\mathbf{r} = \mathbf{Ax} - \sigma\mathbf{Bx}$, and it has the property that $\mathbf{r}^T\mathbf{x} = 0$ when $\sigma = \rho(\mathbf{x})$. The methods of Rayleigh quotient minimization readily extend to the generalized eigenproblem, see for example Schwartz (1977), or the new techniques developed by Longsine and McCormick (1981), where the Rayleigh quotient is minimized over several independent vectors simultaneously.

The concept of a scalar Rayleigh quotient can be generalized to that of a *Rayleigh matrix*, giving rise to the Rayleigh–Ritz approximation procedure, extensively used in the eigenanalysis of sparse matrices. This point is examined in Section 6.9.

6.3. Bounds for eigenvalues

There are several ways for obtaining bounds of eigenvalues. We first introduce three norms for an n by n real matrix **A**, two of which were already used in Chapter 3:

(1) 1-norm $\quad \|\mathbf{A}\|_1 = \max_j \sum_{i=1}^{n} |A_{ij}|$

(2) ∞-norm $\quad \|\mathbf{A}\|_\infty = \max_i \sum_{j=1}^{n} |A_{ij}|$

(3) Euclidean norm $\quad \|\mathbf{A}\|_E = \left(\sum_{i,j=1}^{n} A_{ij}^2 \right)^{1/2}$

Then, if λ is an eigenvalue of **A**, and $\|\mathbf{A}\|$ is any of the norms just introduced:

$$|\lambda| \leqslant \|\mathbf{A}\|. \tag{6.19}$$

Similarly, for the general eigenvalue problem, when λ is an eigenvalue of the symmetric pencil **A**, **B** and **B** is positive definite:

$$|\lambda| \leqslant \|\mathbf{B}^{-1}\mathbf{A}\| \tag{6.20}$$

The theorems of Gerschgorin (1931) are also convenient for obtaining bounds, and sometimes even to isolate intervals which contain a known quantity of eigenvalues. To each row of **A** we associate a *Gerschgorin disc* with centre A_{ii} and radius $\sum_{j \neq i} |A_{ij}|$. The discs are in general defined in the complex plane, although when the eigenvalues are real we can restrict the discs to the real axis and define the *Gerschgorin intervals*. The theorems establish that every eigenvalue of **A** lies in at least one of the discs, and that if s discs form a connected domain which is isolated from the remaining discs, then this domain contains exactly s eigenvalues of **A**. Although when **A** is large it is unlikely that the discs will define disjoint domains, in particular when **A** is conveniently balanced, these theorems usually provide stronger bounds than Equation (6.19) and are cheap to use.

The Rayleigh quotient provides a way for obtaining bounds for the minimum and the maximum eigenvalues of a symmetric **A**. Equation (6.15) can be used with different vectors **y**. For example, taking for **y** the columns of **I** it is easy to obtain that $\lambda_{\min} \leqslant \min_i (A_{ii})$ and $\lambda_{\max} \geqslant \max_i (A_{ii})$. A lower bound for $\lambda_{\min}$ and an upper bound for $\lambda_{\max}$ can be obtained from the Gerschgorin intervals, or from the two values of the following expression (Parlett, 1964):

$$\frac{1}{n}\{t \pm [(n-1)(n\|\mathbf{A}\|_E^2 - t^2)]^{1/2}\}$$

where $t = \sum_i A_{ii}$ is the trace of **A**. This expression is based on Laguerre's iteration for the characteristic polynomial.

It is useful to recall the following elementary properties. If $\{\lambda_i\}$ is the set of eigenvalues of **A**, then:

$$\sum_i \lambda_i = \sum_i A_{ii} \qquad \text{(the trace)}$$

$$\sum_i \lambda_i^2 = \|\mathbf{A}\|_E^2$$

$$\prod_i \lambda_i = \mathrm{Det}(\mathbf{A}) \qquad \text{(the determinant)}$$

In the next section we will discuss the method of bisection, which can also be used to set bounds for eigenvalues.

As an example, consider the following matrix, which was already used as an example in Section 2.13:

$$\mathbf{A} = \begin{vmatrix} 2 & 1 & 1 \\ 1 & 3 & 2 \\ 1 & 2 & 4 \end{vmatrix}.$$

Let the three eigenvalues be $\lambda_1 \leqslant \lambda_2 \leqslant \lambda_3$.

The norms are $\|\mathbf{A}\|_1 = \|\mathbf{A}\|_\infty = 7$, $\|\mathbf{A}\|_E = \sqrt{41} = 6.4031\ldots$, thus $-6.404 < \lambda_1, \lambda_2, \lambda_3 < 6.404$. The Gerschgorin intervals are (0, 4), (0, 6) and

(1, 7), which all overlap and form the connected interval (0, 7), thus $0 \leqslant \lambda_1$, λ_2, $\lambda_3 \leqslant 7$. By examination of the diagonal elements we notice that $\lambda_1 \leqslant 2$ and $\lambda_3 \geqslant 4$. From Laguerre's iteration we obtain $-0.056 < \lambda_1, \lambda_2, \lambda_3 < 6.056$. The Rayleigh quotients for the vectors (1, 1, 0), (1, 0, 1), (0, 1, 1) and (1, 1, 1) are respectively, 3.5, 4, 5.5 and 5.666 ... Taking all these bounds into account:

$$0 \leqslant \lambda_1 \leqslant 2,$$

$$5.666 < \lambda_3 < 6.056.$$

The determinant is 13, the trace is 9, and the eigenvalues are $\lambda_1 = 1.307979$, $\lambda_2 = 1.643104$, $\lambda_3 = 6.048917$, which fulfil all the required relations. **A** is positive definite because all its eigenvalues are positive. Symmetric matrices with a prescribed set of "nice" eigenvalues and eigenvectors, useful for examples, can easily be constructed (Heuvers, 1982).

6.4. The bisection method for eigenvalue calculations

For the general eigenproblem with symmetric **A** and **B**, as well as for the standard eigenproblem with symmetric **A**, it is possible to compute the number of eigenvalues that are less than a given number σ. The procedure is based in Sylvester's inertia theorem (see, e.g., Schwartz, 1977). For the general eigenproblem, Equation (6.2) with **B** positive definite, assume that σ is given and that the factorization $\mathbf{A} - \sigma\mathbf{B} = \mathbf{U}^T\mathbf{D}\mathbf{U}$ can be obtained, where **U** is upper triangular with unit diagonal. Then, the number of eigenvalues less than σ is equal to the number of negative elements of the diagonal matrix **D**. The same statement holds for the standard eigenproblem with $\mathbf{B} \equiv \mathbf{I}$. Note that $\mathbf{A} - \sigma\mathbf{B}$ is symmetric but not positive definite, in general.

The number

$$d_j = \prod_{i=1}^{j} D_{ii}$$

is the determinant of the leading principal j by j submatrix of $\mathbf{A} - \sigma\mathbf{B}$. The sequence $\{d_0 \equiv 1, d_1, \ldots, d_n\}$ is the *Sturm sequence* evaluated for the given σ. Clearly, two consecutive terms of the sequence have different signs when the corresponding D_{ii} is negative, which in turn corresponds to an eigenvalue less than σ. Thus sign disagreements in the Sturm sequence can be used to count eigenvalues less than σ. Sturm sequences are not used for sparse matrices in general because the diagonal matrix **D** obtained from the factorization already contains the necessary information. Their use is restricted to the standard eigenproblem with tridiagonal **A**, because there exists a recurrence relation which allows the calculation of the sequence without factorizing **A** (Wilkinson, 1965, p. 300).

The method of bisection (Barth *et al.*, 1967) uses these properties for finding real eigenvalues. An interval $[\alpha, \beta]$ which contains all the eigenvalues can be found by the methods of Section 6.3. Then we can take $\sigma = (\alpha + \beta)/2$ and find how many of the eigenvalues are less than σ and how many are greater than σ. Note that if σ happens to be equal to an eigenvalue, $\mathbf{A} - \sigma\mathbf{B}$ will be singular and this fact will be detected during the factorization. Repeating the process we can locate any desired eigenvalue with an accuracy given by $(\beta - \alpha)/2^k$ in k steps. Alternatively, when we know beforehand that the desired eigenvalue lies in a given interval, we can improve the accuracy using bisection. The method should be considered for large sparse **A** and **B** when not too many eigenvalues are needed. One evident limitation is that eigenvectors cannot be computed, but when the eigenvalues are known with some accuracy, not necessarily high, the method of inverse iteration (Section 6.8) can be used both to improve the eigenvalues and to compute the eigenvectors. Bisection is implemented in EISPACK (Smith *et al.*, 1976) for tridiagonal matrices only, and also is the combination with inverse iteration.

For an example of bisection, consider the matrix **A** of the preceding section. For $\sigma = 3$ the factorization is:

$$\mathbf{A} - 3\mathbf{I} = \overset{\mathbf{U}^{\mathrm{T}}}{\begin{vmatrix} 1 & & \\ -1 & 1 & \\ -1 & 3 & 1 \end{vmatrix}} \overset{\mathbf{D}}{\begin{vmatrix} -1 & & \\ & 1 & \\ & & -7 \end{vmatrix}} \overset{\mathbf{U}}{\begin{vmatrix} 1 & -1 & -1 \\ & 1 & 3 \\ & & 1 \end{vmatrix}}$$

Thus, **A** has two eigenvalues less than 3.

6.5. Reduction of a general matrix

It has been mentioned before that a given eigenproblem can often be reduced to a simpler form before starting the iterative solution. Reduction is usually achieved by means of a congruence transformation, Equation (6.6) for the standard eigenproblem or Equation (6.9) for the generalized eigenproblem. The reduced form is symmetric *tridiagonal* when the original matrix is symmetric, or *upper Hessenberg* when the original matrix is unsymmetric. Let us examine the definitions and procedures in more detail.

A matrix **C** is *tridiagonal* when it has nonzeros only on the diagonal, the first upper codiagonal (or superdiagonal) and the first lower codiagonal (or subdiagonal); i.e., $C_{ij} = 0$ when $|j - i| > 1$. A matrix **C** is of *upper Hessenberg* or *upper almost-triangular* form if it has nonzeros only in its upper triangle, diagonal and subdiagonal, i.e., if $C_{ij} = 0$ when $j < i - 1$. A symmetric Hessenberg matrix is necessarily tridiagonal, but a tridiagonal matrix may, in general, be either symmetric or not.

In n-dimensional space, the *i, j-plane* is the set of points spanned by the unit vectors $\mathbf{e}_i$ and $\mathbf{e}_j$: $\{\mathbf{x} = \alpha\mathbf{e}_i + \beta\mathbf{e}_j | \alpha, \beta$ any real numbers$\}$, and $\mathbf{e}_i$ is the ith column of the identity matrix $\mathbf{I}$. Consider the matrix $\mathbf{R}(i, j, \theta)$, which is the identity matrix $\mathbf{I}$ except for the following elements (for $i < j$):

$$R_{ii} = R_{jj} = \cos\theta \equiv \gamma$$

$$-R_{ij} = R_{ji} = \sin\theta \equiv \sigma. \tag{6.25}$$

$\mathbf{R}$ (i, j, θ) is elementary (Section 2.2) and orthogonal, i.e., $\mathbf{R}^{-1} = \mathbf{R}^{\mathrm{T}}$. It represents a *plane rotation* on the i, j-plane through an angle θ. A sequence of plane rotations can be used to transform any symmetric $\mathbf{A}$ into tridiagonal form. Consider the orthogonal similarity:

$$\mathbf{A} \rightarrow \mathbf{B} = \mathbf{R}(i, j, \theta)^{\mathrm{T}}\mathbf{A}\mathbf{R}(i, j, \theta). \tag{6.26}$$

$\mathbf{B}$ is symmetric and similar to $\mathbf{A}$. Furthermore, $\mathbf{B}$ is identical to $\mathbf{A}$ except for its lines i and j (a *line* is either a row or a column). Some convenient element of either of these lines (and the corresponding symmetric element) can be made to vanish by taking the appropriate value of the rotation angle θ. If the annihilated elements are A_{ij} and A_{ji} the transformation is a *Jacobi rotation*, otherwise it is a *Givens rotation*. The reduction to tridiagonal form is achieved by means of a sequence of rotations, each of which introduces a new pair of zeros. Provided the rotations are carried out in a convenient order, the zeros introduced by previous rotations will not be destroyed. An extension of Jacobi rotations exists for the generalized eigenproblem with $\mathbf{A}$ symmetric and $\mathbf{B}$ symmetric positive definite, in which the i, j elements of both $\mathbf{A}$ and $\mathbf{B}$ are annihilated by a single congruence transformation.

The same technique can be applied to any general matrix $\mathbf{A}$. In this case, the rotations are used to annihilate elements in the lower triangle, and an upper Hessenberg form is obtained. Each rotation requires that a square root be calculated to obtain γ and σ, and four multiplications are necessary to modify each pair of elements of lines i and j. An improved procedure, called *fast Givens rotations*, which avoids the square root and requires only two multiplications per pair of elements, was proposed by Hammerling (1974) and is very clearly explained by Parlett (1980, p. 100).

Householder's reflections can also be used to reduce a general matrix to upper Hessenberg form, or a symmetric matrix to tridiagonal form. In n-space, a hyperplane is characterized by a vector $\mathbf{u}$ normal to it, and is defined as $\{\mathbf{x} | \mathbf{u}^{\mathrm{T}}\mathbf{x} = 0\}$ (note the difference with the definition of an i, j-plane). A *reflector* or *Householder's matrix* $\mathbf{H}$ is an elementary, orthogonal matrix which reverses $\mathbf{u}$, i.e., $\mathbf{Hu} = -\mathbf{u}$, and leaves any normal vector $\mathbf{x}$ invariant, i.e., $\mathbf{Hx} = \mathbf{x}$ if $\mathbf{u}^T\mathbf{x} = 0$. Then, given any vector $\mathbf{b}$, the hyperplane can be chosen in such a way that $\mathbf{Hb} = \pm|\mathbf{b}|\mathbf{e}_1$, namely:

$$\mathbf{H} = \mathbf{I} - 2\frac{\mathbf{uu}^T}{\mathbf{u}^T\mathbf{u}} \tag{6.27}$$

where

$$\mathbf{u} = \mathbf{b} \mp |\mathbf{b}|\mathbf{e}_1. \tag{6.28}$$

This property is used to annihilate all the appropriate elements of a row with a single reflection. Reflections are more effective than rotations when the given matrix $\mathbf{A}$ is dense and can be stored in main memory. Note, however, that if $\mathbf{w}$ is any vector, then:

$$\mathbf{Hw} = \mathbf{w} - 2\frac{\mathbf{u}^T\mathbf{w}}{\mathbf{u}^T\mathbf{u}}\mathbf{u}, \tag{6.29}$$

which shows that the effect of $\mathbf{H}$ on $\mathbf{A}$ is to subtract a multiple of $\mathbf{u}$ from every column $\mathbf{w}$ of $\mathbf{A}$.

The Algol procedure for symmetric matrices was given and discussed in detail by Martin *et al.* (1968). The Fortran translation is given in EISPACK (Smith *et al.*, 1976) under the names TRED1 and TRED2. For general matrices, the Algol procedure was given by Martin and Wilkinson (1968) and its translation into Fortran is in EISPACK under the name ORTHES. The main application is for small dense matrices. Both rotations and reflections form numerous linear combinations between the lines of $\mathbf{A}$. This is highly unsatisfactory from the point of view of sparseness. When a certain pivotal sequence is given, reflections never produce less fill-in than rotations, and Gaussian similarity transformations are the best (Duff and Reid, 1975). Various pivot ordering for rotations were analysed by Duff (1974b) and Rudolphi (1973). These methods, however, should be considered for very sparse unsymmetric matrices, and Givens rotations have found an important application in the reduction of banded matrices, which is the subject of the next section. Givens rotations are also used for the solution of sparse linear least squares problems (see George and Heath, 1981). Pivotal strategies for plane rotations were considered by Zlatev (1982), and the approach presented was found to be very efficient for some rectangular matrices.

6.6. Reduction of a symmetric band matrix to tridiagonal form

Consider a symmetric band matrix $\mathbf{A}$ of order n and let $2m + 1$ be the bandwidth, i.e., $A_{ij} = 0$ if $|i - j| > m$. It is possible to reduce $\mathbf{A}$ to symmetric tridiagonal form using Givens or fast Givens rotations in such a way that no nonzero elements are introduced outside the band during the reduction. The required rotations are of the form $\mathbf{R}(j-1, j, \theta)$, and A_{kj} and A_{jk} with $k < j-1$ are the pair of elements to be annihilated at each step. We explain the procedure by describing how the first row of **A** is treated, making reference to Fig. 6.2 for an example.

First, element $(1, m+1)$ is annihilated by the rotation $\mathbf{R}(m, m+1, \theta_1)$. This element is indicated as a in Fig. 6.2. The transformation $\mathbf{R}^{\mathrm{T}}\mathbf{A}\mathbf{R}$ modifies lines m and $m+1$ of **A**, which are calculated as linear combinations of the old lines m and $m+1$. Hence, a new nonzero b is introduced at position $(m, 2m+1)$.

Next, element b is annihilated by means of a rotation $\mathbf{R}(2m, 2m+1, \theta_2)$, which combines lines $2m$ and $2m+1$ and introduces the new nonzero c at $(2m, 3m+1)$. This element is in turn annihilated by rotation $\mathbf{R}(3m, 3m+1, \theta_3)$. In our example, no new nonzeros are produced, and the original element $(1, m+1)$ is thus completely eliminated.

In general, elements from the first row are annihilated in the order $(1, m+1), (1, m), \ldots, (1, 3)$, in each case performing all the necessary rotations so that no nonzero remains outside the band. The remaining rows are then processed in order in the same way.

The total number of rotations is bounded by $n^2(m-1)/(2m)$. If Givens rotations are used, each requires one square root and $8m + 13$ operations, but fast rotations can also be used requiring no square roots and approximately one half of the operations. An explicit Algol program was given by Schwartz *et al.* (1971). A Fortran version is in EISPACK (Smith *et al.*, 1976, p. 532). Before the rotations start, the matrix can be permuted in order to minimize the half-bandwidth m, as discussed in Section 4.5.

The same idea was extended to the generalized eigenproblem, Equation (6.2), by Crawford (1973) when both **A** and **B** are banded symmetric of order n and bandwidth m, and **B** is positive definite. A first step produces a

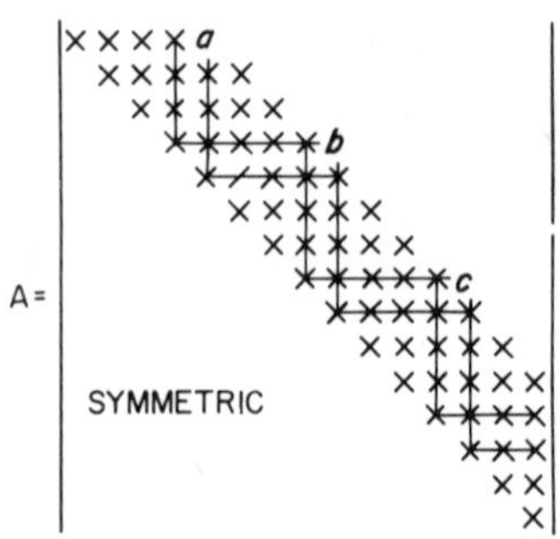

Figure 6.2 Reduction of a band matrix of half-bandwidth $m = 4$ to tridiagonal form.

standard eigenproblem with a banded matrix of the same bandwidth, in $O(n^2m)$ operations. Then, in a second step, the banded matrix can be reduced to tridiagonal form. This is a very useful procedure when extra storage is unavailable, and a further advantage is that powerful methods exist for solving the eigenproblem with a tridiagonal matrix. Crawford's method is a good technique if all the eigenvalues are required, but was found not to be competitive when only partial eigensolutions are sought, as in vibration problems (Jennings, 1981). When **A** and **B** are large and have a narrow bandwidth, other methods which avoid explicit reduction will usually be preferable.

6.7. Eigenanalysis of tridiagonal and Hessenberg matrices

In the preceding sections procedures were discussed for reducing a symmetric matrix to a similar symmetric tridiagonal matrix, or a general matrix to a similar Hessenberg matrix. Tridiagonal matrices are a particular and important class of sparse matrices, but a Hessenberg matrix may be either sparse or not. The case of banded matrices was also considered, and it was mentioned that a symmetric generalized eigenproblem with a banded pencil can be reduced to a standard problem with a symmetric tridiagonal matrix without using extra storage. Besides, it often happens in practice that an eigenproblem is originally given with a tridiagonal matrix. In any of these cases we face the problem of calculating the eigenvalues and eigenvectors of the reduced matrix.

There exist well established algorithms and easily available computer programs for solving this problem. In some sense, the procedures are so powerful that one feels that a problem is solved when reduced to tridiagonal form. The most commonly used are the QR and QL algorithms for the case that all the eigenvalues or all the eigenvalues and all the eigenvectors are needed. QR and QL are not described here because they are sufficiently discussed in the modern literature on dense matrices (e.g., Parlett, 1980). Also employed are the bisection technique based on Sturm sequences for the calculation of the eigenvalues in a specified interval, and inverse iteration for the calculation of the corresponding eigenvectors. These last two techniques are discussed in Sections 6.4 and 6.8 because they are of interest for general sparse matrices. Fortran programs which employ QR, QL, Sturm bisection and inverse iteration for calculating the complete eigensystem, or part of it, of a symmetric tridiagonal or of a Hessenberg matrix, are given in EISPACK (Smith *et al.*, 1976). In the case of a Hessenberg matrix, these programs require it to be stored in full format, and thus they are only convenient for small Hessenberg matrices. On the other hand, they can deal satisfactorily with very large symmetric tridiagonal matrices. Note that the eigenvalues and eigenvectors of a Hessenberg matrix are complex.

It is worth mentioning here that when the matrix is tridiagonal but not symmetric, it can still be transformed to a similar symmetric tridiagonal matrix, provided the product of every pair of corresponding codiagonal elements is positive, and is zero only if both are zero. The eigenvalues of such a matrix are all real. The method is explained by Wilkinson (1965, p. 335) and a Fortran implementation is available with EISPACK. If the given unsymmetric tridiagonal matrix does not have the required special form, then it must be considered as a Hessenberg matrix.

6.8. Direct and inverse iteration

The power method, also known as the method of direct iteration or Stodola's iteration, and the method of inverse iteration are both attractive for large sparse matrices when some eigenvalues *and* the corresponding eigenvectors are required. Both are simple and capable of giving accurate results, and inverse iteration is also used for small dense matrices. The *power method* is as follows. Pick any column vector, say $\mathbf{e}_1$. Pre-multiply it by the given matrix $\mathbf{A}$ and normalize the result. Repeat the same operations until the result converges, say a total of m times. After $m - 1$ steps we have formed $\mathbf{x} = \mathbf{A}^{m-1}\mathbf{e}_1/|\mathbf{A}^{m-1}\mathbf{e}_1|$, where $\mathbf{x}^{\mathrm{T}}\mathbf{x} = 1$. Then, at the mth step, we have discovered that $\mathbf{Ax}/|\mathbf{Ax}| = \mathbf{x}' \cong \mathbf{x}$. Thus $h = |\mathbf{Ax}| = |\mathbf{A}^m\mathbf{e}_1|$ is an eigenvalue of $\mathbf{A}$ and $\mathbf{x}$ is the corresponding eigenvector. The eigenvalue obtained is the dominant one, but other eigenvalues and eigenvectors can easily be obtained as follows.

Assume that several eigenvalues $\lambda_1, \lambda_2, \ldots$ and the corresponding eigenvectors $\mathbf{x}_1, \mathbf{x}_2, \ldots$ have already been found, where the eigenvectors are normalized: $\mathbf{x}_i^{\mathrm{T}}\mathbf{x}_j = \delta_{ij}$. Pick any vector $\mathbf{u}$ and form:

$$\mathbf{w} = \mathbf{u} - (\mathbf{u}^{\mathrm{T}}\mathbf{x}_1)\mathbf{x}_1 - (\mathbf{u}^{\mathrm{T}}\mathbf{x}_2)\mathbf{x}_2 - \ldots \tag{6.30}$$

$\mathbf{w}$ is orthogonal to each one of the eigenvectors $\mathbf{x}_1, \mathbf{x}_2, \ldots$ Then, use $\mathbf{w}$ as the starting vector for the iterations. Convergence will take place to the next dominant eigenvalue not in the set $\lambda_1, \lambda_2, \ldots,$ and the corresponding eigenvector. If calculations were exact, each new vector would be exactly orthogonal to each of the known eigenvectors. However, due to round-off errors, spurious components arise and grow at a rate which is approximately bounded by $|\lambda_1/h|$ per iteration, where h is the current estimate of the eigenvalue under calculation. Therefore, it is necessary to re-orthogonalize the current vector from time to time; the bound just given, and an estimation of the initial error in an orthogonalized vector can be used to determine when the next re-orthogonalization must be carried out.

The procedure by which repeated convergence to the known eigenpairs is avoided is called *deflation*. In the present case deflation was achieved by restricting the iteration vector to the invariant subspace which is the complement of the known eigenvectors. This method is particularly convenient in sparse matrix technology because the original matrix need never be modified, and thus its sparsity is preserved. Other methods of deflation exist but seem less convenient when **A** is sparse. [See Hotelling (1943) and Householder (1961), or Parlett (1980) for a modern presentation.] The power method is very simple to program using the matrix-by-vector multiplication algorithms discussed in Chapter 7.

The power method may not be convenient when only eigenvalues of **A** are needed. This is because each new eigenvalue can only be calculated if the eigenvectors of the previous eigenvalues are available. The eigenvectors are full vectors and may require more storage than **A** itself if more than a few eigenvalues are to be obtained. However, since the eigenvectors are used only for re-orthogonalization, they can be stored in a peripheral device and brought into main storage a few at a time when required.

It still remains to explain why and how direct iterations converge. Consider the orthonormalized eigenvectors $\mathbf{x}_1, \mathbf{x}_2, \ldots, \mathbf{x}_n$ of **A** as forming a basis of n-dimensional space, and the arbitrary vector **u** to have components $(u_1, u_2, \ldots, u_n)$ in that basis. The basis and the components only serve as a device for our argument, because they are unknown for the moment. When **u** is pre-multiplied by **A**, the resulting vector **Au** has components $(\lambda_1 u_1, \lambda_2 u_2, \ldots, \lambda_n u_n)$, where $\lambda_1, \ldots, \lambda_n$ are the eigenvalues of **A**. If λ_1, say, is the dominant eigenvalue and $u_1 \neq 0$, then clearly $|\lambda_1 u_1|/|\lambda_i u_i| > |u_1|/|u_i|$ for any $i \neq 1$ such that $u_i \neq 0$. The new vector has tilted towards $\mathbf{x}_1$, and if pre-multiplication by **A** followed by normalization is repeated a sufficient number of times the sequence will converge to $\mathbf{x}_1$.

If now that $\mathbf{x}_1$ is known a new vector **v** is chosen such that **v** is orthogonal to $\mathbf{x}_1$, i.e. $v_1 = 0$, pre-multiplication of **v** by **A** will produce a tilting towards the eigenvector associated with the next dominant eigenvalue, say λ_2. The process can be continued until the desired eigenpairs are found. If an eigenvalue happens to be multiple, say $\lambda_2 = \lambda_3$, **v** will converge to one of the corresponding eigenvectors, say $\mathbf{x}_2$. Then, taking **w** normal to both $\mathbf{x}_1$ and $\mathbf{x}_2$, it will converge to the other eigenvector, $\mathbf{x}_3$. Of course, any linear combination of $\mathbf{x}_2$ and $\mathbf{x}_3$ is also an eigenvector of the pair $\lambda_2 = \lambda_3$.

The power method converges linearly with the factor

$$c_0 = |\lambda_q|/|\lambda_s| \qquad (6.31)$$

where λ_s and λ_q are the dominant and next dominant eigenvalues, respectively, of the eigenspace spanned by the search vector.

Shifts of origin are frequently used to improve the convergence of iterative methods. If $\{\lambda_i\}$ is the set of eigenvalues of $\mathbf{A}$, then $\mathbf{A} - \sigma\mathbf{I}$ has eigenvalues $\{\lambda_i - \sigma\}$ and the same eigenvectors as $\mathbf{A}$; σ is any real number. If a value is chosen for σ and the power method used for $\mathbf{A} - \sigma\mathbf{I}$, convergence will take place to the eigenvalue λ_s farthest from σ, which is necessarily either the largest or the smallest of the eigenvalues of $\mathbf{A}$ (algebraically). The convergence factor is now

$$c_\sigma = \max_{i \neq s} |\lambda_i - \sigma|/|\lambda_s - \sigma|. \tag{6.32}$$

This value cannot be made very small, so that shifts of origin cannot improve significantly the convergence of the power method.

The method of *inverse iteration* is the power method applied to $\mathbf{A}^{-1}$. It has, however, very different practical properties. If $\mathbf{A}$ is symmetric and nonsingular, and $\mathbf{A}\mathbf{x} = \lambda\mathbf{x}$, then pre-multiplication by $\mathbf{A}^{-1}$ yields:

$$\mathbf{A}^{-1}\mathbf{x} = \frac{1}{\lambda}\,\mathbf{x}, \tag{6.33}$$

which shows that the eigenvalues of $\mathbf{A}^{-1}$ are the inverses of the eigenvalues of $\mathbf{A}$, and that $\mathbf{A}$ and $\mathbf{A}^{-1}$ have the same eigenvectors. Note that $\lambda \neq 0$ because we have assumed that $\mathbf{A}$ is nonsingular.

In the method of inverse iteration, as in the power method, a sequence of vectors $\{\mathbf{y}_k\}$ is computed. Each vector is then normalized

$$\mathbf{x}_k = \mathbf{y}_k/|\mathbf{y}_k| \tag{6.34}$$

so that $\mathbf{x}_k^{\mathrm{T}}\mathbf{x}_k = 1$. The starting vector is arbitrary, say $\mathbf{x}_0 = \mathbf{e}_1$. Each vector is the product of $\mathbf{A}^{-1}$ by the normalized form of the preceding vector:

$$\mathbf{y}_{k+1} = \mathbf{A}^{-1}\mathbf{x}_k. \tag{6.35}$$

In practice, however, it is convenient to avoid explicit computation of $\mathbf{A}^{-1}$ and to obtain each $\mathbf{y}_{k+1}$ by solving the system of linear equations:

$$\mathbf{A}\mathbf{y}_{k+1} = \mathbf{x}_k. \tag{6.36}$$

To solve Equation (6.36), $\mathbf{A}$ is factorized, once and for all before the iterations start, using the efficient techniques available for sparse matrices discussed in Chapters 4 and 5. Then Equation (6.36) is solved in the course of each inverse iteration by forward and back substitution. Iterative techniques can also be used to solve (6.36), see for example Ruhe and Wiberg (1972).

The most desirable feature of inverse iteration is that it converges linearly to the eigenvalue λ_1 of $\mathbf{A}$ which is nearest to zero, and its corresponding eigenvector. If λ_2 is the next eigenvalue nearest to zero, i.e. $|\lambda_1| < |\lambda_2| \leqslant |\lambda_i|$ for $i \neq 1, 2$, then the convergence factor is

$$c_0 = |\lambda_1/\lambda_2|. \tag{6.37}$$

If the origin is shifted by an amount σ, using $\mathbf{A} - \sigma\mathbf{I}$ in place of $\mathbf{A}$, convergence will be to the eigenvalue closest to σ. Thus the user can effectively choose an eigenvalue, a feature which is absent from the power method. If this eigenvalue is λ_s, i.e. if σ and λ_s are such that

$$|\lambda_s - \sigma| = \min_i |\lambda_i - \sigma|, \tag{6.38}$$

then the convergence factor is

$$c_\sigma = |\lambda_s - \sigma| / \min_{i \neq s} |\lambda_i - \sigma|. \tag{6.39}$$

σ is usually taken equal to some approximation of λ_s. If the approximation is good, c_σ is small and the convergence is very rapid. Of course, it is possible to use a different shift at each iteration, taking advantage of the improved approximation of λ_s obtained from the preceding iteration. In Section 6.2 it was explained that, when a normalized approximation $\mathbf{x}_k$ to an eigenvector is known, the best approximation to the corresponding eigenvalue is the Rayleigh quotient $\rho_k = \mathbf{x}_k^{\mathrm{T}}\mathbf{A}\mathbf{x}_k$, cheap to compute when $\mathbf{A}$ is sparse. The idea of using ρ_k as the shift for the next iteration, i.e., $\sigma_{k+1} = \rho_k$, gives rise to the *Rayleigh quotient iteration* method. Although this requires the factorization of $\mathbf{A} - \sigma_k\mathbf{I}$ in each iteration to solve the system (6.36), the idea is very convenient: the convergence is asymptotically cubic and when k is sufficiently large (usually a small digit) the number of correct digits in $\mathbf{x}_k$ triples in each iteration. $\mathbf{A} - \sigma_k\mathbf{I}$ becomes ill-conditioned when σ_k approaches λ_s, but this is a further advantage: the system (6.36) with $\mathbf{A} - \sigma_k\mathbf{I}$ in place of $\mathbf{A}$ can be solved incautiously because the error, even when it is large, is almost entirely in the direction of the desired eigenvector and contributes to improve the speed of convergence. Besides, when σ_k is close to λ_s and $\mathbf{A} - \sigma_k\mathbf{I}$ is ill-conditioned, the solution $\mathbf{y}_{k+1}$ in Equation (6.36) is a very large vector, and $|\mathbf{y}_{k+1}|$, which has to be computed anyway for its use in Equation (6.34), is a good measure of convergence.

An important application of inverse iteration with shift occurs when a set of eigenvalues are known from some other method such as bisection. One single step will frequently suffice to obtain an eigenvector with sufficient accuracy (Peters and Wilkinson, 1971).

Both methods, direct and inverse iteration, can be used for unsymmetric matrices with complex eigenelements.

Both methods can be used to solve the generalized eigenvalue problem, Equation (6.2). The extension of the power method with shift σ is:

$$\mathbf{B}\mathbf{y}_{k+1} = (\mathbf{A} - \sigma\mathbf{B})\mathbf{x}_k$$

$$\mathbf{x}_{k+1} = \mathbf{y}_{k+1}/|\mathbf{y}_{k+1}|. \tag{6.40}$$

This iteration requires the solution of a system of linear equations at each step, with $\mathbf{B}$ as the matrix of coefficients. The extension of inverse iteration with shift σ is:

$$(\mathbf{A} - \sigma\mathbf{B})\mathbf{y}_{k+1} = \mathbf{B}\mathbf{x}_k$$

$$\mathbf{x}_{k+1} = \mathbf{y}_{k+1}/|\mathbf{y}_{k+1}|, \tag{6.41}$$

which also requires the solution of a linear system at each step. The extension of Rayleigh quotient iteration to the generalized eigenproblem is obtained when, at each step, the shift is taken equal to the Rayleigh quotient, Equation (6.17), for that step. If the sequence $\{x_k\}$ converges to an eigenvector, then convergence is cubic, but $\{x_k\}$ does not necessarily converge to an eigenvector.

6.9. Subspaces and invariant subspaces

The set of all n-dimensional column vectors is called a *space* of dimension n. The space is designated $\mathscr{R}^n$ when the vectors have real components, or $\mathscr{C}^n$ when the vectors have complex components. A point in $\mathscr{R}^n$ or $\mathscr{C}^n$ represents a vector. When, besides, an inner product is defined, the space becomes an *Euclidean space* $\mathscr{E}^n$. The inner product between two vectors $\mathbf{x} = (x_1, \ldots, x_n)^{\mathrm{T}}$ and $\mathbf{y} = (y_1, \ldots, y_n)^{\mathrm{T}}$ is defined as follows:

$$(\mathbf{x}, \mathbf{y}) = \mathbf{y}^{\mathrm{H}}\mathbf{x} \equiv \sum_{i=1}^{n} y_i^* x_i \tag{6.42}$$

where y_i^* is the complex conjugate of y_i and H means conjugate transpose. Note the difference from the *dot* or *scalar product*

$$\mathbf{y}^{\mathrm{T}}\mathbf{x} = \sum_{i=1}^{n} y_i x_i. \tag{6.43}$$

When the vectors are real the inner product and the scalar product are the same. A more sophisticated definition of inner product, suitable for the generalized eigenproblem $\mathbf{A}\mathbf{x} = \lambda\mathbf{B}\mathbf{x}$ with $\mathbf{B}$ symmetric and positive definite, is $(\mathbf{x}, \mathbf{y}) = \mathbf{y}^{\mathrm{H}}\mathbf{B}\mathbf{x}$, with the corresponding space being designated $\mathscr{M}^n$. Alternatively, it can be defined $\mathbf{y}^{\mathrm{H}}\mathbf{B}^{-1}\mathbf{x}$.

The full potential of algorithms like Lanczos' and simultaneous iteration cannot be realized without the notion of subspace. A set $\mathbf{S} = \{\mathbf{s}_1, \mathbf{s}_2, \ldots\}$ of n-vectors determines a *subspace* $\mathscr{S}$ of $\mathscr{E}^n$, which is the set of all n-vectors that can be written as linear combinations of $\mathbf{s}_1, \mathbf{s}_2, \ldots$ This definition is expressed as follows

$$\mathscr{S} = \mathrm{span}\ (\mathbf{s}_1, \mathbf{s}_2, \ldots) = \mathrm{span}\ (\mathbf{S}) \tag{6.44}$$

and $\mathbf{S}$ is a *spanning set* of the subspace. A subspace has infinitely many spanning sets with different cardinalities. A *basis* is a spanning set with the minimum cardinality, which is the *dimension* m of the subspace. The m n-vectors of the basis are linearly independent. If, in addition, they are orthonormal, the basis is an *orthonormal basis*. $\mathscr{S}$ has infinitely many orthonormal bases, but any vector of any basis can be written as a linear combination of the vectors of any other basis. An example of subspace is any plane in three-dimensional space $\mathscr{R}^3$. The dimension of the subspace is 2, and any two nonparallel vectors of the plane are a basis.

Let now $\mathbf{A} = \mathbf{A}^{\mathrm{T}}$ be a symmetric matrix (the same arguments are valid in the complex field with a hermitian $\mathbf{A}$). $\mathscr{S}$ is *invariant under* $\mathbf{A}$ if, for any n-vector $\mathbf{x}$ of $\mathscr{S}$, $\mathbf{Ax}$ is also in $\mathscr{S}$. An eigenvector of $\mathbf{A}$ determines an invariant subspace of dimension one, or a set of m orthonormalized eigenvectors of $\mathbf{A}$ form the basis of an invariant subspace of dimension m, which is the span of the m eigenvectors. The important result concerning this point is the following: *any* invariant subspace is the span of a set of eigenvectors of $\mathbf{A}$.

If $\mathbf{Q} = (\mathbf{q}_1, \mathbf{q}_2, \ldots, \mathbf{q}_m)$ is any basis of the invariant subspace $\mathscr{S}$, arranged in the form of the n by m matrix $\mathbf{Q}$, then the action of $\mathbf{A}$ on $\mathbf{Q}$ is just to form a new n by m matrix $\mathbf{AQ}$ of which the columns are linear combinations of the columns of $\mathbf{Q}$. This is because of the invariance of $\mathscr{S}$: each vector $\mathbf{Aq}_i$ is in $\mathscr{S}$. The m linear combinations can conveniently be expressed as $\mathbf{QC}$, where the m by m matrix $\mathbf{C}$ is the *restriction* of $\mathbf{A}$ to $\mathscr{S}$. Thus $\mathbf{AQ} = \mathbf{QC}$, or:

$$\underset{n \times n}{\mathbf{A}}\;\underset{n \times m}{\mathbf{Q}} = \underset{n \times m}{\mathbf{Q}}\;\underset{m \times m}{\mathbf{C}} \tag{6.45}$$

The case where $\mathbf{Q}$ is an orthonormal basis of $\mathscr{S}$ is particularly interesting. From $\mathbf{Q}^{\mathrm{T}}\mathbf{Q} = \mathbf{I}_m$ ($\mathbf{I}_m$ is the m by m identity matrix) we obtain $\mathbf{C} = \mathbf{Q}^{\mathrm{T}}\mathbf{AQ}$, where $\mathbf{C}$ is the symmetric *Rayleigh matrix*. Now consider the eigenvalue problem for $\mathbf{C}$ and let $(\lambda, \mathbf{y})$ be an eigenpair of $\mathbf{C}$, where $\mathbf{y}$ is an m-vector. Thus

$$\mathbf{Cy} = \lambda\mathbf{y}. \tag{6.46}$$

Pre-multiplication by $\mathbf{Q}$ yields $\mathbf{QCy} = \lambda\mathbf{Qy}$, or

$$\mathbf{A}(\mathbf{Qy}) = \lambda(\mathbf{Qy}), \tag{6.47}$$

which means that λ is also an eigenvalue of $\mathbf{A}$ and that $\mathbf{Qy}$ is the corresponding eigenvector. This result is very important: eigenpairs for the large $\mathbf{A}$ can be found by solving the eigenvalue problem for the smaller $\mathbf{C}$.

Of course, the result above is useful only when $\mathscr{S} = \text{span}(\mathbf{Q})$ is invariant under **A**. An invariant $\mathscr{S}$ cannot be chosen beforehand because this would amount to solving the eigenproblem of **A**. Usually span(**Q**) will be only "nearly" invariant and the natural question is how to find good approximations to the eigenpairs of **A** in such a case. The *Rayleigh–Ritz procedure* provides the best approximations:

(1) Orthonormalize **Q** (if necessary) and compute the m by m *Rayleigh matrix* $\mathbf{H} = \mathbf{Q}^T\mathbf{A}\mathbf{Q}$. This is the generalization of the scalar Rayleigh quotient mentioned in Section 6.2, and the use of the symbol **H** in place of **C** accounts for the fact that Equation (6.45) does not now hold exactly.
(2) Find the required $k \leqslant m$ eigenpairs of **H**, say $(\mu_i, \mathbf{h}_i)$, $i = 1, \ldots, k$. Thus $\mathbf{H}\mathbf{h}_i = \mu_i\mathbf{h}_i$.
(3) The *Ritz values* μ_i are the best approximations to the eigenvalues of **A**. The *Ritz vectors* $\mathbf{x}_i = \mathbf{Q}\mathbf{h}_i$ are the corresponding approximations to the eigenvectors of **A**.

The results of Section 6.2 can now be used to obtain error bounds for the eigenvalues of **A**. If $\mathbf{r}_i = \mathbf{A}\mathbf{x}_i - \mu_i\mathbf{x}_i$ is the residual vector for the Ritz pair $(\mu_i, \mathbf{x}_i)$, then there is an eigenvalue of **A** in the interval $[\mu_i - |\mathbf{r}_i|, \mu_i + |\mathbf{r}_i|]$. If the k intervals are disjoint, this guarantees approximations to k eigenvalues of **A**. However, two or more intervals which overlap may contain the same eigenvalue. In this case it is still possible to identify k eigenvalues of **A** (Kahan, 1967; see also Parlett, 1980).

The extension of the Rayleigh–Ritz procedure to the generalized eigenvalue problem is as follows. Let **Q** be any n by m basis of the subspace $\mathscr{S} = \text{span}(\mathbf{Q})$. It is not necessary that **Q** be orthonormalized or **B**-orthonormalized. Then:

(1) Compute the two m by m Rayleigh matrices $\mathbf{H}_A = \mathbf{Q}^T\mathbf{A}\mathbf{Q}$ and $\mathbf{H}_B = \mathbf{Q}^T\mathbf{B}\mathbf{Q}$.
(2) Solve the eigenproblem $\mathbf{H}_A\mathbf{h}_i = \mu_i\mathbf{H}_B\mathbf{h}_i$ for the desired k eigenpairs $(\mu_i, \mathbf{h}_i)$ of the small pencil $(\mathbf{H}_A, \mathbf{H}_B)$.
(3) The Ritz values μ_i are the best approximations to the eigenvalues of **A**, **B**, and the Ritz vectors $\mathbf{x}_i = \mathbf{Q}\mathbf{h}_i$ are the corresponding approximations to the eigenvectors of **A**, **B**.

6.10. Simultaneous iteration

When an arbitrary vector **u** is repeatedly pre-multiplied by **A** and each result normalized, a sequence of vectors is generated which converges to an eigenvector $\mathbf{x}_1$ of **A**. If the same is done with a second vector **v** normal to $\mathbf{x}_1$

but otherwise arbitrary, convergence occurs to another eigenvector $\mathbf{x}_2$ of $\mathbf{A}$. Repeating the process more eigenvectors can be found. This is the Power Method, discussed in Section 6.8. The method of *Simultaneous Iteration* or *Subspace Iteration* is a natural generalization of the idea. A set of k normalized vectors, arranged as the columns of an n by k matrix $\mathbf{U}$, are simultaneously pre-multiplied by $\mathbf{A}$. The vectors must be perpendicular to each other because otherwise they would all converge to the same eigenvector, i.e., $\mathbf{U}$ must be orthonormal: $\mathbf{U}^{\mathrm{T}}\mathbf{U} = \mathbf{I}_k$. $\mathbf{U}$ is thus an orthonormal basis of the subspace $\mathscr{S} = \text{span}(\mathbf{U})$. $\mathscr{S}$ is not invariant, but becomes "nearly" so as the algorithm progresses. Now, we know from the preceding section that the best approximations to the eigenvectors of $\mathbf{A}$ which can be obtained from $\mathscr{S}$ are the Ritz vectors. Thus, we would like to compute the Ritz vectors at each step. Furthermore, if we do and have the Ritz vectors available, it is evidently wise to use them in place of the basis $\mathbf{U}$ as the starting set of k orthonormal vectors for the next step of iteration. In fact we would like the so-far arbitrary basis $\mathbf{U}$ itself to consist precisely of the set of Ritz vectors at each step. The power of the method relies on this beautiful and sophisticated idea. The algorithm can now be restated as follows: at the beginning of step m, the orthonormal basis $\mathbf{U}_{m-1}$ is available. Compute $\mathbf{AU}_{m-1}$ and find the new basis $\mathbf{U}_m$ of span$(\mathbf{AU}_{m-1})$, where the columns of $\mathbf{U}_m$ are the Ritz vectors. Reinsch (1971) suggested an elegant way for obtaining the required quantities. Explicitly, for step m:

(1) An n by k orthonormal matrix $\mathbf{U}_{m-1}$ is available, so that:

$$\overset{k\times n}{\mathbf{U}_{m-1}^{\mathrm{T}}}\ \overset{n\times k}{\mathbf{U}_{m-1}} = \overset{k\times k}{\mathbf{I}_k} \tag{6.48}$$

(2) Pre-multiply $\mathbf{U}_{m-1}$ by $\mathbf{A}$:

$$\overset{n\times k}{\mathbf{C}} = \overset{n\times n}{\mathbf{A}}\ \overset{n\times k}{\mathbf{U}_{m-1}} \tag{6.49}$$

and store $\mathbf{C}$ over $\mathbf{U}_{m-1}$.

(3) $\mathbf{C}$ is not orthonormal. Orthonormalize the columns of $\mathbf{C}$ using the Gram–Schmidt procedure to obtain the orthonormal $\mathbf{Q}$ and the upper triangular $\mathbf{R}$. Thus:

$$\overset{n\times k}{\mathbf{C}} = \overset{n\times k}{\mathbf{Q}}\ \overset{k\times k}{\mathbf{R}} \tag{6.50}$$

where

$$\mathbf{Q}^{\mathrm{T}}\mathbf{Q} = \mathbf{I}_k. \tag{6.51}$$

Store $\mathbf{Q}$ over $\mathbf{C}$.

(4) Compute $\mathbf{R}\mathbf{R}^{\mathrm{T}}$ and solve the eigenproblem for this symmetric positive definite small matrix. Thus, the spectral decomposition is obtained:

$$\overset{k\times k}{\mathbf{R}}\;\overset{k\times k}{\mathbf{R}^{\mathrm{T}}} = \overset{k\times k}{\mathbf{P}}\;\overset{k\times k}{\mathbf{D}}\;\overset{k\times k}{\mathbf{P}^{\mathrm{T}}} \tag{6.52}$$

where $\mathbf{D}$ is diagonal with positive diagonal elements which are the squares of the new Ritz values, and

$$\mathbf{P}^{\mathrm{T}}\mathbf{P} = \mathbf{I}_k. \tag{6.53}$$

(5) Compute the new basis whose columns are the new Ritz vectors:

$$\overset{n\times k}{\mathbf{U}_m} = \overset{n\times k}{\mathbf{Q}}\;\overset{k\times k}{\mathbf{P}} \tag{6.54}$$

Store $\mathbf{U}_m$ over $\mathbf{Q}$. Test for convergence and go to (1) if necessary.

We have to prove that the columns of $\mathbf{U}_m$ are the Ritz vectors from $\mathscr{S} = \mathrm{span}(\mathbf{U}_m)$. We first prove that they are orthonormal:

$$\mathbf{U}_m^{\mathrm{T}}\mathbf{U}_m = (\mathbf{QP})^{\mathrm{T}}\mathbf{QP} = \mathbf{P}^{\mathrm{T}}(\mathbf{Q}^{\mathrm{T}}\mathbf{Q})\mathbf{P} = \mathbf{I}_k$$

where use has been made of Equations (6.54), (6.51) and (6.53), in that order. The following result will be needed:

$$\mathbf{QP} = \mathbf{A}\mathbf{U}_{m-1}\mathbf{R}^{\mathrm{T}}\mathbf{P}\mathbf{D}^{-1}. \tag{6.55}$$

It is easy to obtain Equation (6.55). From Equation (6.53) $\mathbf{D}\mathbf{P}^{\mathrm{T}}\mathbf{P}\mathbf{D}^{-1} = \mathbf{I}_k$, so that $\mathbf{QP} = \mathbf{QPDP}^{\mathrm{T}}\mathbf{PD}^{-1}$. Then, using Equations (6.52), (6.50) and (6.49), in this order, Equation (6.55) is obtained. The following property is also needed: $\mathbf{A}^{-2}$ has the same eigenvectors as $\mathbf{A}$, and, as a consequence, $\mathbf{A}$ and $\mathbf{A}^{-2}$ have the same Rayleigh–Ritz approximations from $\mathscr{S}$. The restriction of $\mathbf{A}^{-2}$ to $\mathscr{S}$ is:

$$\mathbf{U}_m^{\mathrm{T}}\mathbf{A}^{-2}\mathbf{U}_m = (\mathbf{QP})^{\mathrm{T}}\mathbf{A}^{-2}\mathbf{QP} = \mathbf{D}^{-1} \tag{6.56}$$

where Equations (6.54), (6.55), (6.48), (6.52) and (6.53) were used in this order. Thus, $\mathbf{D}^{-1}$ is the Rayleigh matrix for $\mathbf{A}^{-2}$. The normal procedure for computing the Ritz vectors would be to find the spectral decomposition of $\mathbf{D}^{-1}$ and to pre-multiply the matrix of eigenvectors by $\mathbf{U}_m$. The spectral decomposition of $\mathbf{D}^{-1}$ is $\mathbf{I}_p^{\mathrm{T}}\mathbf{D}^{-1}\mathbf{I}_p$, the matrix of eigenvectors is $\mathbf{I}_p$, and $\mathbf{U}_m\mathbf{I}_p = \mathbf{U}_m$, which proves that $\mathbf{U}_m$ itself is the matrix of Ritz vectors for $\mathbf{A}$ or $\mathbf{A}^{-2}$ obtained from $\mathscr{S}$. Besides, the Ritz values for $\mathbf{A}^{-2}$ are the diagonal elements of $\mathbf{D}^{-1}$, so that the diagonal elements of $\mathbf{D}^{1/2}$ are the Ritz values for $\mathbf{A}$, i.e., the best approximations to the eigenvalues of $\mathbf{A}$ which can be obtained from $\mathscr{S}$.

Simultaneous iteration is frequently used with $(\mathbf{A} - \sigma\mathbf{I})^{-1}$ in place of $\mathbf{A}$, as inverse iteration, where σ is the shift. In this way the k eigenvalues of $\mathbf{A}$ closest to σ can be determined, together with the corresponding eigenvectors.

Convergence may be much faster than for simple vector iterations, particularly when clustered eigenvalues are needed. Convergence often depends on the size k of the subspace, and one of the limitations of the method is that k is not known *a priori*, although of course k can easily be modified in the course of the iteration either by adding new columns to the basis or by deflating the basis from converged eigenvectors. Ritz vectors need not be computed at every step. It is perfectly possible to pre-multiply the current basis by **A** several times, or even by some function of **A** such as a polynomial in **A**, before computing the new set of Ritz vectors. The function of **A** is often chosen to be a Chebyshev polynomial, because it has some desirable properties which contribute to improve convergence, giving rise to *Chebyshev acceleration*. Again, rules are absent and heuristics must be used to fix the degree of the polynomial. Rutishauser (1970) has developed an algorithm which incorporates most of the known refinements. A program based on it is listed in the Catalog (Heath, 1982, p. 83), where details concerning its availability are also given.

Simultaneous iteration can be used to solve the generalized eigenvalue problem $\mathbf{Ax} = \lambda\mathbf{Bx}$. The inverse iteration technique with shift σ is usually employed. The shifted eigenproblem is written as follows:

$$(\mathbf{A} - \sigma\mathbf{B})\mathbf{X} = \mathbf{BX\Lambda}. \tag{6.57}$$

Then for step m:

(1) An n by k matrix $\mathbf{U}_{m-1}$ is available. It is not necessary that $\mathbf{U}_{m-1}$ be orthonormal or **B**-orthonormal. The diagonal k by k matrix $\mathbf{\Lambda}_{m-1}$ of approximate eigenvalues is also available.

(2) Compute $\mathbf{R} = \mathbf{BU}_{m-1}\mathbf{\Lambda}_{m-1}$ and solve

$$(\mathbf{A} - \sigma\mathbf{B})\mathbf{C} = \mathbf{R}$$

for n by k **C**. This is derived from Equation (6.57).

(3) Start the computation of the Rayleigh–Ritz approximation from span(**C**), as explained at the end of Section 6.9. For this purpose, find the two k by k Rayleigh matrices:

$$\mathbf{H}_A \equiv \mathbf{C}^{\mathrm{T}}(\mathbf{A} - \sigma\mathbf{B})\mathbf{C} = \mathbf{C}^{\mathrm{T}}\mathbf{R}$$

$$\mathbf{H}_B = \mathbf{C}^{\mathrm{T}}\mathbf{BC}$$

(4) Solve the complete generalized eigenproblem for the small pencil $\mathbf{H}_A$, $\mathbf{H}_B$:

$$(\mathbf{H}_A - \sigma\mathbf{H}_B)\mathbf{P} = \mathbf{H}_B\mathbf{P}\mathbf{\Lambda}_m$$

This produces the new matrix $\mathbf{\Lambda}_m$ of Ritz values and the k by k matrix **P** which is $\mathbf{H}_B$-orthogonal:

$$\mathbf{P}^{\mathrm{T}}\mathbf{H}_B\mathbf{P} = \mathbf{I}_k$$

(5) Form new basis $\mathbf{U}_m = \mathbf{CP}$. The columns of $\mathbf{U}_m$ are the new Ritz vectors. Test for convergence and go to (1) if necessary.

A code which solves the generalized eigenproblem by simultaneous iteration was published by Nikolai (1979) and is listed in the Catalog (Heath, 1982, p. 87a).

6.11. Lanczos algorithm

The Lanczos method (Lanczos, 1950) is derived when the "nearly" invariant subspace $\mathscr{S}$ from which Rayleigh–Ritz approximations are drawn is chosen to be a *Krylov-subspace*. If $\mathbf{b}$ is an arbitrary nonzero vector, a Krylov subspace is defined by:

$$\mathscr{K}^m = \text{span}(\mathbf{b}, \mathbf{Ab}, \mathbf{A}^2\mathbf{b}, \ldots, \mathbf{A}^{m-1}\mathbf{b}). \tag{6.58}$$

This is a sensible choice because $\mathscr{K}^m$ will in fact be nearly invariant under $\mathbf{A}$ when m is sufficiently large. To show this, consider any vector $\mathbf{u}$ in $\mathscr{K}^m$. $\mathbf{u}$ can be written as a linear combination of $\mathbf{b}, \mathbf{Ab}, \ldots, \mathbf{A}^{m-1}\mathbf{b}$. If $\mathbf{u}$ is pre-multiplied by $\mathbf{A}$, the result is a linear combination of $\mathbf{Ab}, \mathbf{A}^2\mathbf{b}, \ldots, \mathbf{A}^m\mathbf{b}$, which is in $\mathscr{K}^m$ except for the last term $\mathbf{A}^m\mathbf{b}$. However, in Section 6.8 it was shown that $\mathbf{A}^{m-1}\mathbf{b}$ converges to an eigenvector of $\mathbf{A}$ for m sufficiently large, so that $\mathbf{A}^m\mathbf{b} = \mathbf{A}(\mathbf{A}^{m-1}\mathbf{b})$ is approximately proportional to $\mathbf{A}^{m-1}\mathbf{b}$ and is "almost" in $\mathscr{K}^m$. Thus, we have proved that for any $\mathbf{u}$ in $\mathscr{K}^m$ most of $\mathbf{Au}$ also is in $\mathscr{K}^m$, which means that $\mathscr{K}^m$ is nearly invariant, and, besides, becomes more so as m increases.

The selection of $\mathscr{K}^m$ brings into play important and desirable properties. The most remarkable are:

(1) The Rayleigh matrix $\mathbf{Q}^\mathrm{T}\mathbf{AQ}$ is tridiagonal. It will be designated with the symbol $\mathbf{T}$. The computation of the Ritz pairs is greatly simplified by this fact as discussed in Section 6.7.
(2) There exists a three term recurrence relation for the calculation of successive columns of the orthonormal *Lanczos basis* $\mathbf{Q}$.
(3) The algorithm of Lanczos usually employs a *sequence* of Krylov subspaces $\mathscr{K}^1, \mathscr{K}^2, \ldots, \mathscr{K}^m$, and computes Ritz pairs for $\mathbf{A}$ from each or from some of the subspaces. The convergence is very fast, an indicative figure being $m \sim 2n^{1/2}$.
(4) $\mathbf{A}$ is only needed for computing its product by certain vectors. It can be represented by a subroutine which returns $\mathbf{Ax}$ for a given $\mathbf{x}$, such as the one given in Section 7.13.

There also exists a flaw:

(5) Round-off errors destroy the orthogonality of $\mathbf{Q}$.

Fortunately the way out is known. When the difficulty is overcome:

(6) The resulting algorithm is very cheap and sufficiently automatic to be used for production. It is the favourite for large sparse matrices.
(7) Versions of the algorithm exist for finding extremal eigenvalues, some interior eigenvalues and even all of the eigenvalues of very large symmetric or hermitian matrices. Some versions can also compute the corresponding eigenvectors. Others do not, but eigenvectors associated with a known eigenvalue can always be easily obtained using, for example, inverse iteration.

A few results must be discussed before the algorithm is given explicitly. From now on we will use $\mathbf{Q}_m$ in place of $\mathbf{Q}$ for the orthonormal basis of $\mathscr{K}^m$. $\mathbf{Q}_m$ shows the dimension of $\mathscr{K}^m$, which we will always assume to be m, i.e., the m vectors $\mathbf{b}, \ldots, \mathbf{A}^{m-1}\mathbf{b}$ in Equation (6.58) are assumed to be independent. To avoid confusion it is important to keep in mind that $\mathbf{Q}_m$ is a rectangular matrix of n by m with its *columns* orthonormalized, i.e. $\mathbf{Q}_m^{\mathrm{T}}\mathbf{Q}_m = \mathbf{I}_m$. From this property and the definition of the Rayleigh matrix $\mathbf{T}_m = \mathbf{Q}_m^{\mathrm{T}}\mathbf{A}\mathbf{Q}_m$ it would not be correct to conclude that $\mathbf{A}\mathbf{Q}_m = \mathbf{Q}_m\mathbf{T}_m$ since $\mathbf{Q}_m\mathbf{Q}_m^{\mathrm{T}} \neq \mathbf{I}_n$ in general. The correct relation is written:

$$\mathbf{A}\mathbf{Q}_m = \mathbf{Q}_m\mathbf{T}_m + \mathbf{R}_m, \qquad (6.59)$$

where $\mathbf{R}_m$ is a *residual matrix* of which the form is given below in Equation (6.64) and in Fig. 6.3. Of course, when $m = n$, then $\mathbf{Q}_n$ is an orthogonal matrix, $\mathbf{R}_n = \mathbf{0}$ and $\mathbf{A}\mathbf{Q}_n = \mathbf{Q}_n\mathbf{T}_n$.

The Krylov subspace $\mathscr{K}$ is determined by Equation (6.58) when the arbitrary starting vector $\mathbf{b}$ is given, but the orthonormal basis $\mathbf{Q}_m = (\mathbf{q}_1, \ldots, \mathbf{q}_m)$ must be constructed. This can be done directly, without

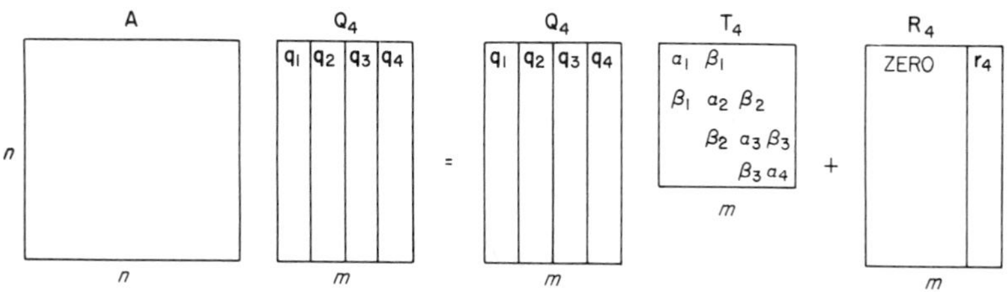

Figure 6.3 Pictorial representation of the Lanczos algorithm, Equation (6.59), for the case $m = 4$.

computing the Krylov sequence. The basis is constructed step by step in such a way that the following relation holds for *every* $j \leqslant m$:

$$\mathscr{K}^j \equiv \text{span}(\mathbf{b}, \mathbf{Ab}, \ldots, \mathbf{A}^{j-1}\mathbf{b}) = \text{span}(\mathbf{q}_1, \mathbf{q}_2, \ldots, \mathbf{q}_j). \tag{6.60}$$

In fact, since $\mathbf{T}_m$ will also be constructed step by step, it will soon become clear that m need not be fixed *a priori*. Rather, m must be regarded as a parameter which grows until "convergence" is achieved. It is this property which makes Lanczos algorithm look as if it were iterative, although it is essentially *not* iterative ($\mathbf{A}$ is *exactly* reduced to a tridiagonal matrix for $m = n$). Therefore we drop j and use m in its place in Equation (6.60):

$$\mathscr{K}^m \equiv \text{span}(\mathbf{b}, \mathbf{Ab}, \ldots, \mathbf{A}^{m-1}\mathbf{b}) = \text{span}(\mathbf{q}_1, \mathbf{q}_2, \ldots, \mathbf{q}_m). \tag{6.61}$$

We now show how successive orthonormal bases $\mathbf{Q}_m$, $m = 1, 2, \ldots$, are constructed in such a way that Equation (6.61) holds for each of them. We define $\mathbf{q}_1 = \mathbf{b}/|\mathbf{b}|$, so that (6.61) holds for $m = 1$. Assume now that (6.61) is true for some m. This means that $\mathbf{q}_m$ can be written as a linear combination of $\mathbf{b}, \ldots, \mathbf{A}^{m-1}\mathbf{b}$; consequently $\mathbf{Aq}_m$ can be written as the same combination of $\mathbf{Ab}, \ldots, \mathbf{A}^m\mathbf{b}$, so that $\mathbf{Aq}_m$ is in $\mathscr{K}^{m+1}$. If, besides, $\mathbf{Aq}_m$ is independent of $\mathbf{q}_1, \ldots, \mathbf{q}_m$, we *define* $\mathbf{q}_{m+1}$ as that vector component of $\mathbf{Aq}_m$ which is orthogonal to $\mathbf{q}_1, \ldots, \mathbf{q}_m$, conveniently normalized. Then:

$$\mathscr{K}^{m+1} = \text{span}(\mathbf{q}_1, \mathbf{q}_2, \ldots, \mathbf{q}_m, \mathbf{q}_{m+1}) \tag{6.62}$$

which proves that Equation (6.61) holds for every m *provided* $\mathbf{q}_{m+1}$ is defined as just explained. If for some m, $\mathbf{Aq}_m$ turns out not to be independent of $\mathbf{q}_1, \ldots, \mathbf{q}_m$, this is a lucky result: $\mathbf{Aq}_m$ is in $\mathscr{K}^m$, which is thus an invariant subspace ready to deliver m exact eigenpairs of $\mathbf{A}$.

Each $\mathbf{q}_i$ is orthogonal to all remaining $\mathbf{q}_j$ with $j \neq i$. In particular, since $\mathbf{Aq}_j$ is in $\mathscr{K}^{j+1}$:

$$\mathbf{q}_i^{\mathrm{T}}\mathbf{Aq}_j = 0 \qquad \text{for } j < i - 1. \tag{6.63}$$

This means that the Rayleigh matrix $\mathbf{T}_m = \mathbf{Q}_m^{\mathrm{T}}\mathbf{AQ}_m$ is of upper Hessenberg form, and since $\mathbf{T}_m$ is symmetric, then $\mathbf{T}_m$ is necessarily tridiagonal. Besides, the transpose of Equation (6.63), written with i and j interchanged and using the symmetry of $\mathbf{A}$, is $\mathbf{q}_i^{\mathrm{T}}\mathbf{Aq}_j = 0$ for $i < j - 1$, which means that $\mathbf{Aq}_j$ is already orthogonal to all $\mathbf{q}_i$ with $i < j - 1$. Thus, to compute $\mathbf{q}_{j+1}$ from $\mathbf{Aq}_j$, it suffices to orthogonalize $\mathbf{Aq}_j$ against $\mathbf{q}_{j-1}$ and $\mathbf{q}_j$ alone, and to normalize the result.

Consider now Equation (6.59) in detail. Figure 6.3 shows its more relevant features for the case $m = 4$, together with some additional notation for $\mathbf{T}_m$

which is of standard use. From Fig. 6.3 the following relations are immediate:

$$\begin{aligned}
\mathbf{Aq}_1 &= \qquad\quad \alpha_1\mathbf{q}_1 + \beta_1\mathbf{q}_2 \\
\mathbf{Aq}_2 &= \beta_1\mathbf{q}_1 + \alpha_2\mathbf{q}_2 + \beta_2\mathbf{q}_3 \\
\mathbf{Aq}_3 &= \beta_2\mathbf{q}_2 + \alpha_3\mathbf{q}_3 + \beta_3\mathbf{q}_4 \\
\mathbf{Aq}_4 &= \beta_3\mathbf{q}_3 + \alpha_4\mathbf{q}_4 \qquad\quad + \mathbf{r}_4
\end{aligned} \tag{6.64}$$

From the definition $\mathbf{T}_m = \mathbf{Q}_m^{\mathrm{T}}\mathbf{A}\mathbf{Q}_m$ we obtain $\alpha_4 = \mathbf{q}_4^{\mathrm{T}}\mathbf{A}\mathbf{q}_4$ and $\beta_3 = \mathbf{q}_3^{\mathrm{T}}\mathbf{A}\mathbf{q}_4$. The last line in Equation (6.64) can thus be written $\mathbf{r}_4 = \mathbf{A}\mathbf{q}_4 - (\mathbf{q}_3^{\mathrm{T}}\mathbf{A}\mathbf{q}_4)\mathbf{q}_3 - (\mathbf{q}_4^{\mathrm{T}}\mathbf{A}\mathbf{q}_4)\mathbf{q}_4$, which is precisely the expression needed to orthogonalize the vector $\mathbf{A}\mathbf{q}_4$ against $\mathbf{q}_3$ and $\mathbf{q}_4$ ($\mathbf{A}\mathbf{q}_4$ was shown to be already orthogonal to $\mathbf{q}_1$ and $\mathbf{q}_2$), in order to compute $\mathbf{q}_5$. Thus $\mathbf{q}_5 = \mathbf{r}_4/\beta_4$, where $\beta_4 = |\mathbf{r}_4|$, and defining $\mathbf{q}_0 = 0$ by convention we have:

$$\mathbf{A}\mathbf{q}_i = \beta_{i-1}\mathbf{q}_{i-1} + \alpha_i\mathbf{q}_i + \beta_i\mathbf{q}_{i+1} \tag{6.65}$$

for $i \leqslant m$, where the equation with $i = m$ defines $\mathbf{r}_m = \beta_m\mathbf{q}_{m+1}$. At the beginning of step m of the algorithm, $\mathbf{r}_{m-1}$ and $\beta_{m-1} = |\mathbf{r}_{m-1}|$ are available; $\mathbf{q}_m$ is computed and $\mathbf{A}\mathbf{q}_m$ is obtained. Instead of computing $\alpha_m = \mathbf{q}_m^{\mathrm{T}}\mathbf{A}\mathbf{q}_m$ from $\mathbf{A}\mathbf{q}_m$ as it is and then orthogonalizing $\mathbf{A}\mathbf{q}_m$ against $\mathbf{q}_{m-1}$ and $\mathbf{q}_m$, it is preferable to improve the numerical accuracy by first orthogonalizing $\mathbf{A}\mathbf{q}_m$ against $\mathbf{q}_{m-1}$, then computing α_m, and finally performing the remaining orthogonalization. Now, the algorithm can be explicitly given. The starting vector $\mathbf{b}$ is selected, taking advantage of any knowledge of the eigenvectors of $\mathbf{A}$ which might be available, or otherwise using some standard form like $(1, 1, \ldots, 1)^{\mathrm{T}}$ or at random. Let $\mathbf{q}_0 = \mathbf{0}$, $\mathbf{r}_0 = \mathbf{b}$ and $\beta_0 = |\mathbf{b}|$. For $m = 1, 2, \ldots,$ repeat:

Step 1 (Extend orthonormal basis). $\mathbf{q}_m \leftarrow \mathbf{r}_{m-1}/\beta_{m-1}$.
Step 2 (Find partial residual). $\mathbf{r}_m \leftarrow \mathbf{A}\mathbf{q}_m - \beta_{m-1}\mathbf{q}_{m-1}$, and store $\mathbf{q}_{m-1}$ on a peripheral device.
Step 3 (Extend diagonal of $\mathbf{T}_m$). $\alpha_m \leftarrow \mathbf{q}_m^{\mathrm{T}}\mathbf{r}_m$.
Step 4 (Complete computation of residual). $\mathbf{r}_m \leftarrow \mathbf{r}_m - \alpha_m\mathbf{q}_m$.
Step 5 (Compute magnitude of residual). $\beta_m \leftarrow |\mathbf{r}_m|$.

This sequence is repeated while necessary. The k Ritz pairs μ_i, $\mathbf{x}_i$ of $\mathbf{A}$, which are the best approximations to the eigenpairs of $\mathbf{A}$, are obtained as in the preceding section by solving the eigenproblem for $\mathbf{T}_m$:

$$\mathbf{T}_m\mathbf{h}_i = \mu_i\mathbf{h}_i, \qquad i = 1, 2, \ldots, k; \qquad k \leqslant m \tag{6.66}$$

and then computing

$$\mathbf{x}_i = \mathbf{Q}_m\mathbf{h}_i. \tag{6.67}$$

To monitor convergence, a good error indicator is $\mathbf{Ax}_i - \mu_i \mathbf{x}_i$, which, by Equations (6.67) and (6.66), is equal to $(\mathbf{AQ}_m - \mathbf{Q}_m \mathbf{T}_m)\mathbf{h}_i$, and by Equation (6.59) to $\mathbf{R}_m \mathbf{h}_i$. Thus, considering the form of $\mathbf{R}_m$ shown in Figure 6.3, we obtain:

$$\mathbf{Ax}_i - \mu_i \mathbf{x}_i = \mathbf{r}_m h_{im} \tag{6.68}$$

where $h_{i\,m}$ is the mth component of $\mathbf{h}_i$; and finally, since $|\mathbf{r}_m| = \beta_m \geqslant 0$:

$$|\mathbf{Ax}_i - \mu_i \mathbf{x}_i| = \beta_m |h_{i\,m}|. \tag{6.69}$$

The reason for computing β_m at Step 5 of the algorithm, rather than at the beginning of the next cycle, is to have β_m available for use in Equation (6.69). Then, when $\mathbf{h}_i$ is obtained from Equation (6.66), the error estimator can be computed without computing $\mathbf{x}_i$, and thus without using $\mathbf{Q}_m$ which was assumed to be kept in peripheral storage. Besides, it is possible to compute h_{im} without computing all of $\mathbf{h}_i$. Using Equation (6.13), we can conclude from Equation (6.69) that there must exist an eigenvalue λ of $\mathbf{A}$ in the range:

$$\mu_i - \beta_m |h_{im}| \leqslant \lambda \leqslant \mu_i + \beta_m |h_{im}|. \tag{6.70}$$

The Lanczos algorithm can be used without any modification to solve the generalized eigenproblem reduced to standard form, Equations (6.11) or (6.12). For example, for Equation (6.11), $\mathbf{U}_B^{-T}\mathbf{A}\mathbf{U}_B^{-1}$ is used in place of $\mathbf{A}$ to compute the required products by the appropriate vectors. For this purpose only $\mathbf{A}$ and $\mathbf{U}_B$ are stored, and a product of the form $\mathbf{z} = \mathbf{U}_B^{-T}\mathbf{A}\mathbf{U}_B^{-1}\mathbf{u}$ is computed as follows: first find $\mathbf{v} = \mathbf{U}_B^{-1}\mathbf{u}$ using, for example, the ideas discussed in Section 7.28; then compute $\mathbf{w} = \mathbf{Av}$, and finally $\mathbf{z} = \mathbf{U}_B^{-T}\mathbf{w}$ using this time the ideas of Chapter 9. The Lanczos algorithm itself remains the same.

The form $\mathbf{B}^{-1}\mathbf{Ax} = \lambda\mathbf{x}$ can also be used without having to calculate $\mathbf{B}^{-1}$ explicitly. The procedure requires the solution of a linear system with $\mathbf{B}$ as the matrix of coefficients at each step, and is particularly convenient when $\mathbf{B}$ cannot be conveniently factorized (because of being too large) and Equation (6.11) cannot be applied. When $\mathbf{B}$ cannot be factorized, the linear equations are solved iteratively. The basic recurrence relation of the Lanczos algorithm, Equation (6.65), written with $\mathbf{B}^{-1}\mathbf{A}$ in place of $\mathbf{A}$, takes the form:

$$\mathbf{Aq}_i = \beta_{i-1}\mathbf{Bq}_{i-1} + \alpha_i \mathbf{Bq}_i + \beta_i \mathbf{Bq}_{i+1}. \tag{6.71}$$

The algorithm proceeds as before, except that the columns of $\mathbf{Q}_m$ are now $\mathbf{B}$-orthogonal: $\mathbf{Q}_m^T\mathbf{B}\mathbf{Q}_m = \mathbf{I}_m$. A tridiagonal matrix $\mathbf{T}_m$ is obtained and the Ritz pairs of the pencil $\mathbf{A}, \mathbf{B}$ are computed as before, using Equations (6.66) and (6.67). When eigenvalues in an interval and the corresponding eigenvectors of $\mathbf{A}, \mathbf{B}$ are wanted, it is advantageous to apply the method on a sequence of shifted and inverted problems of the form $\mathbf{B}, \mathbf{A} - \sigma\mathbf{B}$ (Ericsson and Ruhe,

1980). The program, called STLM and listed on page 86 of the Catalog (Heath, 1982), is available. A very good description of the Lanczos algorithm and a survey of current research on the subject was published by Scott (1981).

6.12. Lanczos algorithm in practice

The actual behaviour of the algorithm in practice differs from theory. Round-off destroys the orthogonality of the columns of $\mathbf{Q}_m$ to the extent that they become linearly dependent. After the works of Paige (1971, 1972, 1976), and of Takahashi and Natori (1972), this phenomenon is known to be associated with the convergence of a Ritz pair to an eigenpair of $\mathbf{A}$. As execution of the algorithm proceeds, a Ritz pair converges and at the same time the columns of $\mathbf{Q}_m$ become linearly dependent. If execution continues, new Ritz pairs may converge; however, since linear independence no longer exists, some of the new Ritz pairs may, and will, approximate the same eigenpair of $\mathbf{A}$. Many redundant copies of old eigenpairs may result, and of course the number of steps of the algorithm is not limited to $m \leqslant n$.

This scheme is still capable of delivering useful information. Paige's suggestion was to continue execution of the algorithm while storage permits, and then to compute all Ritz pairs and discard the redundant ones. The formation of redundant Ritz pairs can be avoided by enforcing orthogonality. The *Lanczos algorithm with reorthogonalization* does so by explicitly orthogonalizing each $\mathbf{q}_{m+1}$ against all $\mathbf{q}_i$, $i = 1, \ldots, m$. The cost is high but can be halved by storing $\mathbf{Q}_m$ in factored form (Golub *et al.*, 1972). The factors are reflector matrices (see Section 6.5). *Selective orthogonalization* (Parlett, 1980; Parlett and Scott, 1979) is based on the observation that $\mathbf{q}_{m+1}$ tilts in the direction of those Ritz vectors $\mathbf{x}_i$ which have converged close to eigenvectors of $\mathbf{A}$. A careful error analysis is used to identify such eigenvectors without computing them and also to detect situations where reorthogonalization is beneficial. Thus, reorthogonalization is not performed at every step, and when performed, only some *threshold* Ritz vectors are involved, with the hope that a reasonable degree of linear independence and global orthogonality, say $\kappa_m \equiv \|\mathbf{I} - \mathbf{Q}_m^{\mathrm{T}}\mathbf{Q}_m\| < 0.01$, will be preserved in this way. Experience shows that κ_m must be within an order of magnitude from $\sqrt{\varepsilon}$, where ε is the machine precision. The main features of the resulting algorithm are the following:

(1) The formation of redundant Ritz pairs is prevented.
(2) The number m of steps is kept to a minimum, and can never exceed n. The procedure terminates when β_m is sufficiently small.
(3) When the multiplicity of an eigenvalue of $\mathbf{A}$, say λ_1, is larger than 1, the

corresponding set of orthonormal eigenvectors can be completely determined. This is so because selective orthogonalization keeps every residual orthogonal to the previously converged eigenvectors of λ_1, but does not prevent roundoff from introducing components of other eigenvectors of λ_1. These components will eventually converge, until the entire eigenspace of λ_1 is spanned.

(4) There are no user-specified tolerances or parameters. The algorithm can be used automatically, without expert advice.

(5) As soon as a Ritz vector is known to have converged, it must be computed and stored even if it is not wanted as a final result. This makes the procedure suitable for computing a few extreme eigenpairs. The eigenvectors corresponding to extreme eigenvalues converge first, so that when some interior eigenpairs are needed, some unwanted eigenvectors usually have to be computed and stored.

There exists a connection between the Lanczos algorithm and the method of conjugate gradients for solving the system of linear equations $\mathbf{Au} = \mathbf{v}_1$, with $\mathbf{u}_0 = 0$ as the starting iterate (Cullum and Willoughby, 1977; 1978). This interpretation has led to a better understanding of the numerical behaviour of the Lanczos procedure in the case where classical requirements of global orthogonality between the vectors $\mathbf{q}_i$ are completely abandoned. If we require every eigenvalue of $\mathbf{T}_m$ to approximate an eigenvalue of $\mathbf{A}$, then some degree of orthogonality of the $\mathbf{q}_i$ must be maintained, but if orthogonality is not maintained, then it is still possible to prove that a subset of the eigenvalues of $\mathbf{T}_m$ are eigenvalues of $\mathbf{A}$. For $m > n$ and sufficiently large it is thus possible to obtain all eigenvalues of $\mathbf{A}$, or all eigenvalues of $\mathbf{A}$ in a specified interval. The main features of the resulting *Lanczos algorithm with no orthogonalization* are as follows:

(1) $\mathbf{T}_m$ is computed for $m > n$, disregarding the total loss of global orthogonality of the vectors $\mathbf{q}_i$. The maximum value of m depends on $\mathbf{A}$'s spectrum. For a reasonably uniform distribution $m \sim 2n$ is sufficient in practice. If $\mathbf{A}$ has clusters of eigenvalues, approximations to each cluster are usually obtained with $m = 2n$, but $m = 6n$ may be required to resolve individual eigenvalues in the clusters. Cases requiring $m = 10n$ are known.

(2) Storing all $\mathbf{q}_i$ when n is large and $m > n$ would be a practical impossibility. Thus, simply, the $\mathbf{q}_i$ are not stored and the algorithm is restricted to the computation of eigenvalues. The storage requirements are remarkably low. Eigenvectors can be computed, if necessary, using, for example, inverse iteration.

(3) The algorithm is now essentially iterative. A test is needed to discard spurious eigenvalues and to find out when the correct ones have

converged sufficiently. A test based on a comparison between the eigenvalues of $\mathbf{T}_m$ and those of $\mathbf{T}_{m-1}$ (van Kats and van der Vorst, 1977) requires user-specified tolerances. A better test is based on the matrix $\hat{\mathbf{T}}_m$ of order $m - 1$, obtained from $\mathbf{T}_m$ by deleting the first row and the first column. The key observation is that, if μ is an eigenvalue of $\mathbf{T}_m$ of multiplicity 1, then there is an eigenvalue λ of $\mathbf{A}$ such that the bound for $|\lambda - \mu|$ is inversely proportional to $d = \mathrm{Det}(\mu\mathbf{I} - \hat{\mathbf{T}}_m)$. If μ is close to an eigenvalue of $\hat{\mathbf{T}}_m$, this bound is large and μ may not be a good approximation to any eigenvalue of $\mathbf{A}$. On the other hand, if μ is sufficiently far from any eigenvalue of $\hat{\mathbf{T}}_m$, then $1/d$ is small and there must be an eigenvalue of $\mathbf{A}$ very close to μ, and μ must be kept as an approximation to an eigenvalue of $\mathbf{A}$. Otherwise μ is labelled as spurius, each eigenvalue of $\hat{\mathbf{T}}_m$ being allowed to eliminate at most one eigenvalue from $\mathbf{T}_m$. An eigenvalue of $\mathbf{T}_m$ which has a multiplicity greater than 1 is accepted as good. Theoretically $\mathbf{T}_m$ cannot have such eigenvalues, but numerically it does.

(4) A limitation for the test comes from the fact that the algorithm does not detect the multiplicities of the eigenvalues of $\mathbf{A}$. Thus, counting the eigenvalues found at some step will not provide an answer to the fundamental question as to whether all eigenvalues of $\mathbf{A}$ have been discovered. This difficulty is overcome by comparing the number of good eigenvalues obtained for two different values of m, say m_0 and $m_0 + n/2$. Termination occurs when both numbers coincide. When multiplicities are required, they can be obtained by bisection.

(5) If $\mathbf{A}$ is sparse and $\mathbf{Ax}$ can be computed in kn operations where $k \ll n$, then all eigenvalues of $\mathbf{A}$ can be computed with $O(m\, n)$ operations and using $O(m)$ storage. All the eigenvalues of $\mathbf{T}_m$ can be found in $O(m^2)$ operations and $O(m)$ storage. If m is a small multiple of n, then $O(n^2)$ operations and $O(n)$ storage are needed to compute the complete spectrum of $\mathbf{A}$.

A version of the Lanczos algorithm with *periodic reorthogonalization* has been suggested (Grcar, 1981). Several Lanczos programs for solving both the standard and the generalized eigenvalue problem are listed in the Catalog (Heath, 1982) and available.

6.13. Block Lanczos and band Lanczos algorithms

If $\mathbf{b}$ is an arbitrary starting vector and $\mathbf{q}_1 = \mathbf{b}/|\mathbf{b}|$, Equation (6.60) defines the simple Krylov subspace. This definition can be generalized: starting with a set of k arbitrary orthonormal vectors, arranged as the columns of the n by k

matrix $\mathbf{Q}_1$, the subspace is defined by

$$\hat{\mathscr{K}}^{km} = \text{span}(\mathbf{Q}_1, \mathbf{AQ}_1, \ldots, \mathbf{A}^{m-1}\mathbf{Q}_1). \tag{6.72}$$

The basic Lanczos algorithm can be correspondingly generalized. Each column n-vector now becomes an n by k matrix, and each scalar, a k by k matrix. The tridiagonal matrix is now $\hat{\mathbf{T}}_m$, a block-tridiagonal symmetric matrix, with k by k blocks on the diagonal and both codiagonals. The blocks on the upper codiagonal are lower triangular, and those on the lower codiagonal are upper triangular, so that $\hat{\mathbf{T}}_m$ is in fact a band matrix with bandwidth $2k + 1$. The generalization was described by Cullum and Donath (1974) and by Golub and Underwood (1977).

We need the following result: let $\mathbf{R}$ be any nonnull n by k matrix, and let $r = \text{rank}(\mathbf{R})$. Then $\mathbf{R}$ has a unique factorization $\mathbf{R} = \mathbf{QB}$, where $\mathbf{Q}$ is n by r with its columns orthonormalized: $\mathbf{Q}^{\mathrm{T}}\mathbf{Q} = \mathbf{I}_r$, and $\mathbf{B}$ is of r by k with zeros in its lower triangle: $B_{ij} = 0$ if $j < i$. Note that $r \leqslant k$. In particular, if $k <$ n and $\mathbf{R}$ has full rank $r = k$, then $\mathbf{B}$ is square upper triangular of k by k. This result is the matrix formulation of the Gram–Schmidt orthonormalization procedure when applied to the columns of $\mathbf{R}$ in the natural order.

Figure 6.4 displays the fundamental relation $\mathbf{A}\hat{\mathbf{Q}}_m = \hat{\mathbf{Q}}_m\hat{\mathbf{T}}_m + \hat{\mathbf{R}}_m$ for the case $m = 4$. Equations (6.64) now take the form:

$$\begin{aligned}
\mathbf{AQ}_1 &= \phantom{\mathbf{Q}_1\mathbf{B}_1^{\mathrm{T}} + {}} \mathbf{Q}_1\mathbf{A}_1 + \mathbf{Q}_2\mathbf{B}_1 \\
\mathbf{AQ}_2 &= \mathbf{Q}_1\mathbf{B}_1^{\mathrm{T}} + \mathbf{Q}_2\mathbf{A}_2 + \mathbf{Q}_3\mathbf{B}_2 \\
\mathbf{AQ}_3 &= \mathbf{Q}_2\mathbf{B}_2^{\mathrm{T}} + \mathbf{Q}_3\mathbf{A}_3 + \mathbf{Q}_4\mathbf{B}_3 \\
\mathbf{AQ}_4 &= \mathbf{Q}_3\mathbf{B}_3^{\mathrm{T}} + \mathbf{Q}_4\mathbf{A}_4 \qquad\quad + \mathbf{R}_4
\end{aligned} \tag{6.73}$$

We assume for generality that the Krylov subspace is defined by giving k independent n-vectors, which, for the sake of recurrence, are stored in $\mathbf{R}_0$. Then, the first step of the following algorithm computes $\mathbf{Q}_1$, while $\mathbf{B}_0$, which is also obtained, is not needed. We also assume, for simplicity, that $\mathbf{A}^{m-1}\mathbf{Q}_1$ has full rank k, and as a consequence so also have all $\mathbf{B}_i$. The block Lanczos

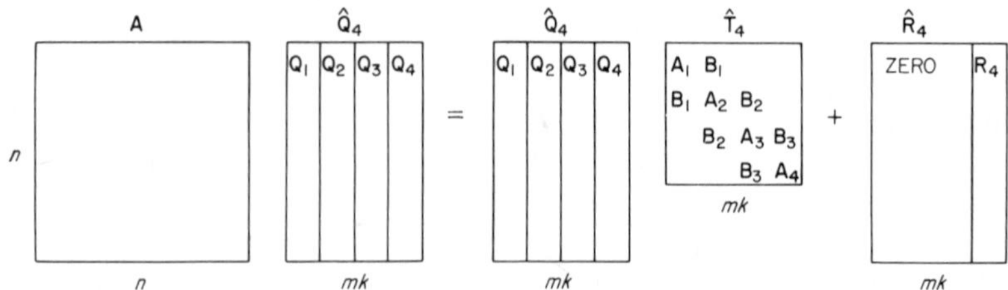

Figure 6.4 Pictorial representation of the block-Lanczos algorithm for the case $m = 4$.

algorithm is similar to the simple algorithm given in Section 6.11, except that now the first step is the factorization of $\mathbf{R}_{m-1}$ to obtain both $\mathbf{Q}_m$ and $\mathbf{B}_{m-1}$. Let $\mathbf{Q}_0 = 0$. For $m = 1, 2, \ldots,$ repeat:

Step 1 (Factorize $\mathbf{R}_{m-1}$ to compute $\mathbf{Q}_m$ and the upper triangular $\mathbf{B}_{m-1}$). $\mathbf{R}_{m-1} = \mathbf{Q}_m\mathbf{B}_{m-1}$.
Step 2 (Find partial residual). $\mathbf{R}_m \leftarrow \mathbf{A}\mathbf{Q}_m - \mathbf{Q}_{m-1}\mathbf{B}_{m-1}^{\mathrm{T}}$, and store $\mathbf{Q}_{m-1}$ on a peripheral device.
Step 3 (Extend diagonal of $\hat{\mathbf{T}}_m$). $\mathbf{A}_m \leftarrow \mathbf{Q}_m^{\mathrm{T}}\mathbf{R}_m$.
Step 4 (Complete computation of residual). $\mathbf{R}_m \leftarrow \mathbf{R}_m - \mathbf{Q}_m\mathbf{A}_m$.

The desired Ritz pairs are computed from $\hat{\mathbf{T}}_m\mathbf{h}_i = \mu_i\mathbf{h}_i$ and $\mathbf{x}_i = \hat{\mathbf{Q}}_m\mathbf{h}_i$. The approximations are tested as before, until sufficient accuracy is achieved. This algorithm encounters the same numerical difficulties as the simple one, and can be used with complete reorthogonalization of each $\mathbf{Q}_m$ against every preceding $\mathbf{Q}_i$, with selective reorthogonalization, or without any reorthogonalization. Despite its greater complexity, the advantages are remarkable:

(1) Multiple eigenvalues of $\mathbf{A}$ with a multiplicity not exceeding k can be predicted in a straightforward manner, not just because spurious vector components generated by round-off grow, as in the case of the simple algorithm with selective reorthogonalization.
(2) The bounds on the rate of convergence are better than those of the simple algorithm. The block Lanczos algorithm is superior to the single vector version in a way which is similar in many respects to the way that simultaneous iteration is superior to the simple power method. This result holds for exact computation, and was obtained by Saad (1980).

The cost of computing the eigenvalues of $\hat{\mathbf{T}}_m$ is high. Besides, the band is full. In practice this forces k to be a small number, usually 2, 3, or 4, when $\mathbf{A}$ is large. $\mathbf{A}$ itself may have a few nonzeros per row, and other methods may be competitive unless the blocks are small.

An alternative formulation of the block Lanczos algorithm was presented by Ruhe (1979). The original matrix $\mathbf{A}$ is directly reduced to band form by means of recurrence relations written in terms of n-vectors, not n by k matrices. The algorithm is identical to block Lanczos, but has the advantage that no factorization of a matrix is necessary.

Programs which employ the block Lanczos algorithm to solve the standard and the generalized eigenproblem are listed in the Catalog (Heath, 1982).

Singular values of unsymmetric or rectangular matrices can be computed using this procedure (Cullum *et al.*, 1981). A technique which employs an augmented system and avoids destroying sparsity has been suggested by Golub *et al.* (1981).

6.14. Trace minimization

This method computes simultaneously the p smallest or largest eigenvalues and corresponding eigenvectors of the generalized eigenproblem, or of its particular case the standard eigenproblem. This is achieved by minimizing the trace of a p by p matrix subject to quadratic constraints. Consider the set of all n by p matrices **Y** which have **B**-orthonormalized columns:

$$\mathbf{Y}^{\mathrm{T}}\mathbf{B}\mathbf{Y} = \mathbf{I}_p. \tag{6.74}$$

For each such **Y** consider trace $(\mathbf{Y}^{\mathrm{T}}\mathbf{A}\mathbf{Y})$. The minimum value of this trace is obtained when $\mathbf{Y} = \mathbf{X}_p$, where the p columns of $\mathbf{X}_p$ are the eigenvectors corresponding to the smallest eigenvalues. Besides, this minimum trace is equal to the sum of the p smallest eigenvalues. Thus:

$$\min_{\mathbf{Y}} \{\mathrm{trace}(\mathbf{Y}^{\mathrm{T}}\mathbf{A}\mathbf{Y}) \mid \mathbf{Y}^{\mathrm{T}}\mathbf{B}\mathbf{Y} = \mathbf{I}_p\} = \mathrm{trace}(\mathbf{X}_p^{\mathrm{T}}\mathbf{A}\mathbf{X}_p) = \sum_{i=1}^{p} \lambda_i \tag{6.75}$$

The method is stated as a quadratic minimization problem:

$$\text{minimize trace}(\mathbf{Y}^{\mathrm{T}}\mathbf{A}\mathbf{Y}) \tag{6.76}$$

subject to the constraints given by Equation (6.74). The approach to use for solving this problem is to compute a sequence of iterates $\mathbf{Y}_{k+1} = f(\mathbf{Y}_k)$ such that

$$\mathrm{trace}(\mathbf{Y}_{k+1}^{\mathrm{T}}\mathbf{A}\mathbf{Y}_{k+1}) < \mathrm{trace}(\mathbf{Y}_k^{\mathrm{T}}\mathbf{A}\mathbf{Y}_k) \tag{6.77}$$

and Equation (6.74) is satisfied. The rate of convergence is that of simultaneous inverse iteration, i.e., column j of **Y** globally converges to the eigenvector $\mathbf{x}_j$ with a rate bounded by $|\lambda_j/\lambda_{p+1}|$. The method appears to be competitive with Lanczos algorithm, at least for matrices of moderate size. It has been developed by Wisniewski (1981), and the program is available (Heath, 1982, p. 87).

6.15. Eigenanalysis of hermitian matrices

The eigenvalue problem $\mathbf{A}\mathbf{x} = \lambda\mathbf{x}$ where **A** is hermitian, i.e., $\mathbf{A}^{\mathrm{H}} = \mathbf{A}$, can be solved in the real field by defining a real symmetric matrix $\mathbf{A}'$ of twice the order. Let $\mathbf{A} = \mathbf{P} + \mathrm{i}\mathbf{Q}$, where **P** and **Q** are real, $\mathbf{P}^{\mathrm{T}} = \mathbf{P}$, $\mathbf{Q}^{\mathrm{T}} = -\mathbf{Q}$. Let $\mathbf{x} = \mathbf{u} + \mathrm{i}\mathbf{v}$, where **u** and **v** are real. All eigenvalues of **A** are real. The eigenvalue problem

$$(\mathbf{P} + \mathrm{i}\mathbf{Q})(\mathbf{u} + \mathrm{i}\mathbf{v}) = \lambda(\mathbf{u} + \mathrm{i}\mathbf{v}) \tag{6.78}$$

can be written

$$\mathbf{A}'\mathbf{w} = \lambda \mathbf{w}, \tag{6.79}$$

where

$$\mathbf{A}' = \begin{vmatrix} \mathbf{P} & -\mathbf{Q} \\ \mathbf{Q} & \mathbf{P} \end{vmatrix}.$$

For each λ and $\mathbf{x}$, there are two different solutions $\mathbf{w}$:

$$\mathbf{w}_1 = \begin{vmatrix} \mathbf{u} \\ \mathbf{v} \end{vmatrix} \qquad \mathbf{w}_2 = \begin{vmatrix} -\mathbf{v} \\ \mathbf{u} \end{vmatrix}. \tag{6.80}$$

Similarly, the generalized eigenproblem $\mathbf{Ax} = \lambda \mathbf{Bx}$ with $\mathbf{A}^{\mathrm{H}} = \mathbf{A} = \mathbf{P} + \mathrm{i}\mathbf{Q}$, $\mathbf{B}^{\mathrm{H}} = \mathbf{B} = \mathbf{R} + \mathrm{i}\mathbf{S}$, becomes

$$\mathbf{A}'\mathbf{w} = \lambda \mathbf{B}'\mathbf{w} \tag{6.81}$$

where

$$\mathbf{A}' = \begin{vmatrix} \mathbf{P} & -\mathbf{Q} \\ \mathbf{Q} & \mathbf{P} \end{vmatrix}; \qquad \mathbf{B}' = \begin{vmatrix} \mathbf{R} & -\mathbf{S} \\ \mathbf{S} & \mathbf{R} \end{vmatrix}$$

and $\mathbf{x} = \mathbf{u} + \mathrm{i}\mathbf{v}$. The eigenvectors $\mathbf{w}_1$ and $\mathbf{w}_2$ are also correct in this case.

Software for real matrices can thus be used to solve eigenproblems with complex hermitian matrices. However, when the available computer features a good implementation of complex arithmetic, it should be preferable to work with the original hermitian matrix.

6.16. Unsymmetric eigenproblems

A real unsymmetric matrix $\mathbf{A}$ of order n has n eigenvalues, which in general may be complex and of any multiplicities up to n. When the eigenvalues are distinct, to each one there corresponds an eigenvector, the n eigenvectors being linearly independent. These are the *right-hand eigenvectors* because they are solutions of $\mathbf{Ax} = \lambda \mathbf{x}$, and they may be, in general, complex. The transpose matrix $\mathbf{A}^{\mathrm{T}}$ has the same eigenvalues as $\mathbf{A}$, and its eigenvectors, solutions of $\mathbf{A}^{\mathrm{T}}\mathbf{y} = \lambda \mathbf{y}$ or $\mathbf{y}^{\mathrm{T}}\mathbf{A} = \lambda \mathbf{y}^{\mathrm{T}}$, are the *left-hand eigenvectors* of $\mathbf{A}$. Both sets fulfil $\mathbf{x}_i^{\mathrm{T}}\mathbf{y}_j = 0$ if $\lambda_i \neq \lambda_j$, and $\mathbf{x}_i^{\mathrm{T}}\mathbf{y}_i \neq 0$, so that they form a biorthogonal system. However, when multiple eigenvalues exist, the system of eigenvectors may be defective and it may not be possible to diagonalize $\mathbf{A}$.

Unsymmetric eigenproblems arise in practice, an important example being the analysis of structures where fluid damping forces are present, such as in aircraft flutter analysis. When facing such a problem, it is convenient to see whether the given matrix can be permuted to block triangular form, using the techniques discussed in Sections 5.9 and 5.10. The eigenvalues of the whole matrix are just the union of those of the diagonal blocks, and the eigenvectors can easily be obtained once the eigenvalues are known. Besides, it may happen that some blocks of order 1 are obtained, each consisting of a single element; in this case each single diagonal element is an eigenvalue. The procedure, combined with balancing to improve numerical accuracy of the succeeding calculations, is discussed in detail by Parlett and Reinsch (1969), and is implemented in EISPACK (Smith *et al.*, 1976).

The problem for each diagonal block can be solved using Sturm sequences or simultaneous iteration (Gupta, 1976; Dong, 1977). In particular the latter method has been well tried for large sparse unsymmetric matrices (Clint and Jennings, 1971; Jennings and W. J. Stewart, 1975; G. W. Stewart, 1976b). An algorithm which obtains both right-hand and left-hand eigenvectors for the standard unsymmetric eigenproblem has been published by W. J. Stewart and Jennings (1981), and a different technique was suggested by Saad (1981). The Lanczos method can also be used for the unsymmetric eigenproblem (Paige, 1974; Brännström, 1973). Saad (1982) presents the *Lanczos biorthogonalization algorithm* and other methods for large unsymmetric systems, reporting both theoretical results and numerical experiments. Reduction should also be considered for very sparse unsymmetric matrices, see Section 6.5. Lewis (1977) reduces the unsymmetric eigenproblem to a series of symmetric problems, using a generalization of Rayleigh quotient iteration with singular vectors; this algorithm can find a few interior eigenvalues.

CHAPTER 7

Sparse Matrix Algebra

7.1. Introduction

In this chapter we discuss the elementary operations of sparse matrix algebra: transposition, permutation of rows and columns, ordering of a sparse representation, addition and multiplication of two sparse matrices, and multiplication of a sparse matrix and a vector. Addition and multiplication of sparse vectors was considered in Chapter 1, and the reader is expected to be familiar with this material.

We also consider the triangular factorization of a symmetric positive definite sparse matrix, where diagonal pivoting is numerically stable, and sparse forward and backward substitution. The purpose is to examine the algorithmic aspects of elimination in the case where the lower triangle of the matrix, which contains the nonzero elements to be eliminated, is not explicitly stored in the computer, and the row-wise format makes column scanning difficult to program efficiently.

Sparse matrix algebra is an important part of sparse matrix technology. There are abundant examples of algorithms which employ operations with sparse matrices: hypermatrix and supersparse techniques (Section 1.11), assembly of finite element equations (Chapter 8), ordering of a row-wise representation before Gauss elimination, and many others. All the operations are trivial for full matrices, and even for band matrices, but they are not for matrices stored in sparse format. Here we concentrate on algorithms which use the sparse row-wise format discussed in Sections 1.8 and 1.9. The algorithms require expert programming if good results are expected. The central idea is to design the algorithms in such a way that the total storage and the number of arithmetic operations required to perform a certain matrix operation, be linear with, or be bounded by some slowly increasing function of, the number of nonzeros in the matrix rather than the total number of elements.

Not much attention has been paid to sparse matrix algebra in the literature. The subject was systematically explored by Gustavson at the Watson Research Center of IBM. Several reports and papers were published in the period from 1972 to 1976. Much of the material we present in connection with sparse matrix algebra is based on these developments, although a few other authors have also been concerned with the subject, and have made useful contributions.

Fortran is now a universally accepted language. The algorithms in this chapter are given directly in Fortran, and Fortran symbols are used in the text whenever possible in order to avoid unnecessary duplication of symbols. The algorithms are not written as subroutines because they can be used either as subroutines or as sections of other programs. Transforming them into subroutines only requires a SUBROUTINE statement, which can easily be prepared by the user because input parameters and results are clearly specified. Of course, a RETURN and an END statement are also needed. All comments are made separately, but the reader can optionally punch the text on comment cards. The algorithms have been used and tested during several years. They are carefully explained and expected to be efficient and compatible with most existing installations.

A few remarks must be made. Consider the following DO loop, where IA is an array of row pointers for the row-wise representation of a sparse matrix:

```
      DO 10 K=IA(I),IA(I+1)-1
      ...
10    CONTINUE
      ...
```

The meaning of the DO statement is clear: the loop must be executed for values of K ranging from IA(I) to IA(I+1)−1 in increments of 1. If IA(I+1) −1 < IA(I), a situation which arises when row I of the matrix is empty, the loop must not be executed. However, some installations will reject the spelling of the DO statement, or will execute the loop once even when IA(I + 1) − 1 < IA(I). Both difficulties are avoided and the code is made compatible with most installations by writing it as follows:

```
      IAA=IA(I)
      IAB=IA(I+1)-1
      IF(IAB.LT.IAA) GO TO 20
      DO 10 K=IAA,IAB
      ...
10    CONTINUE
20    ...
```

Some compilers optimize DO loops by taking outside every calculation which is independent of the DO parameter. The programmer can write complete expressions inside the loop. The resulting code resembles the mathematical formulae and is easy to understand, but will not operate efficiently in installations without DO optimization. It lacks transportability. Our codes are, instead, already optimized. They are slightly more difficult to understand, but will operate efficiently on any computer.

Modern pipelined computers employing systolic arrays of processors can be used for performing matrix operations like multiplication and **LU** factorization efficiently (Kung and Leiserson, 1979).

7.2. Transposition of a sparse matrix

There is a simple algorithm which transforms a row-wise representation of a matrix into a column-wise representation of the same matrix, or vice versa (Gustavson, 1976a, 1978). Since a column-wise representation of the matrix is a row-wise representation of the transpose, the algorithm effectively transposes the matrix. A further property of the algorithm is that the resulting representation is ordered in the sense that the column indices of the elements in each row are obtained in the natural increasing order. Therefore, if the algorithm is used twice to transpose a matrix originally given in an unordered representation, an ordered representation of the same matrix is obtained. When the matrix is symmetric and the representation complete, it is sufficient to transpose it only once to order the representation, although usually upper rather than complete representations are employed for symmetric matrices. The same algorithm, with slight modifications, can be used to permute rows and/or columns of a sparse matrix.

An interesting and important possibility arises when a certain matrix operation is performed using an algorithm which comprises a symbolic and a numerical section, and it is desired that the result be ordered. Since the structure of the matrix, as determined by the symbolic section of the algorithm, will not be altered by the numerical section, it is convenient to order the structure alone *before* performing the numerical computations. The sequence of procedures is as follows:

(1) Determine the structure of the resulting matrix by using the symbolic section of the given algorithm.
(2) Order the structure by using the transposition algorithm twice.
(3) Compute the numerical values using the numerical section of the given algorithm.

This sequence is particularly convenient when many matrices, having the same structure but different numerical values, have to be computed. Another important case is Gauss elimination, which can be performed numerically only if the structure of the resulting matrix is ordered.

The algorithm of Gustavson was extended by Szyld and Vishnepolsky (1982). Their version runs faster in some cases, particularly if the resulting matrix is used with its indices unordered, and can be used to obtain a submatrix of a sparse matrix. They have also developed an algorithm for permuted transposition when only the original matrix is kept in core and the resulting one is written on secondary storage.

Let IA, JA, AN be some sparse representation of a matrix with N rows and M columns. We wish to obtain IAT, JAT, ANT, the sparse representation of the transposed matrix. The question "what are the elements in a given column of IA, JA, AN?" would lead to a very inefficient inspection of IA and JA. Instead, we define M lists of integers, initially empty, each with a pointer to the first free place, initially the first place. Another M lists of real numbers are also defined. Next, we run over all the nonzeros of the matrix. For each nonzero I, J, we add I to the J-th list of integers and the value of the nonzero to the J-th list of real numbers, and we increment the corresponding pointer. The following example illustrates the procedure.

Consider the following sparse matrix where, for simplicity, the numerical values of the nonzeros are omitted:

$$\mathbf{A} = \begin{array}{c|cccccc|} & 1 & 2 & 3 & 4 & 5 & 6 \\ \hline 1 & 0 & 0 & x & 0 & x & x \\ 2 & x & 0 & 0 & x & 0 & 0 \\ 3 & 0 & 0 & x & x & 0 & 0 \\ 4 & x & 0 & x & x & 0 & 0 \\ 5 & 0 & x & 0 & 0 & x & x \end{array} \qquad (7.1)$$

which is described in RR(C)U by:

IA = 1 4 6 8 11 14
JA = 5 6 3, 4 1, 3 4, 4 3 1, 2 6 5
row = 1 2 3 4 5

The array AN is omitted in this example. Since the matrix has 6 columns, we define six lists. Then we run over row 1, which contains the column indices 5, 6 and 3, and add 1 to the lists 5, 6 and 3:

1:
2:
3: 1
4:
5: 1
6: 1

Next, we add 2 to the lists 4 and 1:

1: 2
2:
3: 1
4: 2
5: 1
6: 1

After all five rows have been processed, the lists are:

1: 2 4
2: 5
3: 1 3 4
4: 2 3 4
5: 1 5
6: 1 5

or:

JAT = 2 4, 5, 1 3 4, 2 3 4, 1 5, 1 5
column 1 2 3 4 5 6

which is (except for IAT and ANT) a CR(C)O of the given matrix, or a RR(C)O of the transposed matrix. IAT is obtained simply by counting the elements in each list, and ANT, if required, can also be obtained by adding the actual value of each nonzero, stored in AN, to the lists of real numbers, immediately after each integer is added to the lists of integers.

In practice, the lists are defined directly in the arrays JAT and ANT, and the pointers to the first free place in each list are stored directly in IAT. Thus, no additional storage is required, and data movement in the computer memory is minimized. The complete algorithm is presented and discussed in detail in the next section.

7.3. Algorithm for the transposition of a general sparse matrix

Input:	IA, JA, AN	given matrix in RR(C)U.
	N	number of rows of the matrix.
	M	number of columns of the matrix.
Output:	IAT, JAT, ANT	transposed matrix in RR(C)O.

```
          MH=M+1
          NH=N+1
          DO 10 I=2,MH
    10    IAT(I)=0
          IAB=IA(NH)-1
          DO 20 I=1,IAB
          J=JA(I)+2
          IF(J.LE.MH)IAT(J)=IAT(J)+1
    20    CONTINUE
          IAT(1)=1
          IAT(2)=1
```

```
12.             IF(M.EQ.1)GO TO 40
13.             DO 30 I=3,MH
14.     30      IAT(I)=IAT(I)+IAT(I-1)
15.     40      DO 60 I=1,N
16.             IAA=IA(I)
17.             IAB=IA(I+1)-1
18.             IF(IAB.LT.IAA)GO TO 60
19.             DO 50 JP=IAA,IAB
20.             J=JA(JP)+1
21.             K=IAT(J)
22.             JAT(K)=I
23.             ANT(K)=AN(JP)
24.     50      IAT(J)=K+1
25.     60      CONTINUE
```

This algorithm transposes an N × M sparse matrix. M lists are defined in each of the arrays JAT and ANT. Pointers to the first place of each list are set in the array IAT as follows. The number of elements in each list is determined in lines 6 to 9: just after line 9 has been processed, IAT(J) contains the number of elements in the column J − 2 of the matrix, for J in the range 3 to M + 1. The pointers themselves are constructed in lines 13 and 14: when line 14 has been processed, IAT(I) points to the position in JAT and ANT where the list number I − 1 starts, for I − 1 in the range 1 to M. In this way, when elements are added to the list I − 1 and its pointer IAT(I) is incremented, IAT(I) automatically becomes the pointer to the first place of the list I, which follows immediately after the list I − 1 in the arrays JAT and ANT. This result, which is in agreement with the definition of the pointers given in Chapter 1, is obtained here with a minimum of computational effort.

The loop DO 60 runs over each row of the matrix and adds elements to the lists defined in the arrays JAT and ANT. In line 20, a nonzero is found in row I, column J − 1 of the matrix. In line 21, K points to the position in JAT and ANT corresponding to the first free position of the list J − 1. In lines 22 and 23, the row index I and the value AN(JP) of the nonzero are added to the lists JAT and ANT, respectively, and in line 24 the pointer IAT(J) is incremented.

7.4. Ordering a sparse representation

When the algorithm in Section 7.3 is applied twice, an ordered representation of the given matrix is obtained (Gustavson, 1976a, 1978). Ordered representations are required for some applications, such as Gauss elimination and for output purposes. We note that ordering a list of n numbers usually requires

$n(n-1)/2$ comparisons, since each number has to be compared with all the numbers which follow in the list. Here, instead, ordering can be achieved with only $a\mathrm{N} + b\mathrm{M} + c\mathrm{Z}$ elementary computations, where a, b and c are small numbers and Z is the total number of nonzeros. The asymptotic complexity of the sparse algorithm is, thus, linear.

In some cases, it is required to transpose or order only the structure IA, JA of a matrix. For this purpose the algorithm of Section 7.3 is used, except that the statement in line 23 is omitted, and the example becomes an algorithm for the symbolic transposition of a general sparse matrix. Two important examples are: finite element mesh connectivity and Gauss elimination (or triangular factorization). These examples are carefully discussed in Chapter 8 and this chapter, respectively. Here we will only mention that a connectivity matrix is a Boolean matrix, its elements being either 0 or 1. In sparse format the values of the nonzeros are not stored and, as a consequence, the matrix is entirely represented by its structure. For Gauss elimination, an ordered representation is required. However, since Gauss elimination is performed first symbolically and then numerically, and since an ordered representation is not required for the symbolic step, the usual procedure is the one described in Section 7.2: perform symbolic Gauss elimination, transpose the resulting unordered structure twice, and use the resulting ordered structure to perform the numerical step of Gauss elimination. The transposition required by this procedure is only symbolic.

The ordering algorithm was independently rediscovered by Alvarado (1979), with the name *simultaneous radix sort*. An alternative algorithm which is faster in some cases was developed by Szyld and Vishnepolsky (1982).

7.5. Permutation of rows or columns of a sparse matrix: First procedure

The ideas just outlined can be used for permuting rows and/or columns of a matrix in sparse format (Gustavson, 1976a). Let:

$$K = (k_1, k_2, \ldots, k_{\mathrm{N}}) \tag{7.2}$$

be the desired permutation of the N rows of the matrix **A** of N × M, where $(k_1, k_2, \ldots, k_{\mathrm{N}})$ is some permutation of $(1, 2, \ldots, \mathrm{N})$. A permutation matrix **P** of N × N can be defined as follows:

$$P_{i,k_i} = 1, \qquad P_{ij} = 0 \text{ otherwise.} \tag{7.3}$$

Every row and every column of **P** contains just one unity element, and **P** is orthogonal ($\mathbf{P}^{\mathrm{T}} = \mathbf{P}^{-1}$). If **A** is pre-multiplied by **P**, the original row k_i of **A** will become row i of the resulting matrix **PA**. The pre-multiplication of **A** by **P** can be carried out by the algorithm of Section 7.3 with only a slight modification: at stage I, refer to row k_I of **A** instead of row I. Only lines 16, 17 and 22 have to be modified. If an array KK with N positions is used to define the permutation, the new rows are:

```
16.         IAA=IA(KK(I))
17.         IAB=IA(KK(I)+1)-1
22.         JAT(K)=KK(I)
```

and the output from the algorithm is the transpose of the permuted matrix, or $(\mathbf{PA})^T$. The algorithm of Section 7.3 can be used twice to permute both the rows and the columns of **A**. The problem is stated as follows: given the permutation matrix **P** of N × M for the rows, and the permutation matrix **Q** of M × N for the columns, we wish to compute $\mathbf{PAQ}^T$. We write:

$$\mathbf{PAQ}^T = (\mathbf{Q}(\mathbf{PA})^T)^T. \tag{7.4}$$

The first application of the algorithm to **A** with **P** as the permutation matrix delivers $(\mathbf{PA})^T$. The second application, to $(\mathbf{PA})^T$ with **Q** as the permutation matrix, produces the desired result. This procedure is convenient when both the rows and the columns have to be permuted. When only the rows, or only the columns have to be permuted, the following procedure may be advantageous.

7.6. Permutation of rows or columns of a sparse matrix: Second procedure

Consider first the permutation of the columns of **A**. Let the permutation be defined by an array J(I), indicating that the original column I of **A** will become column J(I) of the resulting matrix. Note that this definition is different from that of the array KK in the preceding section. Then, we merely run over all elements of the array of column indices JA, and replace each JA(I) by J(JA(I)). The numerical values of the nonzeros, stored in AN, remain the same. The reader can easily write the corresponding algorithm.

Consider now the permutation of the rows of **A**, and let J(I) be the array which defines the permutation as before. The column indices and numerical values of the elements of row I of **A** are stored in the positions IA(I) to IA(I + 1) − 1 of JA and AN. These numbers have to be moved to new positions in new arrays JB and BN, corresponding to row J(I). For this purpose, a new array of pointers IB has to be constructed using the information in IA and J. Then, the new arrays of column indices and numerical values JB and BN are constructed simply by moving the numbers from the positions IA(I) to IA(I + 1) − 1 of JA and AN into the positions IB(J(I)) to IB(J(I) + 1) − 1 of JB and BN.

7.7. Ordering of the upper representation of a sparse symmetric matrix

There is still another case which arises in practice: ordering the upper representation of a sparse symmetric matrix **A**. This case can be reduced conceptually to that of a general matrix simply by considering it to be the complete representation of another matrix **B**, which has the upper triangle identical to that of **A**, but the lower triangle and the diagonal filled with zeros. Then, **B** is ordered by means of two applications of the algorithm of Section 7.3, and the result is the ordered upper representation of **A**.

Note that the representation of $\mathbf{B}^T$, obtained after the first application of the transposition algorithm, is in fact a RR(L)O of $\mathbf{A}^T$ (or a CR(U)O of **A**), while what we are seeking is a RR(U)O of **A**. In other words, two transpositions are required to order a symmetric matrix given in upper representation, but each transposition involves only one half of the matrix. When the representation is complete, one transposition of the entire matrix is required.

7.8. Addition of sparse matrices

Matrix addition is one of the operations of matrix algebra. Since subtraction of a matrix is equivalent to addition of the matrix with the signs of its nonzeros reversed, we refer to both addition or subtraction as addition. Addition of sparse matrices is performed by two algorithms: a symbolic algorithm, which determines the structure of the resulting matrix, and a numerical algorithm which determines the values of the nonzeros, taking advantage of the previous knowledge of their positions. It is possible to perform the addition numerically in just one step, but little is gained by doing so. On the other hand, splitting the addition procedure in two steps introduces an additional degree of freedom in the program which may be very convenient, for example, for iterative calculations where the structures are fixed but the numerical values change, or when an ordered representation is required and can be obtained by ordering the structure alone before numerical values are obtained. We note here that the result of the symbolic algorithm will be an unordered structure even if the structures of all the addend matrices are ordered. On the other hand, the numerical algorithm requires the structure as an input and will not change it.

The symbolic addition algorithm employs the multiple switch technique introduced in Section 1.14. The addition is performed row by row. Since each row is uniquely characterized by the row index and the row indices are used in ascending order, each row index can be used directly as the switch selector. The numerical addition is also performed row by row and an expanded array is used for the accumulation of the nonzeros, as explained in Section 1.15.

Procedures for the addition of two or more general sparse matrices are presented in this chapter. The same procedures can be used for the addition of two or more symmetric matrices given in upper representations. The need to add symmetric plus general matrices seldom arises and will not be discussed here. The procedures can be easily extended to the case where the addend matrices have different numbers of rows and columns. The algorithmic aspects of sparse matrix addition are discussed in the following section with the help of an example. The basic ideas were discussed by Gustavson (1972, 1976c) and by Eisenstat *et al.* (1975).

7.9. Example of addition of two sparse matrices

Consider the following addition of two matrices **A** and **B**, giving the resulting matrix **C**:

$$
\begin{vmatrix} 0 & 0 & 2 & 0 & -1 & 0 \\ 4 & 0 & 3 & 3 & 7 & 0 \\ -2 & 0 & 0 & 0 & 0 & -1 \\ 0 & 1 & 0 & 1 & 0 & 0 \end{vmatrix}
+
\begin{vmatrix} 1 & 0 & -1 & 0 & 0 & 5 \\ 0 & 0 & 0 & 0 & -2 & 0 \\ 4 & 6 & 0 & 2 & 0 & 0 \\ 0 & -1 & 1 & 0 & 0 & 0 \end{vmatrix}
$$

$$
= \begin{vmatrix} 1 & 0 & 1 & 0 & -1 & 5 \\ 4 & 0 & 3 & 3 & 5 & 0 \\ 2 & 6 & 0 & 2 & 0 & -1 \\ 0 & 0 & 1 & 1 & 0 & 0 \end{vmatrix} \tag{7.5}
$$

The matrices **A** and **B** are given in RR(C)O as follows:

$$
\begin{array}{rl}
\mathrm{JA} = & 5\ \ 3,\ \ 4\ \ 3\ \ 1\ \ 5,\ \ 1\ \ \ 6,\ \ 4\ \ 2 \\
\mathrm{AN} = & -1\ \ 2,\ \ 3\ \ 3\ \ 4\ \ 7,\ \ -2\ \ -1,\ \ 1\ \ 1 \\
\mathrm{row} = & \quad 1 \qquad\quad 2 \qquad\qquad 3 \qquad\quad 4
\end{array}
$$

$$
\begin{array}{rl}
\mathrm{JB} = & 1\ \ 6\ \ \ 3,\ \ \ 5,\ \ 4\ \ 2\ \ 1,\ \ \ 2\ \ 3 \\
\mathrm{BN} = & 1\ \ 5\ \ -1,\ \ -2,\ \ 2\ \ 6\ \ 4,\ \ -1\ \ 1 \\
\mathrm{row} = & \quad 1 \qquad\qquad 2 \quad\ 3 \qquad\quad 4
\end{array}
$$

where for simplicity the arrays of pointers IA and IB have been omitted and the row indices are explicitly shown. Since the resulting matrix **C** has 6 columns we define the multiple switch vector to be the integer array IX with 6 positions. IX is initialized to 0:

$$\text{IX} = 0 \quad 0 \quad 0 \quad 0 \quad 0 \quad 0$$

To obtain the matrix **C**, we first construct JC by merging JA and JB row by row. For the first row, this implies merging 5 3 and 1 6 3. These numbers are sequentially added to the list JC. When 5 is added to JC, the row index 1 is also stored in IX(5). Then 3 is added to JC and 1 is stored in IX(3). In order to avoid repeating elements in JC, before adding each element we check IX for the value 1. For example, before adding the last number 3 to JC we check IX(3) and find it to be equal to 1 (the switch is "on") which means that 3 has already been included in JC. When row 1 has been processed we have the following situation:

$$\text{JC} = 5 \quad 3 \quad 1 \quad 6$$
$$\text{IX} = 1 \quad 0 \quad 1 \quad 0 \quad 1 \quad 1$$

IC is easily constructed with the help of a pointer which points to the first free position of JC. E.g., in this case, IC(1) = 1, IC(2) = 5.

Next, we have to merge the second row 4 3 1 5 and 5. Since the row index is now 2, we store 2 in IX and check IX for the value 2. The effect of the multiple switch technique is now clear: resetting IX to 0 after processing each row is avoided, since, just before processing row i, only numbers less than i are stored in IX and will not interfere with the use of i as the switch for row i. For example, after processing row 2 we have:

$$\text{JC} = 5 \quad 3 \quad 1 \quad 6, \ 4 \quad 3 \quad 1 \quad 5 \quad 2$$
$$\text{IX} = 2 \quad 0 \quad 2 \quad 2 \quad 2 \quad 1$$

and IX is ready to process row 3. We note here that IX can be economically reset to 0 after processing each row, where "economically" means that the number of operations will be proportional to the number of nonzeros rather than to the number of elements in the row. This is done by using the information stored in JC. For example, when JC = 5 3 1 6 we reset only IX(5), IX(3), IX(1) and IX(6). This procedure may be convenient to save computer memory in cases where IX can be packed or stored in less memory locations by declaring it to be LOGICAL*1 or simply an array of bits: each bit can store only 0 or 1, and thus IX has to be reset to 0 after processing each row.

Now, we have to construct CN, the array containing the numerical values of the nonzeros of the matrix **C**. This is the numerical part of the algorithm.

We use an expanded array X to accumulate the values of the nonzeros of each row, stored in AN and BN. Starting with row 1, we first use JC to set to 0 the positions 5, 3, 1 and 6 of X. Then we use JA = 5 3 to store the values -1 and 2 of AN in the positions 5 and 3, respectively, of X. Next, we use JB and BN to accumulate the values, 1, 5 and -1 in the positions 1, 6 and 3 of X, respectively. Finally, we use JC again to retrieve from the positions 5, 3, 1 and 6 of X the final values to be stored in CN. The remaining rows are processed in exactly the same way. It is interesting to note that $C_{4,2} = 0$. However, since the symbolic section of the algorithm does not have any knowledge of the numerical values of the elements, the element $C_{4,2}$ will be treated as a nonzero and its value of 0 will be included in CN. Exact cancellation of an element seldom occurs, and the presence of a few zeros in CN causes no problems. In some cases, however, cancellation can be frequent, e.g. for matrices having all nonzeros equal to either 1 or -1. In such cases it may be convenient to generate JC and CN together, row by row, and immediately reprocess JC and CN to eliminate any zeros which may have appeared.

It is also clear that the same ideas just outlined can be very easily extended to add more than two matrices. It is also possible to add matrices with different numbers of rows or columns. We now proceed to the description of the symbolic and the numerical algorithms.

7.10. Algorithm for the symbolic addition of two sparse matrices with N rows and M columns

Input:	IA, JA	structure of the first matrix in RR(C)U.
	IB, JB	structure of the second matrix in RR(C)U.
	N	number of rows of the matrices.
	M	number of columns of the matrices.
Output:	IC, JC	structure of the resulting matrix in RR(C)U.
Working space:	IX	multiple switch, dimension M.

```
         IP=1
         DO 10 I=1,M
   10    IX(I)=0
         DO 50 I=1,N
         IC(I)=IP
         IAA=IA(I)
         IAB=IA(I+1)-1
         IF(IAB.LT.IAA)GO TO 30
         DO 20 JP=IAA,IAB
         J=JA(JP)
```

```
11.           JC(IP)=J
12.           IP=IP+1
13.   20      IX(J)=I
14.   30      IBA=IB(I)
15.           IBB=IB(I+1)-1
16.           IF(IBB.LT.IBA)GO TO 50
17.           DO 40 JP=IBA,IBB
18.           J=JB(JP)
19.           IF(IX(J).EQ.I)GO TO 40
20.           JC(IP)=J
21.           IP=IP+1
22.   40      CONTINUE
23.   50      CONTINUE
24.           IC(N+1)=IP
```

In this algorithm, IP is used as the pointer to JC. IP is initialized to 1 at line 1 and is incremented each time an element is added to the list JC, at lines 12 and 21. IP is also used to construct the array of pointers IC at lines 5 and 24. The multiple switch array IX is initialized to 0 at lines 2 and 3. I, defined at line 4, identifies each row. The DO 20 loop scans row I of the first given matrix: the column indices, if any, are stored in JC at line 11 and the row index is stored in IX at line 13, thus turning "on" the corresponding switch. The DO 40 loop runs over row I of the second matrix. For each column index J, defined at line 18, the multiple switch is tested at line 19: if the value of IX(J) is I, then the switch is on, which means that J has already been added to the list JC and should not be added again. Otherwise, J is added to JC at line 20. The reader may expect that the sentence IX(J)=I should appear between lines 21 and 22 in order to record the fact that the column index J has been added to the list JC. However, such a record is now not necessary because, during the processing of row I, the same value of J will never be found again: there are no repeated column indices in the representation of row I in the array JB.

7.11. Algorithm for the numerical addition of two sparse matrices with N rows

Input:	IA, JA, AN	first given matrix in RR(C)U.
	IB, JB, BN	second given matrix in RR(C)U.
	IC, JC	structure of the resulting matrix in RR(C)U.
	N	number of rows of the matrices.

Output: CN — numerical values of the nonzeros of the resulting matrix.

Working space: X — expanded array used to accumulate the nonzeros; the dimension of X is M, the number of columns of the matrices.

```
 1.          DO 70 I=1,N
 2.          IH=I+1
 3.          ICA=IC(I)
 4.          ICB=IC(IH)-1
 5.          IF(ICB.LT.ICA)GO TO 70
 6.          DO 10 IP=ICA,ICB
 7.   10     X(JC(IP))=0.
 8.          IAA=IA(I)
 9.          IAB=IA(IH)-1
10.          IF(IAB.LT.IAA)GO TO 30
11.          DO 20 IP=IAA,IAB
12.   20     X(JA(IP))=AN(IP)
13.   30     IBA=IB(I)
14.          IBB=IB(IH)
15.          IF(IBB.LT.IBA)GO TO 50
16.          DO 40 IP=IBA,IBB
17.          J=JB(IP)
18.   40     X(J)=X(J)+BN(IP)
19.   50     DO 60 IP=ICA,ICB
20.   60     CN(IP)=X(JC(IP))
21.   70     CONTINUE
```

This algorithm uses the expanded array X to accumulate the nonzeros of each row of the given matrices, as explained in Section 7.9. In lines 6 and 7, those positions of X which correspond to nonzeros of row I of the resulting matrix are initialized to zero. Then the nonzeros from row I of the first addend matrix, if any, are loaded into X at lines 11 and 12. The nonzeros from row I of the second addend matrix are accumulated in X at line 18. Finally, the resulting nonzero elements are loaded into CN at line 20. Note that this algorithm takes advantage of the previous knowledge of the positions of the nonzeros, given by IC, JC, to operate only with the nonzeros.

We note also that this algorithm preserves the order in which JC is given to it, and constructs CN in the same order. As a consequence, if IC, JC are given in a RR(C)O as a result of using twice the algorithm for symbolic transposition of Section 7.2 after the algorithm for symbolic addition of Section 7.10, the result of the numerical addition of this example will also be in a RR(C)O.

7.12. Product of a general sparse matrix by a column vector

We will now examine the multiplication of a sparse matrix by a column vector, and that of a row vector by a sparse matrix. The result of such operations is a full vector, rather than a sparse matrix. Thus, the multiplication algorithms perform the numerical computations directly, the symbolic section being unnecessary.

Different algorithms are employed, depending on the representation in which the given matrix is stored. The simplest case is that of a general matrix, rectangular or square, stored in RR(C)U. Note that even a symmetric matrix can be given in this type of representation, and that an ordered representation is a particular case of an unordered one: the algorithm will operate efficiently for any type of matrix provided it is stored in RR(C)U or RR(C)O. When the matrix is symmetric, however, it is more convenient to use a RR(DU)U or a RR(U)U. In a RR(DU)U only the nonzeros on the diagonal and upper triangle of the matrix are stored in the sparse arrays IA, JA, AN, while in a RR(U)U the diagonal elements are stored separately in a full array AD. A considerable reduction of storage requirements is obtained because the lower triangle of the matrix is not stored in the computer memory.

An important application of these algorithms is the calculation of Lanczos vectors, necessary for the iterative solution of linear equations by the conjugate gradient method, and for the calculation of the eigenvalues and eigenvectors of a matrix (Chapter 6). The advantage of these procedures, from the computational point of view, is that the only matrix operation required is the repeated multiplication of the matrix by a number of full vectors, the matrix remaining unchanged. The Gauss–Seidel method for the solution of linear equations (see Chapter 9) has the same property.

In this section we examine the product of a general sparse matrix $\mathbf{A}$ stored in IA, JA, AN in RR(C)U by a full column vector $\mathbf{b}$ stored in an array B. The result is another full vector $\mathbf{c}$ to be stored in the array C:

$$\mathbf{c} = \mathbf{A}\mathbf{b}. \tag{7.6}$$

Let N be the number of rows of the matrix. If $\mathbf{b}$ is full its elements stored in B can be accessed randomly. If $\mathbf{b}$ is sparse and is stored in B in compact form, we must first form an array of pointers IP; then, as explained in Section 1.17, each time that we need an element b_i we merely access B(IP(i)). Then, the order in which the inner products are performed is simply determined by the arbitrary order in which the elements of the matrix are stored. For each row I of the matrix, we use IA to obtain the initial pointer IAA, and the final pointer IAB, to the positions in JA and AN where row I is described. Then, to calculate the inner product of row I by the vector B, we simply scan JA and AN from IAA to IAB: each value stored in JA is a column index and is used to retrieve from the array B the element which has to be multiplied by the corresponding value of AN. The result of each multiplication is accumulated in C(I). The following algorithm does the job in the case of a full vector **b**.

7.13. Algorithm for the product of a general sparse matrix by a full column vector

Input:	IA, JA, AN	Given matrix in RR(C)U.
	B	given full vector.
	N	number of rows of the matrix.
Output:	C	resulting vector, of order N.

```
1.            DO 20 I=1,N
2.            U=0.
3.            IAA=IA(I)
4.            IAB=IA(I+1)-1
5.            IF(IAB.LT.IAA)GO TO 20
6.            DO 10 K=IAA,IAB
7.     10     U=U+AN(K)*B(JA(K))
8.     20     C(I)=U
```

The DO 20 loop scans the N rows of the matrix. The variable U, initialized at line 2, is used instead of C(I) to accumulate the products in line 7 because Fortran compilers generate more efficient machine instructions when nonsubscripted variables are used. In addition, a higher precision can be carried in U in order to increase the accuracy of the accumulation in line 7, and then to round the final result in line 8 (Gustavson, 1972, p. 51; Wilkinson, 1965, p. 228). Note that C(I)=0. when row I of the matrix is empty. The purpose of the sentence at line 5 is to detect empty rows of the matrix. At line 6, K is a pointer to JA and AN, and JA(K), at line 7, is the column index corresponding to the element AN(K).

7.14. Product of a row vector by a general sparse matrix

The row vector $\mathbf{b}^T$ is stored in the array B, and the general sparse matrix **A** in the arrays IA, JA, AN in RR(C)U. It is desired to pre-multiply the matrix by the vector, the result being the full row vector $\mathbf{c}^T$ to be stored in the array C:

$$\mathbf{c}^T = \mathbf{b}^T\mathbf{A}. \tag{7.7}$$

One possibility is to write this expression as $\mathbf{c} = \mathbf{A}^T\mathbf{b}$, where T means transpose, and to use the algorithm of Section 7.13. The transposition of sparse matrices was discussed in Section 7.2, and vectors do not have to be transposed because **b** and $\mathbf{b}^T$, or **c** and $\mathbf{c}^T$, are stored in exactly the same way in the computer memory. However, the complexity of the matrix transposition algorithm is comparable to that of the multiplication algorithm, and it also requires additional storage for $\mathbf{A}^T$. It is thus better to compute $\mathbf{c}^T = \mathbf{b}^T\mathbf{A}$ directly. The example of Section 7.15 illustrates how this can be accomplished, and the corresponding algorithm is given in Section 7.16.

7.15. Example of product of a full row vector by a general sparse matrix

Let us consider the following product:

$$(c_1 \quad c_2 \quad c_3) = (b_1 \quad b_2)\begin{vmatrix} A_{11} & A_{12} & A_{13} \\ A_{21} & A_{22} & A_{23} \end{vmatrix}. \tag{7.8}$$

We have:

$$\begin{aligned} c_1 &= b_1A_{11} + b_2A_{21} \\ c_2 &= b_1A_{12} + b_2A_{22} \\ c_3 &= b_1A_{13} + b_2A_{23}. \end{aligned} \tag{7.9}$$

Direct use of these equations is not convenient because the elements of matrix **A**, which are stored by rows, would have to be accessed by columns. Instead, the equations are written as follows:

$$\begin{aligned} c_1 &\leftarrow b_1A_{11} \\ c_2 &\leftarrow b_1A_{12} \\ c_3 &\leftarrow b_1A_{13} \\ c_1 &\leftarrow c_1 + b_2A_{21} \\ c_2 &\leftarrow c_2 + b_2A_{22} \\ c_3 &\leftarrow c_3 + b_2A_{23} \end{aligned} \tag{7.10}$$

where "$\leftarrow$" indicates the Fortran assignment statement. Now the elements of **A** are accessed in the sequence in which they are stored in the row-wise representation, and the algorithm operates efficiently.

7.16. Algorithm for the product of a full row vector by a general sparse matrix

Input:	IA, JA, AN	given matrix in RR(C)U.
	B	given full vector.
	N	number of rows of the matrix.
	M	number of columns of the matrix.
Output:	C	resulting row vector.

```
 1.           DO 10 I=1,M
 2.    10     C(I)=0.
 3.           DO 30 I=1,N
 4.           IAA=IA(I)
 5.           IAB=IA(I+1)-1
 6.           IF(IAB.LT.IAA)GO TO 30
 7.           Z=B(I)
 8.           DO 20 K=IAA,IAB
 9.           J=JA(K)
10.    20     C(J)=C(J)+AN(K)*Z
11.    30     CONTINUE
```

This algorithm performs the computations discussed in the preceding section. The M elements of the array C are initialized to 0. by the DO 10 loop. The DO 30 loop scans the N rows of the matrix. Empty rows are detected and by-passed at line 6. The DO 20 loop scans all the elements of each row I. At line 9, J is the column index of one such element, and AN(K), at line 10, its numerical value. The multiplier B(I) common to all elements of row I of the matrix, is stored in Z at line 7 and used to calculate the products at line 10. The results of the partial inner products are accumulated in C(J). Note that the values of J will appear in a random sequence, in general, because we have assumed that the representation is unordered, and the elements of C will be accessed at random. In this case, it is not possible to accumulate the inner products in a nonsubscripted variable, as was done in the algorithm of Section 7.13.

7.17. Product of a symmetric sparse matrix by a column vector

In this section we examine the product of a symmetric sparse matrix IA, JA, AN, AD given in RR(U)U, and a full vector in array B. This algorithm is very similar to the one described in Section 7.12, except that, now, each value stored in AN describes two symmetric elements of the matrix which have to be multiplied by *different* elements of the array B and accumulated in *different* places of the array C. As a consequence, the accumulation has to be made in the array C directly. The algorithm is given in the following section.

7.18. Algorithm for the product of a symmetric sparse matrix by a full column vector

Input:	IA, JA, AN, AD	given matrix, in RR(U)U.
	B	given full column vector.
	N	order of the matrix.
Output:	C	resulting column vector.

```
 1.          DO 10 I=1,N
 2.    10    C(I)=AD(I)*B(I)
 3.          DO 30 I=1,N
 4.          IAA=IA(I)
 5.          IAB=IA(I+1)-1
 6.          IF(IAB.LT.IAA)GO TO 30
 7.          U=C(I)
 8.          Z=B(I)
 9.          DO 20 K=IAA,IAB
10.          J=JA(K)
11.          U=U+AN(K)*B(J)
12.    20    C(J)=C(J)+AN(K)*Z
13.          C(I)=U
14.    30    CONTINUE
```

The elements of the array C are initialized at line 2 by the DO 10 loop. The DO 30 loop scans the N rows of the matrix. Empty rows are detected and bypassed at line 6. The index K at line 9 scans all the nonzeros of a row I which is not empty. Each nonzero AN(K) plays a double role as both element I, J and element J, I of the matrix, where J is defined at line 10. Thus, two inner products have to be accumulated for each K, at lines 11 and 12. U and Z are used instead of C(I) and B(I) to improve the efficiency of the DO 20 loop.

There exist a few more cases of multiplication between a sparse matrix and a vector. The reader can easily write the corresponding algorithms with the help of the previous discussions. However, such cases seldom arise in practice.

It is worth noticing that products of the type "row vector by matrix" can be reduced to the type "matrix by column vector" when the matrix is symmetric, by simple transposition. In fact, the representations in memory of a row vector and a column vector are identical, and a symmetric matrix is its own transpose. Thus, the algorithm of this section can be used directly.

7.19. Multiplication of sparse matrices

In this section we examine the algorithms which are used to calculate the product of two sparse matrices. Given the matrices **A** of $p \times q$ and **B** of $q \times r$, the product matrix **C** of $p \times r$ is given by:

$$C_{ik} = \sum_{j=1}^{q} A_{ij} B_{jk} \qquad \text{for } i = 1, \ldots, p \qquad (7.11)$$
$$k = 1, \ldots, r$$

This formula gives the element C_{ik} as the inner product of row i of **A** and column k of **B**. The columns of **B**, however, are not directly available when **B** is given in row-wise format. One possible solution to this problem is to transpose **B** using the transposition algorithm described in Section 7.3. Then, Equation (7.11) becomes:

$$C_{ik} = \sum_{j=1}^{q} A_{ij} (B^{\mathrm{T}})_{kj}, \qquad (7.12)$$

which requires only rows of **A** and $\mathbf{B}^{\mathrm{T}}$. A more efficient and elegant method will be described here, which does not require the transposition of **B** and allows both **A** and **B** to be given in row-wise format (Gustavson, 1976c). The basic idea of the method is to change the order in which the products required by Equation (7.11) are performed: for fixed i and j, the element A_{ij} is multiplied by all the elements B_{jk} of row j of **B**, and the partial results are accumulated in the positions k of an expanded real accumulator X. When all the elements of row i of **A** have been processed in this way, X contains the complete row i of **C**. The example in Section 7.20 illustrates this concept in a simple way. The symbolic algorithm is given in Section 7.21 and the numerical algorithm in Section 7.22. The symbolic and numerical processing can also be performed in a single run. The symbolic algorithm employs the multiple switch technique, with IX as the switch array, as explained in Section 1.14. The use of the expanded accumulator X in the numerical algorithm was explained in Section 1.15. Alternatively, the sparse rows of the resulting matrix can be used directly as accumulators with the help of an expanded integer array of pointers, as discussed in Section 1.16. The resulting matrix **C** is obtained in an an unordered representation, even if the representations of both **A** and **B** are ordered. An ordered representation of **C** can be obtained by using the algorithm for numerical transposition twice. When symbolic and numerical multiplication are done separately, it is better to order the structure of **C** alone by two applications of the algorithm for symbolic transposition. Then, since the numerical processing preserves the order, the final result will be ordered.

There is an alternative way of looking at matrix multiplication. We write the $p \times q$ matrix $\mathbf{A}$ as a set of q column vectors of length p, and the $q \times r$ matrix $\mathbf{B}$ as a set of q row vectors of length r:

$$\mathbf{A} = (\mathbf{a}_1, \mathbf{a}_2, \ldots, \mathbf{a}_q) \tag{7.13}$$

$$\mathbf{B} = \begin{vmatrix} \mathbf{b}_1^{\mathrm{T}} \\ \mathbf{b}_2^{\mathrm{T}} \\ \vdots \\ \mathbf{b}_q^{\mathrm{T}} \end{vmatrix}$$

A product of the form $\mathbf{a}_i\mathbf{b}_i^{\mathrm{T}}$ is a rank one matrix of size $p \times r$. Rank one matrices were considered in Section 2.2. The product $\mathbf{C} = \mathbf{AB}$, Equation (7.11), can now be written as the sum of q matrices of rank one:

$$\mathbf{AB} = \sum_{i=1}^{q} \mathbf{a}_i\mathbf{b}_i^{\mathrm{T}}. \tag{7.14}$$

One of the applications of Equation (7.14) is to calculate the number of multiplications necessary to form $\mathbf{C}$ when $\mathbf{A}$ and $\mathbf{B}$ are sparse. Let $n(\mathbf{v})$ be the number of nonzeros in a vector $\mathbf{v}$. Then, clearly $n(\mathbf{a}_i)n(\mathbf{b}_i)$ multiplications are required to obtain the rank one matrix $\mathbf{a}_i\mathbf{b}_i^{\mathrm{T}}$, and the complete product $\mathbf{AB}$ requires

$$n(\mathbf{AB}) = \sum_{i=1}^{q} n(\mathbf{a}_i)n(\mathbf{b}_i) \tag{7.15}$$

multiplications. The number of additions is the same provided we count a fill-in as an addition.

7.20. Example of product of two matrices which are stored by rows

Consider the following matrix product:

$$\begin{vmatrix} a_{11} & a_{12} \\ a_{21} & a_{22} \end{vmatrix} \times \begin{vmatrix} b_{11} & b_{12} \\ b_{21} & b_{22} \end{vmatrix} = \begin{vmatrix} c_{11} & c_{12} \\ c_{21} & c_{22} \end{vmatrix}. \tag{7.16}$$

We have:

$$\begin{aligned} c_{11} &= a_{11}b_{11} + a_{12}b_{21} \\ c_{12} &= a_{11}b_{12} + a_{12}b_{22} \\ c_{21} &= a_{21}b_{11} + a_{22}b_{21} \\ c_{22} &= a_{21}b_{12} + a_{22}b_{22}. \end{aligned} \tag{7.17}$$

Instead of forming the products in this way, we calculate them in the following order:

$$x_1 \leftarrow a_{1\,1}b_{1\,1}$$
$$x_2 \leftarrow a_{1\,1}b_{1\,2}$$
$$x_1 \leftarrow x_1 + a_{1\,2}b_{2\,1}$$
$$x_2 \leftarrow x_2 + a_{1\,2}b_{2\,2}$$
$$c_{1\,1} \leftarrow x_1$$
$$c_{1\,2} \leftarrow x_2$$
$$x_1 \leftarrow a_{2\,1}b_{1\,1}$$
$$x_2 \leftarrow a_{2\,1}b_{1\,2}$$
$$x_1 \leftarrow x_1 + a_{2\,2}b_{2\,1}$$
$$x_2 \leftarrow x_2 + a_{2\,2}b_{2\,2}$$
$$c_{2\,1} \leftarrow x_1$$
$$c_{2\,2} \leftarrow x_2$$

where "←" represents the Fortran assignment statement. Note that each element of the first matrix is multiplied sequentially by all the elements of a row of the second matrix, which are easily available when the second matrix is given in row-wise format.

7.21. Algorithm for the symbolic multiplication of two sparse matrices given in row-wise format

Input:	IA, JA	structure of the first matrix in RR(C)U.
	IB, JB	structure of the second matrix in RR(C)U.
	NP	number of rows of the first matrix.
	NQ	number of columns of the first matrix and of rows of the second matrix.
	NR	number of columns of the second matrix.
Output:	IC, JC	structure of the resulting matrix in RR(C)U.
Working space:	IX	of dimension NR, multiple switch.

```
1.            IP=1
2.            DO 10 I=1,NR
3.    10      IX(I)=0
4.            DO 40 I=1,NP
```

```
 5.          IC(I)=IP
 6.          IAA=IA(I)
 7.          IAB=IA(I+1)-1
 8.          IF(IAB.LT.IAA)GO TO 40
 9.          DO 30 JP=IAA,IAB
10.          J=JA(JP)
11.          IBA=IB(J)
12.          IBB=IB(J+1)-1
13.          IF(IBB.LT.IBA)GO TO 30
14.          DO 20 KP=IBA,IBB
15.          K=JB(KP)
16.          IF(IX(K).EQ.I)GO TO 20
17.          JC(IP)=K
18.          IP=IP+1
19.          IX(K)=I
20.    20    CONTINUE
21.    30    CONTINUE
22.    40    CONTINUE
23.          IC(NP+1)=IP
```

In this algorithm, IP is the pointer to the first free place in JC. IP is initialized at line 1, and is incremented at line 18, each time a new element is added to the list JC. IP is also used to determine the array IC at lines 5 and 23. The multiple switch array IX is initialized to zero at lines 2 and 3. The loop DO 40 scans the NP rows of the first given matrix. The loop DO 30 at line 9 scans the nonzeros of row I, which have the column indices J defined at line 10. For each of them, the loop DO 20, at line 14, scans the nonzeros of row J of the second given matrix, which have the column index K defined at line 15. At line 16 the switch array IX is tested to determine whether the element K has already been added to the description of row I in the list JC. Otherwise, K is added to JC at line 17 and this fact is recorded in IX at line 19.

7.22. Algorithm for the numerical multiplication of two sparse matrices given in row-wise format

Input:	IA, JA, AN	first given matrix in RR(C)U.
	IB, JB, BN	second given matrix in RR(C)U.
	IC, JC	structure of the resulting matrix in RR(C)U.
	NP	number of rows of the first given matrix and of the resulting matrix.

Output: CN — numerical values of the nonzeros of the resulting matrix.

Working space: X — expanded accumulator, of dimension equal to the number of columns of the resulting matrix.

```
 1.          DO 50 I=1,NP
 2.          ICA=IC(I)
 3.          ICB=IC(I+1)-1
 4.          IF(ICB.LT.ICA)GO TO 50
 5.          DO 10 J=ICA,ICB
 6.    10    X(JC(J))=0.
 7.          IAA=IA(I)
 8.          IAB=IA(I+1)-1
 9.          DO 30 JP=IAA,IAB
10.          J=JA(JP)
11.          A=AN(JP)
12.          IBA=IB(J)
13.          IBB=IB(J+1)-1
14.          IF(IBB.LT.IBA)GO TO 30
15.          DO 20 KP=IBA,IBB
16.          K=JB(KP)
17.    20    X(K)=X(K)+A*BN(KP)
18.    30    CONTINUE
19.          DO 40 J=ICA,ICB
20.    40    CN(J)=X(JC(J))
21.    50    CONTINUE
```

In this example I refers to a row of the first given matrix and of the resulting matrix. For each row I, those positions of the expanded accumulator X which correspond to nonzeros in the resulting matrix are initialized to 0 at lines 5 and 6. Note that the program reaches line 9 only when row I of the resulting matrix is not empty, which in turn means that row I of the first matrix is not empty, so that IAB $\geqslant$ IAA and the statement IF(IAB.LT.IAA)GO TO β preceding line 9 (see Section 7.1) is not necessary in this case. The loop DO 30 scans the nonzeros of row I of the first matrix. The value of the element I, J is stored in the nonsubscripted variable A at line 11. Then the loop DO 20 scans the nonzeros of row J of the second matrix, for each element J, K calculates the partial product as described in Section 7.20, and accumulates the result in X(K). When the DO 30 loop is complete, the array X contains the expanded version of row I of the resulting matrix, which is then loaded into CN at lines 19 and 20. This procedure was discussed in Section 1.15. Alternatively, the accumulation could be done directly in CN with the help of an expanded integer array of pointers, as explained in Section 1.16. Writing the corresponding algorithm is left as an exercise to the reader.

We note also that this algorithm does not change the ordering of JC. As a consequence, if IC, JC is given in a RR(C)O as a result of using the algorithm for symbolic transposition of Section 7.3 twice after the algorithm for symbolic multiplication of Section 7.21, the result of the numerical multiplication will also be in a RR(C)O: the order is preserved.

7.23. Triangular factorization of a sparse symmetric matrix given in row-wise format

In this section we assume that a sparse symmetric matrix **A** is stored in upper row-wise sparse format, and that Gauss elimination is to be performed on **A**, with pivots selected orderly down the diagonal. This is not a trivial problem, because the nonzeros to be eliminated are in the lower triangle of **A**, which is not explicitly stored in memory. Besides, the representation being row-wise, it is not easy to scan a column.

The version of Gauss elimination by rows is more convenient for a matrix given in row-wise format than the more usual version by columns. In the version by rows we subtract from each row I of **A**, element by element, multiples of all the preceding rows, so that the new row I contains only zeros to the left of the diagonal. Then we divide the remaining elements of the row by the diagonal element to form the upper triangular factor **U**, and store the diagonal element separately to form the diagonal matrix **D**. The procedure was examined in detail in Section 2.8.

The triangular factorization of a sparse matrix is performed first symbolically and then numerically. The symbolic factorization requires the structure IA, JA of **A** in an unordered representation, and generates the structure IU, JU of **U** also in an unordered representation. However, the numerical factorization requires IU, JU to be ordered, while IA, JA, AN can still be given in an unordered representation. This means that the symbolic transposition algorithm described in Section 7.3 has to be used twice to order IU, JU, after the symbolic factorization and before the numerical factorization.

The algorithmic difficulties encountered when a sparse symmetric matrix given in an upper representation is factorized, are best understood with the help of an explicit example.

Consider the following symmetric matrix, where for simplicity we omit the numerical values of the nonzeros:

$$
\mathbf{A} = \begin{array}{r|ccccccccccc|}
 & 1 & 2 & 3 & 4 & 5 & 6 & 7 & 8 & 9 & 10 & 11 \\
1 & x & 0 & 0 & 0 & 0 & x & 0 & 0 & 0 & x & 0 \\
2 & 0 & x & 0 & x & 0 & 0 & 0 & 0 & x & 0 & 0 \\
3 & 0 & 0 & x & 0 & x & 0 & x & 0 & 0 & 0 & x \\
4 & 0 & x & 0 & x & 0 & 0 & x & 0 & 0 & 0 & 0 \\
5 & 0 & 0 & x & 0 & x & 0 & 0 & x & 0 & 0 & 0 \\
6 & x & 0 & 0 & 0 & 0 & x & 0 & 0 & x & 0 & 0 \\
7 & 0 & 0 & x & x & 0 & 0 & x & 0 & 0 & 0 & x \\
8 & 0 & 0 & 0 & 0 & x & 0 & 0 & x & 0 & 0 & x \\
9 & 0 & x & 0 & 0 & 0 & x & 0 & 0 & x & 0 & x \\
10 & x & 0 & 0 & 0 & 0 & 0 & 0 & 0 & 0 & x & x \\
11 & 0 & 0 & x & 0 & 0 & 0 & x & x & x & x & x
\end{array} \qquad (7.18)
$$

The triangular factorization of this matrix starts with the fourth row, since none of the previous rows has any nonzeros to the left of the diagonal. From row 4 we subtract row 2, element by element, multiplied by a convenient constant so as to cancel element $A_{4\,2}$. On doing this, a new nonzero is introduced in row 4: the element $A_{4\,9}$. Next, a multiple of the third row is subtracted from row 5 to remove $A_{5\,3}$, and new nonzeros are introduced at positions $A_{5\,7}$ and $A_{5\,11}$. Next, $A_{6\,1}$ is eliminated, introducing a new nonzero at $A_{6\,10}$. Assuming that the factorization is complete up to this point, we will examine in detail how row 7 is processed in order to eliminate $A_{7\,3}$ and $A_{7\,4}$.

The first difficulty is that only the upper triangle and the diagonal of $\mathbf{A}$ are represented in the computer. There is no information telling us that $A_{7\,3}$ and $A_{7\,4}$ are different from zero and have to be removed. Nor is there any information telling us that a new nonzero will be introduced at $A_{7\,5}$ when row 3 is subtracted, and that $A_{7\,5}$ will have to be eliminated in turn. What we do know is that the symmetric elements $A_{3\,7}$ and $A_{4\,7}$ are nonzeros, and that a new nonzero was introduced at $A_{5\,7}$, the symmetric of $A_{7\,5}$, when row 5 was processed. In other words, we have to examine the nonzeros in *column* 7 above the diagonal to find the nonzeros in row 7 to the left of the diagonal which have to be removed.

Now, we know that all the elements of row 7 to the left of the diagonal will be equal to 0 after row 7 has been processed. Therefore, we do not have to calculate those elements. Only the elements on or to the right of the diagonal have to be calculated, and for this purpose only the elements of the preceding rows which are on or to the right of column 7 are required. The last sentence, generalized, would read: "find the elements of row i which have column indices equal or greater than j, where j is greater than i". Computational efficiency then requires an ordered representation for the rows of $\mathbf{U}$.

However, we will see below that this requirement only holds for the numerical part of Gauss elimination and not for the symbolic part.

Let us now assume that all steps necessary to locate the required nonzeros have been performed, and that we have available the following lists of column indices corresponding to elements on column 7 or to its right:

row 3: 7 11
row 4: 7 9
row 5: 7 8 11
row 7: 7 11

These lists of column indices have to be merged in order to obtain the structure of the new row 7. If this is done using the multiple switch technique described in Section 1.14, the result would be:

new row 7: 7 11 9 8

in an unordered representation. At this point, however, we may take advantage of the following property of Gauss elimination by rows (Rose *et al.*, 1976): it is necessary and sufficient to take into account only those rows for which the nonzero on column 7 is the *first* nonzero of the row to the right of the diagonal, in addition to row 7 itself. In this case, row 3 is not taken into account because its first nonzero to the right of the diagonal is $A_{3\,5}$, which is to the left of column 7. In fact, since $A_{3\,5} \neq 0$, then by symmetry $A_{5\,3} \neq 0$; this means that $A_{5\,3}$ was removed when processing row 5 by subtracting row 3, and on doing this all the nonzeros of row 3 were merged with those of row 5; then, when we take the nonzeros of row 5 we are in fact taking also the nonzeros of row 3 to the right of column 7, as is indeed the case. Therefore, we have to consider only the following structures:

row 4: 7 9
row 5: 7 8 11
row 7: 7 11

which are merged to obtain the correct new structure:

new row 7: 7 9 8 11

Note that these considerations, which deal with the symbolic part of Gauss elimination, do not require the representations of the rows to be ordered. In fact, we only have to record which rows have their *first* nonzero to the right of the diagonal on a given column. This means that the remaining nonzeros of such rows are positioned *to the right* of the column, and therefore we use them *all* to generate the structure of the new row no matter what their ordering is, eventually with the help of the multiple switch technique. The symbolic part of Gauss elimination, therefore, does not require an ordered representation. This is a fortunate result, since, as shown in the example, the symbolic algorithm actually generates unordered structures.

In order to record the rows having their first nonzero on a given column, we have to associate a set of rows with each column. For example, rows 4 and 5 belong to the set associated with column 7. In practice, we find the lowest column index of each row at the time the structure of the row is generated, and then we add the row index to the set associated with that column. For example, when assembling the structure of row 7 we find that 8 is the smallest column index to the right of the diagonal, and we immediately inscribe row 7 in the set associated with column 8. At the time that row 8 is processed, the row index 7 will be found in the corresponding set, and the structure of row 7 will be used.

Note also that the sets of rows associated with each column are disjoint, in the sense that each row belongs to one and only one column. Therefore, all the sets can be stored in a single array IP of length N, where N is the order of the matrix, in the form of circular chains, as discussed in Section 1.3. In fact, at the time that a row I is being processed, only the I − 1 initial locations of IP are used to store all the sets, because only the rows 1 to I − 1 are inscribed in the sets at that time. The remaining locations of IP are used to store column pointers to all the chains, because only the columns I to N are of interest at that time. Further details can be found in Section 7.25, where we present and discuss an algorithm for symbolic Gauss elimination.

The array IU can also be used for a double purpose. At the time that row I is being processed, the row pointers to JU corresponding to the preceding rows are stored in locations 1 to I − 1 of IU. The remaining locations are free. Since only column indices equal to or larger than I will be inscribed in the list JU, the locations I to N of IU are used as the multiple switch expanded array.

7.24. Numerical triangular factorization of a sparse symmetric matrix given in row-wise format

In this section we consider the same matrix given in Section 7.23. Assuming that the symbolic factorization and ordering of the structure have been accomplished and that we have IU, JU in an ordered row-wise upper format, we are now interested in the numerical part of Gauss elimination. We will also assume that the elimination is complete up to and including row 6, and we will examine how row 7 is processed. We know that row 7 has nonzeros at positions 7, 8, 9 and 11. In order to find their values we have to examine column 7, find that rows 3, 4 and 5 have nonzeros on this column, find the elements of these rows which have column indices equal to or greater than 7, and finally multiply them by convenient constants and subtract from row 7. There are several steps involved in this procedure, and three of them will be examined in detail.

(1) Find the elements of a given row (say row 3) which have column indices equal to or greater than the index of the processed row (say 7). The initial and final pointers to the description of row 3 in JU and UN, are IU(3) and IU(4) – 1. Row 3 is ordered and has nonzeros at positions:

row 3: 5 7 11

However, we are only interested in that portion of row 3 which starts at column 7. This requires a different initial pointer, which we will call IUP, while IU(4) – 1 can still be used as the final pointer. At the time that row 7 is processed, IUP(3) points to the nonzero of row 3 which is on column 7. As soon as row 3 is used in the process of row 7, IUP(3) is incremented. Since row 3 is ordered, IUP(3) will now point to the *next* nonzero of row 3, which is 11, and *will remain there* until row 11 is processed. This is so because row 3 does not have any nonzeros on columns 8, 9 or 10 and thus row 3 will not be used and IUP(3) will not be modified when processing rows 8, 9 or 10.

(2) Find which rows have nonzeros in a given column (say column 7). Every row having a nonzero at column 7 is now required. The situation is different from that discussed in Section 7.23, where only the rows having their first nonzero at column 7 were needed for the symbolic process. The rows are also inscribed in sets associated with the columns, but, after each row is used, it is not discarded as in the previous example but is inscribed in the set corresponding to the *next* nonzero of that row. Except for this detail, all the sets are stored as previously in the first I – 1 positions of an array IP of dimension N, while the remaining positions of IP are used to store column pointers to the sets.

(3) Subtract multiples of portions of selected rows from the row being processed (say row 7). The elements of each row, say row 3, have to be multiplied by a factor, which is the ratio of the elements $A_{3\,7}$ (equal to $A_{7\,3}$ by symmetry) and $A_{3\,3}$. Since IUP(3) points to $A_{3\,7}$, and $A_{3\,3}$ is DI(3) (in fact, DI(3) is the inverse of $A_{3\,3}$, because it is convenient to store in DI not the elements of the diagonal matrix **D** but their inverses), the ratio mentioned above can easily be calculated. An expanded accumulator is also required to add the sparse real vectors. For this purpose we use the positions I to N of the array DI, which are free at the time that row I is being processed. A very efficient use of the available storage is made in this way.

In Sections 7.25 and 7.26 we present the algorithms for symbolic and numerical triangular factorization.

7.25. Algorithm for the symbolic triangular factorization of a symmetric sparse matrix A

Input:	IA, JA	structure of given matrix **A** in RR(U)U.
	N	order of matrix **A** and of matrix **U**.
Output:	IU, JU	structure of resulting matrix **U** in RR(U)U.
Working space:	IP	of dimension N. Chained lists of rows associated with each column. The array IU is also used as the multiple switch array.

```
         NM=N-1
         NH=N+1
         DO 10 I=1,N
         IU(I)=0
   10    IP(I)=0
         JP=1
         DO 90 I=1,NM
         JPI=JP
         JPP=N+JP-I
         MIN=NH
         IAA=IA(I)
         IAB=IA(I+1)-1
         IF(IAB.LT.IAA)GO TO 30
         DO 20 J=IAA,IAB
         JJ=JA(J)
         JU(JP)=JJ
         JP=JP+1
         IF(JJ.LT.MIN)MIN=JJ
   20    IU(JJ)=I
   30    LAST=IP(I)
         IF(LAST.EQ.0)GO TO 60
         L=LAST
   40    L=IP(L)
         LH=L+1
         IUA=IU(L)
         IUB=IU(LH)-1
         IF(LH.EQ.I)IUB=JPI-1
```

```
28.            IU(I)=I
29.            DO 50 J=IUA,IUB
30.            JJ=JU(J)
31.            IF(IU(JJ).EQ.I)GO TO 50
32.            JU(JP)=JJ
33.            JP=JP+1
34.            IU(JJ)=I
35.            IF(JJ.LT.MIN)MIN=JJ
36.    50      CONTINUE
37.            IF(JP.EQ.JPP)GO TO 70
38.            IF(L.NE.LAST)GO TO 40
39.    60      IF(MIN.EQ.NH)GO TO 90
40.    70      L=IP(MIN)
41.            IF(L.EQ.0)GO TO 80
42.            IP(I)=IP(L)
43.            IP(L)=I
44.            GO TO 90
45.    80      IP(MIN)=I
46.            IP(I)=I
47.    90      IU(I)=JPI
48.            IU(N)=JP
49.            IU(NH)=JP
```

The principles upon which this algorithm operates have been described in Section 7.23. Here we will only mention some hints for the better understanding of the program. At lines 4 and 5, the multiple switch array IU and the chained sets array IP are initialized to 0. The pointer to the first free position in JU is JP, which is initialized to 1 at line 6 and incremented at lines 17 and 33, each time a new column index is added to the list JU.

The DO 90 loop scans the rows of the matrix. For each row I, the current value of JP is temporarily stored in JPI at line 8, and then permanently stored in IU(I) at line 47, when the position I of IU will not be needed any more for multiple switching. The purpose of the DO 20 loop is to transfer the column indices JJ, corresponding to row I of **A**, from JA to JU; as usual, the switch index I is stored in the multiple switch array IU at line 19; at line 18, the smallest column index is obtained in MIN, which was already initialized at line 10.

The pointer to the circular chain where the rows associated with column I are listed, is retrieved from IP(I) at line 20 and stored in LAST. LAST is in fact the index of one such row, the "last" row. Line 21 takes care of the case where no rows are associated with column I. At line 23, L is the "next" element in the chain. Line 27 takes care of the fact that IU(I) is not yet defined as a pointer, and at line 28 the switch index I is stored in position I of IU to avoid the inscription of I as a column index in JU. The DO 50 loop scans row L of matrix **U**. The switch array IU is checked at line 31, the necessary column indices JJ are added to JU at line 32, and a further inscription of JJ in JU is prevented by storing I in IU(JJ) at line 34. The minimum column index is found at line 35.

JPP, defined at line 9, is the value that JP would achieve if *all* the possible nonzeros were actually present in row I to the right of the diagonal. This condition is tested at line 37, and if the test gives a positive result, further computation is by-passed in order to save computer time. This situation may happen frequently, particularly for the last rows of a matrix.

If L is not the "last" row in the chain associated with column I, then the program will branch from line 38 to line 23, where the next row in the chain will be selected. When the chain has been exhausted, the algorithm reaches line 39, where the condition MIN = NH would mean that row I of **U** is empty to the right of the diagonal, in which case the program branches to line 47. Otherwise, one or more nonzeros exist in row I, and row I has to be inscribed in the chain associated with column MIN. At line 40 the pointer L to this chain is detected, the chain is broken at line 42 and row I is inscribed at line 43. If the chain is still empty, the algorithm branches from line 41 to line 45, where the pointer to the chain is set, and the chain is created with the single element I at line 46.

7.26. Algorithm for the numerical triangular factorization of a symmetric positive definite sparse matrix A

Input:	IA, JA, AN, AD	given matrix **A** in RR(U)U.
	IU, JU	structure of resulting matrix **U** in RR(U)O.
	N	order of matrices **A** and **U**.
Output:	UN	numerical values of the nonzeros of matrix **U** in RR(U)O.
	DI	inverse of the diagonal matrix **D**.
Working space:	IP	of dimension N. Chained lists of rows associated with each column.
	IUP	of dimension N. Auxiliary pointers to portions of rows.
	DI	is used as the expanded accumulator.

```
      DO 10 J=1,N
10    IP(J)=0
```

```
      DO 130 I=1,N
      IH=I+1
      IUA=IU(I)
      IUB=IU(IH)-1
      IF(IUB.LT.IUA)GO TO 40
      DO 20 J=IUA,IUB
20    DI(JU(J))=0.
      IAA=IA(I)
      IAB=IA(IH)-1
      IF(IAB.LT.IAA)GO TO 40
      DO 30 J=IAA,IAB
30    DI(JA(J))=AN(J)
40    DI(I)=AD(I)
      LAST=IP(I)
      IF(LAST.EQ.0)GO TO 90
      LN=IP(LAST)
50    L=LN
      LN=IP(L)
      IUC=IUP(L)
      IUD=IU(L+1)-1
      UM=UN(IUC)*DI(L)
      DO 60 J=IUC,IUD
      JJ=JU(J)
60    DI(JJ)=DI(JJ)-UN(J)*UM
      UN(IUC)=UM
      IUP(L)=IUC+1
      IF(IUC.EQ.IUD)GO TO 80
      J=JU(IUC+1)
      JJ=IP(J)
      IF(JJ.EQ.0)GO TO 70
      IP(L)=IP(JJ)
      IP(JJ)=L
      GO TO 80
70    IP(J)=L
      IP(L)=L
80    IF(L.NE.LAST)GO TO 50
90    DI(I)=1./DI(I)
      IF(IUB.LT.IUA)GO TO 120
      DO 100 J=IUA,IUB
100   UN(J)=DI(JU(J))
      J=JU(IUA)
      JJ=IP(J)
```

```
45.          IF(JJ.EQ.0)GO TO 110
46.          IP(I)=IP(JJ)
47.          IP(JJ)=I
48.          GO TO 120
49.   110    IP(J)=I
50.          IP(I)=I
51.   120    IUP(I)=IUA
52.   130    CONTINUE
```

In this algorithm, IP is initialized to 0 at lines 1 and 2 in order to record the fact that all chained lists of rows are initially empty. The DO 120 loop scans the rows of the matrices **A** and **U**, which are identified by the index I. When the row I of **U** contains no off-diagonal nonzeros, the program branches from line 7 to line 15, where the diagonal element, assumed to be always positive, is processed. Otherwise, the positions of the expanded array DI which correspond to nonzeros are initialized at line 9, and the nonzeros from row I of **A**, if any, are loaded into DI at line 14. The diagonal element of row I is loaded at line 15.

The pointer to the circular chain where the rows associated with column I are listed, is retrieved from IP(I) at line 16 and stored in LAST. If the chain is empty, LAST will be equal to 0 and the algorithm will branch from line 17 to line 39. Otherwise, LAST is the index of one of the rows which has a nonzero on column I, the "last" in the chain, and L, at line 19, is the index of the "next" row, the "first" in the list. At line 21, IUC=IUP(L) points precisely to the nonzero of row L at column I, while IUD, at line 22, points to the end of row L. The factor by which the nonzeros of row L have to be multiplied before accumulation is calculated at line 23 and stored in UM. The DO 60 loop finally accumulates the elements of row L multiplied by UM.

We have mentioned before that the elements of each row have to be normalized by dividing them by the diagonal element in order to form the upper triangular factor **U**. This operation is performed at line 27, where UM was determined at line 23 and DI(L) is in fact the reciprocal of the diagonal element (see line 39 and note that $L < I$). It is important to note that each row I is generated and stored in an unnormalized form. Each nonzero of each row is normalized later, at the time that it is needed for use as a multiplier for row L at lines 23 and 27. Proceeding in this way, a number of multiplications are avoided (Tinney and Walker, 1967, p. 1805). Since lines 23 and 27 are executed once and only once for each nonzero, it is guaranteed that every element will be conveniently normalized.

The auxiliary pointer IUP, which points to the nonzero of row L at column I, is incremented at line 28 in order to point to the next nonzero of row L, if any. If there are no more nonzeros in row L, the program branches from line

29 to line 38, where the scanning of the chain is resumed. Otherwise, at lines 30 to 37, row L is inscribed in the chain associated with column J, which is the column index of the next nonzero of row L. Note the difference from the symbolic algorithm of Section 7.25, where a row L was used only once and then discarded.

The execution reaches line 39 when all the rows associated with column I, if any, have been processed. If the resulting row I is not empty, the nonzeros, still unnormalized, are retrieved from the expanded accumulator DI and stored in UN by the DO 100 loop. The new row I is then inscribed in the chain associated with the column index J of its first nonzero. This operation is performed by lines 43 to 50. Finally, before proceeding to the next row, the auxiliary pointer IUP(I) is set to the first nonzero of row I at line 51.

7.27. Example of forward and backward substitution

In this section we present a simple example of forward and backward substitution, which serves as introductory material for the algorithm presented in the next section. Let $\mathbf{Ax} = \mathbf{b}$ be the linear system we wish to solve and $\mathbf{A} = \mathbf{U}^{\mathrm{T}}\mathbf{DU}$ be the factorization of the symmetric matrix $\mathbf{A}$. The general case was discussed in Section 2.13. The symmetric case is very similar: the linear system becomes $\mathbf{U}^{\mathrm{T}}\mathbf{DUx} = \mathbf{b}$, which, if $\mathbf{z} = \mathbf{DUx}$ and $\mathbf{w} = \mathbf{Ux}$, can be written:

$$\begin{aligned} \mathbf{U}^{\mathrm{T}}\mathbf{z} &= \mathbf{b} \\ \mathbf{Dw} &= \mathbf{z} \\ \mathbf{Ux} &= \mathbf{w} \end{aligned} \tag{7.19}$$

The system (7.19) is solved, first for $\mathbf{z}$, then for $\mathbf{w}$, and finally for $\mathbf{x}$. Since $\mathbf{U}$ and $\mathbf{U}^{\mathrm{T}}$ are triangular and $\mathbf{D}$ is diagonal, the solution of (7.19) is straightforward. Consider the following example:

$$\mathbf{A} = \begin{vmatrix} 1 & 0 & 0 \\ d & 1 & 0 \\ e & f & 1 \end{vmatrix} \begin{vmatrix} a & 0 & 0 \\ 0 & b & 0 \\ 0 & 0 & c \end{vmatrix} \begin{vmatrix} 1 & d & e \\ 0 & 1 & f \\ 0 & 0 & 1 \end{vmatrix} \tag{7.20}$$

Then, the first Equation (7.19) is

$$\begin{vmatrix} 1 & 0 & 0 \\ d & 1 & 0 \\ e & f & 1 \end{vmatrix} \begin{vmatrix} z_1 \\ z_2 \\ z_3 \end{vmatrix} = \begin{vmatrix} b_1 \\ b_2 \\ b_3 \end{vmatrix} \tag{7.21}$$

from which we immediately compute, by forward substitution:

$$\begin{aligned} z_1 &= b_1 \\ z_2 &= b_2 - dz_1 \\ z_3 &= b_3 - ez_1 - fz_2 \end{aligned} \tag{7.22}$$

The second equation of the system (7.19) is:

$$\begin{vmatrix} a & 0 & 0 \\ 0 & b & 0 \\ 0 & 0 & c \end{vmatrix} \begin{vmatrix} w_1 \\ w_2 \\ w_3 \end{vmatrix} = \begin{vmatrix} z_1 \\ z_2 \\ z_3 \end{vmatrix} \tag{7.23}$$

so that:

$$\begin{aligned} w_1 &= z_1/a \\ w_2 &= z_2/b \\ w_3 &= z_3/c \end{aligned} \tag{7.24}$$

Since usually the inverse of **D** is stored in memory, rather than **D** itself, Equation (7.24) involves only multiplications, which are faster than divisions on most computers. Finally, the last Equation of (7.19) is:

$$\begin{vmatrix} 1 & d & e \\ 0 & 1 & f \\ 0 & 0 & 1 \end{vmatrix} \begin{vmatrix} x_1 \\ x_2 \\ x_3 \end{vmatrix} = \begin{vmatrix} w_1 \\ w_2 \\ w_3 \end{vmatrix} \tag{7.25}$$

The final solution is easily obtained by backward substitution:

$$\begin{aligned} x_3 &= w_3 \\ x_2 &= w_2 - fx_3 \\ x_1 &= w_1 - dx_2 - ex_3 \end{aligned} \tag{7.26}$$

7.28. Algorithm for the solution of the system $\mathbf{U}^T\mathbf{DUx} = \mathbf{b}$

Input:	IU, JU, UN	given upper triangular matrix with unit diagonal **U** in RR(U)U.
	DI	inverses of the diagonal elements of the diagonal matrix **D**.
	B	right-hand side vector **b**.
	N	order of the system, N > 1.
Output:	X	vector of unknowns **x**.

```
 1.          NM=N-1
 2.          DO 10 I=1,N
 3.    10    X(I)=B(I)
 4.          DO 40 K=1,NM
 5.          IUA=IU(K)
 6.          IUB=IU(K+1)-1
 7.          XX=X(K)
 8.          IF(IUB.LT.IUA)GO TO 30
 9.          DO 20 I=IUA,IUB
10.    20    X(JU(I))=X(JU(I))-UN(I)*XX
11.    30    X(K)=XX*DI(K)
12.    40    CONTINUE
13.          X(N)=X(N)*DI(N)
14.          K=NM
15.    50    IUA=IU(K)
16.          IUB=IU(K+1)-1
17.          IF(IUB.LT.IUA)GO TO 70
18.          XX=X(K)
19.          DO 60 I=IUA,IUB
20.    60    XX=XX-UN(I)*X(JU(I))
21.          X(K)=XX
22.    70    K=K-1
23.          IF(K.GT.0)GO TO 50
```

The operation of this algorithm is best understood if reference is made to the example in Section 7.27. The algorithm starts by calculating the vector **z**, Equation (7.22) in the array X. This array is initialized at lines 2 and 3. Then, the DO 40 loop scans the rows of **U** and performs the operations indicated in Equation (7.22) by columns, since in this way the matrix **U** is accessed by rows. Immediately after each row of **U** has been processed, X(K) is multiplied by the inverse of the K-th element of **D**, stored in DI(K), at line 11. This operation is required by Equation (7.24). When line 13 has been executed, the vector **y** is developed in the array X.

The solution of Equation (7.25) starts at line 14. The array X is already initialized with the elements of the vector **y**. The DO 60 loop performs the operations indicated by Equation (7.26), this time row by row, since in this way **U** has to be accessed again by rows. The final solution **x** is developed in X.

CHAPTER 8

Connectivity and Nodal Assembly

8.1. Introduction

In this chapter we continue the description of some useful algorithms, specifically designed for sparse matrices stored in row-wise format. We are now interested in mesh problems. Typical mesh problems arise when the domain of a partial differential equation is discretized and the *Finite Element Method* (Zienkiewicz, 1977) is used to find a solution. Mesh problems also arise when a partial differential equation is solved using the *Boundary Element Method* (Brebbia, 1978). In this case only the boundary of the domain is discretized. If the domain is a three-dimensional region enclosed by a surface, the surface must be discretized and there results a two-dimensional mesh, similar to a two-dimensional finite element mesh.

To be specific, we are interested here in the algorithmic aspects of storage allocation and data manipulation required to obtain the *nodal assembly* sparse matrix associated with the mesh. Let us suppose that the given domain has been approximated by a set of m adjoining elements, which are disjoint except that contiguous elements share their common boundary. Nodes have been defined at the corners of the elements, and optionally also at other points of the boundary and interior of the elements. Thus, we may say that a node which is on the boundary between two elements belongs to both, and a node at a corner or edge belongs to all the elements which share that corner or that edge. Let n be the number of nodes. The m elements are numbered consecutively in an arbitrary order from 1 to m. So also are the n nodes, from 1 to n. An example of a two-dimensional mesh with numbered nodes and elements is shown in Fig. 8.1. The *connectivity matrix* **E** is a Boolean sparse matrix defined as follows:

E is rectangular of order m by n.

$E_{ij} = 1$ if node j belongs to element i.

$E_{ij} = 0$ otherwise.

Thus, a row of **E** corresponds to an element, and the ones in that row correspond to the reference numbers of the nodes of that element. The transposed matrix $\mathbf{E}^T$ is also frequently used. $\mathbf{E}^T$ is of order n by m. A row of $\mathbf{E}^T$ corresponds to a node, and the ones in that row correspond to the elements to which that node belongs. In sparse row-wise format, both matrices, being Boolean, are represented only by their structures. We will use the arrays IE, JE for **E**, and IET, JET for $\mathbf{E}^T$. Since the array JE contains the column indices of the nonzeros of each row of **E**, and the column indices are precisely the reference numbers of the nodes of the element corresponding to that row, it is immediately obvious that JE is a list of the reference numbers of the nodes which belong to each element. Usually, the nodes of each element are listed in JE in some conventional order, which describes some topological property of the discretization. For example, for a two-dimensional element with nodes on its boundary and corners, the nodes are listed counter-clockwise, starting at an arbitrary corner. If interior nodes exist, they are listed afterwards. From the point of view of the sparse row-wise format, this corresponds to an unordered representation. It is interesting to note that this ordering convention is impossible if a full format is used for **E**.

Similar considerations can be made for $\mathbf{E}^T$. The array JET is a list of the elements to which each node belongs. Here, however, it is not usually

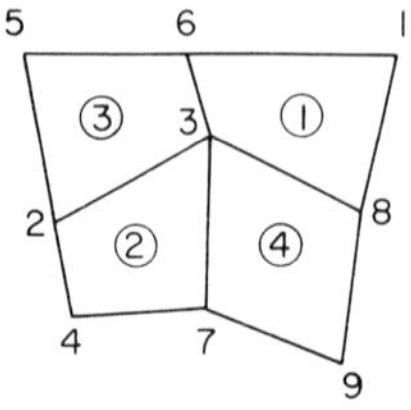

Figure 8.1 A simple finite element mesh.

necessary to make any convention concerning the order in which the elements are listed. In our context, this is a fortunate fact: the representation IET, JET of $\mathbf{E}^T$ is obtained by transposition of the representation IE, JE of **E**, using the algorithm given in Section 7.3, which constructs JET with the elements listed in the increasing order of their reference numbers for each node.

The problem of constructing the connectivity matrix **E** falls into a more general category of problems, those related with *mesh generation* [see for example Pissanetzky (1981)].

The functional subspace from which approximations to the solution of the differential equation will be obtained, is defined by specifying the set of *shape functions*, which are usually simple functions and are in correspondence with the nodes of the mesh. The specification is complete when the positions of all nodes and the shapes of all elements are given with respect to some coordinate system. However, we will not need this information for our purposes.

As explained in Section 4.14, element methods require that a matrix **A** be assembled, and that either a system of linear equations

$$\mathbf{A}\mathbf{x} = \mathbf{b} \tag{8.1}$$

or an eigenvalue problem

$$\mathbf{A}\mathbf{x} = \lambda\mathbf{x} \tag{8.2}$$

be solved. For scalar probems, there is one unknown associated with each node, and thus **A** is of order n. **A** is the *nodal assembly* matrix, and is also frequently called *stiffness matrix*, a name which originated from structural analysis. **A** is calculated as the sum of element matrices $\mathbf{A}^{(e)}$, as in Equation (4.28), and A_{ij} is nonzero only when there is an element to which nodes i and j belong, in which case we say that nodes i and j are *connected*. Since a node is connected with only a few other nodes in the mesh, **A** has only a few nonzeros in each row, and, even more important, the number of nonzeros per row is independent of the size of the mesh. Thus, **A** is sparse and the total number of nonzeros is proportional to the number of nodes in the mesh. Its structure is symmetric, and frequently **A** itself is symmetric and positive definite.

The element matrices $\mathbf{A}^{(e)}$ are usually calculated by a DO loop which, for each element, computes the corresponding matrix and immediately adds or *assembles* it into **A**. When required, and element vector is also computed and assembled into **b** to form the system (8.1). The actual calculation of the element matrices and vectors depends on the differential equation to be solved, on the approximation subspace and on the numerical method. It is of no interest to us because we are concerned with the details of the assembly and not with the numerical values to be assembled. Since $A_{ij}^{(e)} \neq 0$ only if i and j are nodes of element e, $\mathbf{A}^{(e)}$ is usually stored and processed as a full submatrix of order equal to the number of nodes of element e.

8.2. Boundary conditions for scalar problems

In some cases when the linear system (8.1) is being assembled, the values of the unknowns associated with some nodes of the mesh may be prescribed. This is the case for nodes which fall on boundaries or portions of a boundary where Dirichlet boundary conditions are given. We will refer to such nodes as *Dirichlet nodes*. The only equation associated with a Dirichlet node is thus the obvious one:

$$x_i = \bar{x}_i, \tag{8.3}$$

where $\bar{x}_i$ is the given value prescribed for the unknown x_i. This obvious equation is usually assembled with the system, giving rise to a row in the matrix $\mathbf{A}$ which contains a 1 on the diagonal as the only nonzero, and the prescribed value as the right-hand side. The reason for keeping the Dirichlet nodes in the formulation is that other nodes are connected to Dirichlet nodes and have equations in which terms containing Dirichlet unknowns are present. Since the Dirichlet "unknowns" are in fact known, such terms must be eliminated from the equations by subtracting them from the corresponding right sides, an operation which becomes computationally simpler to perform when the Dirichlet nodes are present in the formulation. This technique is particularly convenient when sparse formats are used due to the ease with which empty rows in $\mathbf{A}$ can be managed, without causing any overhead.

A common practice is to assemble the linear system (8.1) from element matrices, as usual, including equation i. Then row i of $\mathbf{A}$ is filled with zeros and a 1 is placed on the diagonal. Then, zeros are placed at the off-diagonal positions of column i, and the elements previously stored at these positions are multiplied by $\bar{x}_i$ and subtracted from $\mathbf{b}$. Finally b_i is set equal to $\bar{x}_i$. If $\mathbf{A}$ is symmetric, it is evident that these operations do not destroy the symmetry. If in addition $\mathbf{A}$ is positive definite, a simple proof shows that the modified matrix is also positive definite. For, consider without loss of generality that $i = n$. Since $\mathbf{A}$ is symmetric positive definite, we know from Property 4 of Section 2.2 that the principal minors of orders $1, 2, \ldots, n-1$, of $\mathbf{A}$, have positive determinants. When zeros are introduced in row n and in column n, and a 1 at position (n, n), it is clear that the determinant of the resulting matrix will also be positive. According to Property 6 of Section 2.2, these conditions are necessary and sufficient for the modified matrix to be positive definite.

A common practice is to store and process **A** as a banded matrix. Since the bandwidth increases as the number of nodes in the mesh increases, a large number of zeros are stored and processed when the mesh is large. Thus, for large problems, sparse matrix techniques are computationally more convenient. A further advantage of sparse matrix notation is that it places no restrictions on the numbering of the nodes and elements, which is completely arbitrary, the concept of bandwidth being nonexistent. A further disadvantage of banded matrix procedures is that Dirichlet nodes may cause an unnecessary increase in bandwidth.

8.3. Boundary conditions for vector problems

The finite element method is frequently used to solve problems where the unknown function is a vector field. In such cases each component of the vector field is treated separately as if it were a scalar function, and is represented over the mesh in terms of an independent set of nodal unknowns. There are, therefore, several unknowns associated with each node of the mesh. For example, in three-dimensional elasticity, where the model is an elastic body, the unknowns associated with each node i are its three displacements $x_{i\,1}$, $x_{i\,2}$, $x_{i\,3}$ along the coordinate directions. In fluid mechanics, the model is a fluid and the unknowns are the components of the fluid velocity at each node. In electromagnetism, the unknowns are the components of an electric or a magnetic field.

There are different types of boundary conditions for vector problems. The vector at a certain node may be prescribed, i.e., all its components have prescribed values. Or the vector at a node may be required to lie along a given direction in two or three dimensions, or to be parallel to a given plane when the problem is three-dimensional. For example, a point of an elastic body may be given a known displacement, or may be constrained to move along a line or in a plane. For a fluid, if part of the boundary of the region where the problem is being solved is an axis or a plane of symmetry, the velocity must lie in the plane or along the axis, while at other points of the boundary the velocity may be prescribed. When the vector has a prescribed value, or when the given line is parallel to a coordinate direction, or when the given plane is perpendicular to a coordinate direction, conditions of the type of Equation (8.3) are obtained, which are easily handled by the standard procedures already discussed. We will now consider the more difficult situations where the line is not parallel to any coordinate direction, or the plane is not perpendicular to any coordinate direction.

To fix ideas we restrict the analysis to three-dimensional problems. If the vector of components (x_{i1}, x_{i2}, x_{i3}) at node i must lie in a given plane, then:

$$v_1 x_{i1} + v_2 x_{i2} + v_3 x_{i3} = 0, \tag{8.4}$$

where (v_1, v_2, v_3) is a vector normal to the plane. If the unknown vector (x_{i1}, x_{i2}, x_{i3}) must be parallel to a line, then:

$$\begin{aligned} v_1 x_{i1} + v_2 x_{i2} + v_3 x_{i3} &= 0 \\ w_1 x_{i1} + w_2 x_{i2} + w_3 x_{i3} &= 0, \end{aligned} \tag{8.5}$$

where (v_1, v_2, v_3) and (w_1, w_2, w_3) are two given noncollinear vectors perpendicular to the line. Equations such as (8.4) and (8.5) can be assembled with the system of linear equations, as we did with Equation (8.3). However, if **A** is symmetric, the symmetry is lost. We will now describe an alternative procedure based on a transformation of variables, which preserves both the symmetry and the positive definiteness of **A**.

For node i, we take a local coordinate system ξ, η, ζ, where in the case of a given plane ζ is taken perpendicular to the plane as shown in Fig. 8.2, while in the case of a line ξ is taken along the line as Fig. 8.3 shows. The vector (x_{i1}, x_{i2}, x_{i3}) at node i is expressed as follows:

$$\begin{vmatrix} x_{i1} \\ x_{i2} \\ x_{i3} \end{vmatrix} = \begin{vmatrix} \lambda_1 & \mu_1 & \nu_1 \\ \lambda_2 & \mu_2 & \nu_2 \\ \lambda_3 & \mu_3 & \nu_3 \end{vmatrix} \begin{vmatrix} \xi \\ \eta \\ \zeta \end{vmatrix} \tag{8.6}$$

where $(\lambda_1, \lambda_2, \lambda_3)$, (μ_1, μ_2, μ_3) and (ν_1, ν_2, ν_3) are the direction cosines of the axes ξ, η and ζ, respectively, and (ξ, η, ζ) are the components of the vector in the local system. The matrix in Equation (8.6) is orthogonal. The vector is parallel to the plane when $\zeta = 0$, or is parallel to the line when $\eta = \zeta = 0$. Thus, if we use ξ, η, ζ as coordinates for node i, the desired condition can be

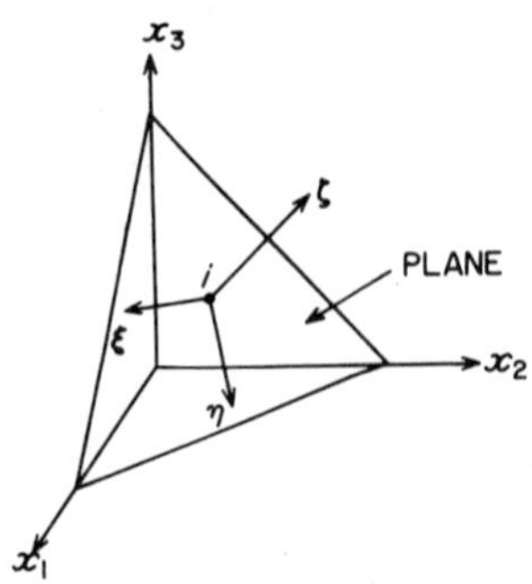

Figure 8.2 Local coordinate system for a plane.

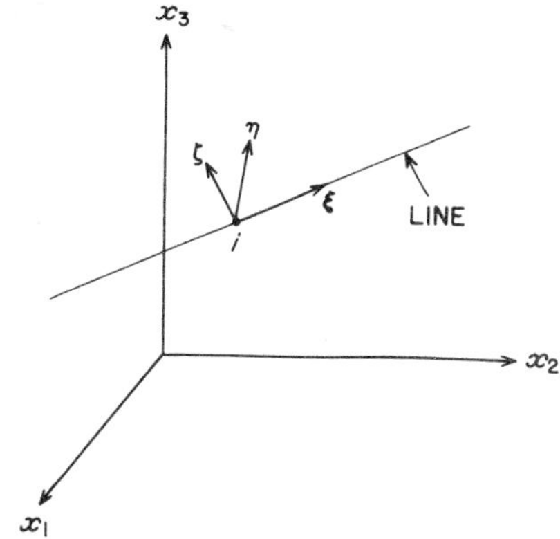

Figure 8.3 Local coordinate system for a line.

very easily enforced. In place of the usual column vector $\mathbf{x}$ of nodal unknowns:

$$\mathbf{x} = (x_{1\,1}, x_{2\,1}, x_{3\,1}, \ldots, x_{i\,1}, x_{i\,2}, x_{i\,3}, \ldots, x_{n1}, x_{n2}, x_{n3})^{\mathrm{T}} \tag{8.7}$$

the following column vector $\mathbf{x}'$ is used:

$$\mathbf{x}' = (x_{1\,1}, x_{2\,1}, x_{3\,1}, \ldots, \xi, \eta, \zeta, \ldots, x_{n1}, x_{n2}, x_{n3})^{\mathrm{T}} \tag{8.8}$$

From Equation (8.6) we have:

$$\mathbf{x} = \mathbf{R}\mathbf{x}' \tag{8.9}$$

where:

$$\mathbf{R} = \begin{array}{c|ccc:ccc:ccc|}
 & 1\,1 & & & i\,1 & i\,2 & i\,3 & & & n\,3 \\
\hline
1\,1 & 1 & & & & & & & & \\
 & & \ddots & & & \mathbf{0} & & & \mathbf{0} & \\
 & & & 1 & & & & & & \\
\hdashline
i\,1 & & & & \lambda_1 & \mu_1 & \nu_1 & & & \\
i\,2 & & \mathbf{0} & & \lambda_2 & \mu_2 & \nu_2 & & \mathbf{0} & \\
i\,3 & & & & \lambda_3 & \mu_3 & \nu_3 & & & \\
\hdashline
 & & & & & & & 1 & & \\
 & & \mathbf{0} & & & \mathbf{0} & & & \ddots & \\
n\,3 & & & & & & & & & 1
\end{array} \tag{8.10}$$

Matrix **R** is also orthogonal, since $\mathbf{R}\mathbf{R}^{\mathrm{T}} = \mathbf{I}$ or $\mathbf{R}^{\mathrm{T}} = \mathbf{R}^{-1}$. In general, there may be a set of nodes with given planes and another set with given lines. Matrix **R** will then have several 3×3 blocks placed at different positions along the diagonal, with ones at the remaining positions, and vector $\mathbf{x}'$ will contain several groups of three local coordinates. **R** will still be orthogonal. The system of linear equations

$$\mathbf{A}\mathbf{x} = \mathbf{b} \tag{8.11}$$

is asembled from element matrices in the usual way. Using Equation (8.9) and pre-multiplying Equation (8.11) by $\mathbf{R}^{\mathrm{T}}$ we obtain

$$\mathbf{R}^{\mathrm{T}}\mathbf{A}\mathbf{R}\mathbf{x}' = \mathbf{R}^{\mathrm{T}}\mathbf{b} \tag{8.12}$$

or, if $\mathbf{B} = \mathbf{R}^{\mathrm{T}}\mathbf{A}\mathbf{R}$ and $\mathbf{b}' = \mathbf{R}^{\mathrm{T}}\mathbf{b}$:

$$\mathbf{B}\mathbf{x}' = \mathbf{b}'. \tag{8.13}$$

In Equation (8.13), **B** is symmetric positive definite (Property 8 of Section 2.2). The conditions $\zeta = 0$ or $\eta = \zeta = 0$ are introduced in **B** in the usual way: placing zeros at all off-diagonal positions of the corresponding row and column, a one at the diagonal position, and a zero at the corresponding position of $\mathbf{b}'$. This preserves both the symmetry and positive definiteness of **B**, as discussed previously. Then the system (8.13) is solved and $\mathbf{x}'$ is obtained. Finally, Equation (8.9) is used to obtain the solution vector **x** in terms of the global coordinate system.

It may be easily seen that, since conditions of the type $\zeta = 0$ or $\eta = \zeta = 0$ are being applied, the same result is obtained with less computational effort if we take:

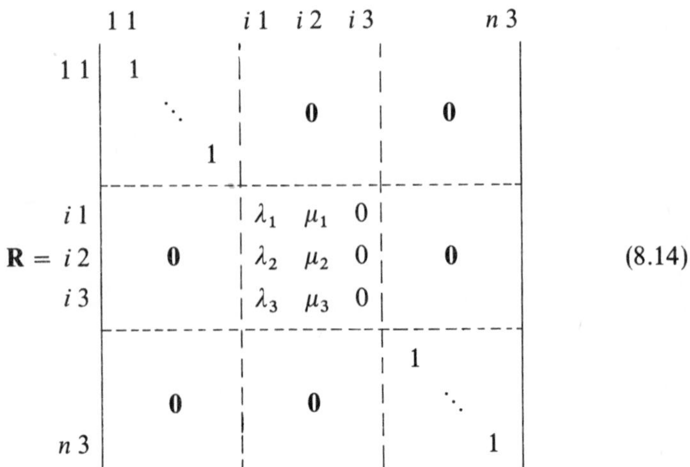

for a plane at node i, and:

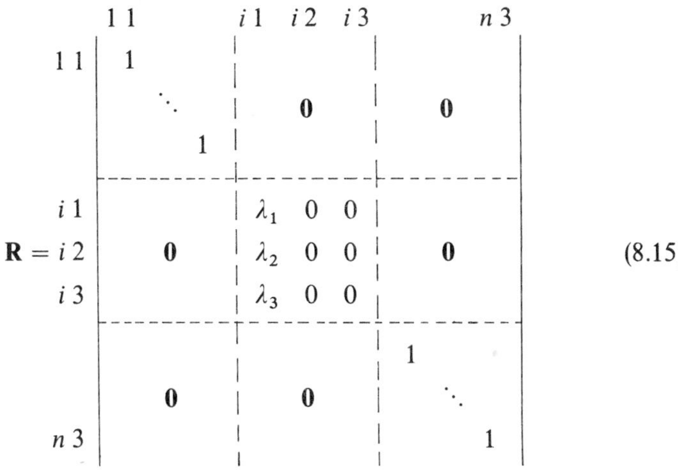

for a line at node i. $\mathbf{B}$ results with the corresponding rows and columns already filled with zeros, and it suffices to insert a one at each of the diagonal positions and the required zeros in $\mathbf{b}'$. $\mathbf{B}$ is still symmetric positive definite, and Equation (8.9) is still valid with the simplified $\mathbf{R}$. Since the 3×3 blocks in $\mathbf{A}$ are usually full, this procedure not only preserves sparsity but actually *improves* it. The procedure is basically similar to the well-known eigenvalue economizer method (Irons, 1963). An alternative procedure for manipulating vector boundary conditions, which also employs the concept of coordinate transformation, is *condensation* [see for example Gallagher (1975)].

8.4. Example of a connectivity matrix

Consider the two-dimensional mesh shown in Fig. 8.1, with $N = 9$ nodes and $M = 4$ elements, numbered in an arbitrary way. The numbers of the elements are encircled. The $M \times N$ connectivity matrix $\mathbf{E}$ for this mesh is:

$$
\mathbf{E} = \begin{array}{c|ccccccccc|}
 & 1 & 2 & 3 & 4 & 5 & 6 & 7 & 8 & 9 \\
1 & 1 & 0 & 1 & 0 & 0 & 1 & 0 & 1 & 0 \\
2 & 0 & 1 & 1 & 1 & 0 & 0 & 1 & 0 & 0 \\
3 & 0 & 1 & 1 & 0 & 1 & 1 & 0 & 0 & 0 \\
4 & 0 & 0 & 1 & 0 & 0 & 0 & 1 & 1 & 1
\end{array}
$$

Each row of this matrix is associated with an element, and each column with a node. Row 1 has nonzeros at positions 1, 3, 6 and 8, thus expressing the fact that nodes 1, 3, 6 and 8 belong to element 1. The nonzeros of column 7 are at positions 2 and 4, because node 7 belongs to both elements 2 and 4. In this notation, the nodal reference numbers are given in ascending order for each element. But when **E** is represented in sparse row-wise format, they can be given in the conventional order accepted for elements. For example, a usual convention for two-dimensional elements is the counter-clockwise order, in which case we have in RR(C)U

IE = 1 5 9 13 17

JE = 3 8 1 6, 7 3 2 4, 5 2 3 6, 7 9 8 3

Only the structure of **E** is given since the nonzeros are all equal to one. This representation is unordered according to the definition of sparse format; however, it is ordered in a certain sense because the reference numbers of the nodes of each element are given in the conventional order, only the selection of the first node of each sequence being arbitrary.

We can also represent the transpose $\mathbf{E}^T$ of matrix **E** in sparse format:

IET = 1 2 4 8 9 10 12 14 16 17

JET = 1, 2 3, 1 2 3 4, 2, 3, 1 3, 2 4, 1 4, 4

in RR(C)O. This representation can easily be obtained from IE, JE using the transposition algorithm of Section 7.3. In JET are listed the reference numbers of the elements associated with each node, e.g., 2, 3 in row 2 indicate that node 2 belongs only to elements 2 and 3. For some computations both representations IE, JE and IET, JET are required simultaneously.

8.5. Example of a nodal assembly matrix

The nodal assembly or "stiffness" matrix for the mesh shown in Fig. 8.1 is the following:

A =

	1	2	3	4	5	6	7	8	9
1	x	0	x	0	0	x	0	x	0
2	0	x	x	x	x	x	x	0	0
3	x	x	x	x	x	x	x	x	x
4	0	x	x	x	0	0	x	0	0
5	0	x	x	0	x	x	0	0	0
6	x	x	x	0	x	x	0	x	0
7	0	x	x	x	0	0	x	x	x
8	x	0	x	0	0	x	x	x	x
9	0	0	x	0	0	0	x	x	x

where only the structure is shown since the numerical values can only be determined by calculating and assembling the element matrices associated with each element and with the problem which is being solved. In many practical cases **A** is symmetric, and its structure is always symmetric. Assuming that **A** is symmetric in this example, its structure can be represented as follows in RR(U)O:

IA = 1 4 9 15 16 17 18 20 21 21

JA = 3 6 8, 3 4 5 6 7, 4 5 6 7 8 9, 7, 6, 8, 8 9, 9

This representation (though unordered) can be obtained from IE, JE and IET, JET using the algorithm of Section 8.6. Note that there are only 20 off-diagonal nonzeros. If **A** were a banded matrix, the minimum half-bandwidth would be 5 for this example, and the number of off-diagonal elements would be 26, which shows the advantage of sparse representations even for such a small mesh.

As was explained in Section 8.2, it is computationally convenient that equations associated with Dirichlet nodes remain in the system, corresponding to rows in **A** with a one on the diagonal as the only nonzero. It was also explained that the terms which connect other nodes with Dirichlet nodes must be removed from the corresponding equations by subtracting them from the right sides. Let us assume that nodes 2, 4 and 5 of Fig. 8.1 are Dirichlet nodes. The nodal assembly matrix in this case is:

$$
\mathbf{A} = \begin{array}{c|ccccccccc|}
 & 1 & 2 & 3 & 4 & 5 & 6 & 7 & 8 & 9 \\
1 & x & 0 & x & 0 & 0 & x & 0 & x & 0 \\
2 & 0 & 1 & 0 & 0 & 0 & 0 & 0 & 0 & 0 \\
3 & x & 0 & x & 0 & 0 & x & x & x & x \\
4 & 0 & 0 & 0 & 1 & 0 & 0 & 0 & 0 & 0 \\
5 & 0 & 0 & 0 & 0 & 1 & 0 & 0 & 0 & 0 \\
6 & x & 0 & x & 0 & 0 & x & 0 & x & 0 \\
7 & 0 & 0 & x & 0 & 0 & 0 & x & x & x \\
8 & x & 0 & x & 0 & 0 & x & x & x & x \\
9 & 0 & 0 & x & 0 & 0 & 0 & x & x & x
\end{array}
$$

where the diagonal elements 2, 4 and 5 are now equal to one. In RR(U)O we have:

IA = 1 4 4 8 8 8 9 11 12 12

JA = 3 6 8, 6 7 8 9, 8, 8 9, 9

which has only 11 off-diagonal nonzeros, while the banded representation would still have 26 off-diagonal elements.

8.6. Algorithm for the symbolic assembly of a symmetric nodal assembly matrix

Input:	IE, JE	mesh connectivity matrix in RR(C)U.
	IET, JET	transpose of IE, JE, in RR(C)U.
	N	number of nodes in the mesh.
	IA	array of dimension N which contains the value N in the positions corresponding to Dirichlet nodes and 0 elsewhere.
Output:	IA, JA	structure of the nodal assembly matrix of dimension N × N, in RR(U)U.

```
          JP=1
          NM=N-1
          DO 30 I=1,NM
          JPI=JP
          IF(IA(I).EQ.N)GO TO 30
          IETA=IET(I)
          IETB=IET(I+1)-1
          DO 20 IP=IETA,IETB
          J=JET(IP)
          IEA=IE(J)
          IEB=IE(J+1)-1
          DO 10 KP=IEA,IEB
          K=JE(KP)
          IF(K.LE.I)GO TO 10
          IF(IA(K).GE.I)GO TO 10
          JA(JP)=K
          JP=JP+1
          IA(K)=I
  10      CONTINUE
  20      CONTINUE
  30      IA(I)=JPI
          IA(N)=JP
          IA(N+1)=JP
```

This algorithm is essentially similar to symbolic multiplication, Section 7.21, where the factors are $\mathbf{E}^T$ and $\mathbf{E}$, and the result is the structure of $\mathbf{A}$ (Gustavson, 1976c). The array IA plays three different roles: on input it identifies the Dirichlet nodes, if any; during execution, it is used as the multiple switch array (see section 1.14); and on output it is the array of pointers to JA. During the processing of row I, the pointers to the I − 1 initial rows are stored in positions 1 to I − 1 of IA, while positions I to N of IA are used as the multiple switch. This is done with no additional processing because only column indices larger than I are of interest for row I, the representation being upper.

The pointer to the list JA is JP, initialized at line 1 and incremented at line 17. Only N − 1 rows are processed by the DO 30 loop since row N is necessarily empty, having no elements to the right of the diagonal. Line 5 takes care of equations associated with Dirichlet nodes: the corresponding rows are left empty. The DO 20 loop at line 8 scans all the elements to which node I belongs; note that IETB ⩾ IETA, since every node belongs to at least one element. At line 9, J is the reference number of one of the elements of node I. The DO 10 loop at line 12 scans all the nodes of element J; note that necessarily IEB > IEA since there are no elements with less than two nodes. At line 13, K is the reference number of a node of element J. At line 14, all nodes which do not fall to the right of the diagonal are discarded. At line 15, the multiple switch is tested; note, however, that IA(K) = I would mean that node K has already been added to the list JA and does not have to be added a second time, while IA(K) = N means that K is a Dirichlet node and does not have to be inscribed in JA at all. The remaining nodes are inscribed in JA at line 16 and the multiple switch is consequently blocked at line 18. JP, the pointer to the list JA, is used to store the values of the row pointers in IA at lines 21, 22 and 23.

8.7. Algorithm for the numerical assembly of an element matrix and vector into the nodal assembly matrix A and right-hand vector b: Symmetric case

Input:	IA, JA	structure of matrix **A** in RR(U)U. The order of **A** is N.
	IDIR	array which identifies Dirichlet nodes; it contains 1 for a Dirichlet node, 0 otherwise.
	AE, BE	element matrix and element vector, respectively, to be assembled in AN, AD and B.
	JEP	reference numbers of the nodes associated with the rows and columns of AE.
	NN	order of AE and BE.
Output:	AN, AD	numerical values of nonzeros of **A** in RR(U)U.
	B	right-hand vector of system of linear equations.
Working space:	IP	of dimension N, initialized to 0. IP is used and then reset to 0. IP is the expanded integer array of pointers.
Note:		the prescribed values of the Dirichlet unknowns should be stored in the corresponding positions of B. In other

words, if i is a Dirichlet node with boundary condition C_i, then, before using this algorithm, set IDIR(i) = 1, B(i) = C_i.

```
 1.         DO 40 L=1,NN
 2.         I=JEP(L)
 3.         IF(IDIR(I).NE.0)GO TO 40
 4.         K=L-NN
 5.         AD(I)=AD(I)+AE(K+L*NN)
 6.         B(I)=B(I)+BE(L)
 7.         KK=0
 8.         DO 20 LL=1,NN
 9.         K=K+NN
10.         IF(LL.EQ.L)GO TO 20
11.         J=JEP(LL)
12.         IF(IDIR(J).NE.0)GO TO 10
13.         IF(J.LT.I)GO TO 20
14.         IP(J)=K
15.         KK=1
16.         GO TO 20
17.   10    B(I)=B(I)-B(J)*AE(K)
18.   20    CONTINUE
19.         IF(KK.EQ.0)GO TO 40
20.         IAA=IA(I)
21.         IAB=IA(I+1)-1
22.         DO 30 J=IAA,IAB
23.         K=IP(JA(J))
24.         IF(K.EQ.0)GO TO 30
25.         AN(J)=AN(J)+AE(K)
26.         IP(JA(J))=0
27.   30    CONTINUE
28.   40    CONTINUE
```

This algorithm accumulates the element matrix AE of NN × NN into the appropriate positions of the nodal assembly matrix AN, AD of N × N, and the element vector BE of length NN into the corresponding positions of the right-hand vector B of length N. Equations associated with Dirichlet nodes are not asembled (line 3) and terms connecting normal nodes with Dirichlet nodes are directly subtracted from B (line 17). This algorithm is essentially one of addition, and the techniques employed are those discussed in Section 7.8. The expanded integer array IP is used to store pointers to the elements of AE which have to be assembled. Since AE is stored column-wise, the element (L, LL) is at position K = L + (LL − 1)*NN. The parameter K is initialized at line 4, within the DO 40 loop, which scans the NN rows of AE. At line 2, I is the global row index associated with row L of AE. The diagonal element of this row is assembled at line 5, and the right-hand element at line 6.

The DO 20 loop scans the remaining elements of row L of AE, the diagonal one being discarded at line 10. K is redefined at line 9 in such a way that its value is in fact K = L + (LL − 1)*NN. The global column index J is calculated at line 11. At line 13, all elements which are in the lower triangle of **A** are discarded. When the execution reaches line 14, the decision has been made that the element (L, LL) of AE, at position AE(K), has to be accumulated in position (I, J) of the global matrix **A**. This fact is recorded by storing K in IP(J).

KK is used to detect situations in which none of the elements of row L of AE must be assembled. Such situations arise at least once for each element matrix in the symmetric case: row I for which the largest column index is equal to I, is not assembled. KK is initialized at line 7 and defined at line 15 when an element to the right of the diagonal is found in row I. Then, if KK = 0 at line 19, execution of the DO 30 loop is avoided.

The DO 30 loop scans row I of matrix **A**. At line 23 the values of K are retrieved from IP and at line 25 the corresponding element from AE is accumulated in the correct position of AN. IP is reset to 0 at line 26.

Note that the elements of AE cannot be directly accumulated in AN because the lists JEP and JA of column indices are not ordered. This algorithm runs first over JEP setting the expanded pointers IP, and then over JA using the expanded pointers to find the required elements in AE. In this way, a fixed number of operations is performed for each element of **A**, and the total number of operations is thus linearly proportional to the total number of nonzeros.

We should also note that execution of the statements at lines 23 and 24 is somewhat inefficient. If we compare NN − 1, the number of off-diagonal nonzeros in a row of AE, with NZ, the maximum number of nonzeros in a row of **A** to the right of the diagonal, we have, for some typical finite element applications:

(a) Plane mesh composed of triangles: NN − 1 = 2, NZ = 8.
(b) Plane mesh composed of quadrilaterals: NN − 1 = 3, NZ = 8.
(c) Three-dimensional mesh composed of hexahedrons: NN − 1 = 7, NZ = 26.

In the last case, for example, lines 23 and 24 will be executed 26 times, but only 7 nonzeros will be assembled at line 25. There seems to be no economic solution to this difficulty. However, as an alternative procedure we may consider the use of an expanded real array X, in place of IP, as discussed in Section 1.15. We scan JA, loading the nonzeros from AN into the corresponding positions of X; then we accumulate the nonzeros from row L of AE into X, and finally we again scan JA and load all the corresponding elements back into AN. Some elements are unnecessarily loaded into X and then back into AN, but this additional cost may be comparable with that of executing statements 23 and 24 unnecessarily the same number of times.

8.8. Algorithm for the numerical assembly of an element matrix and vector into the nodal assembly matrix A and right-hand vector b: General case

Input:	IA, JA	structure of matrix **A** in RR(C)U. The order of **A** is N.
	IDIR	array which identifies Dirichlet nodes; it contains 1 for a Dirichlet node, 0 otherwise.
	AE, BE	element matrix and vector, respectively, to be assembled in AN, AD and B.
	JEP	reference numbers of the nodes associated with the rows and columns of AE.
	NN	order of AE and BE.
Output:	AN	numerical values of nonzeros of **A** in RR(C)U.
	B	right-hand vector of system of linear equations.
Working space:	IP	of dimension N, initialized to 0. IP is used and then reset to 0. IP is the expanded integer array of pointers.
Note:		the prescribed values of the Dirichlet unknowns should be stored in the corresponding positions of B. In other words, if i is a Dirichlet node with prescribed value C_i, then, before using this algorithm, set IDIR(i)=1 , B(i)=C_i.

```
          DO 40 L=1,NN
          I=JEP(L)
          IF(IDIR(I).NE.0)GO TO 40
          K=L-NN
          B(I)=B(I)+BE(L)
          DO 20 LL=1,NN
          K=K+NN
          J=JEP(LL)
          IF(IDIR(J).NE.0)GO TO 10
          IP(J)=K
          GO TO 20
   10     B(I)=B(I)-B(J)*AE(K)
```

```
13.   20    CONTINUE
14.         IAA=IA(I)
15.         IAB=IA(I+1)-1
16.         DO 30 J=IAA,IAB
17.         K=IP(JA(J))
18.         IF(K.EQ.0)GO TO 30
19.         AN(J)=AN(J)+AE(K)
20.         IP(JA(J))=0
21.   30    CONTINUE
22.   40    CONTINUE
```

This algorithm is essentially similar to that presented in Section 8.7. However, some important differences deserve consideration. The algorithm of this section is used when matrix **A** is unsymmetric and is thus stored in a complete representation, AD being absent. All elements of each row of AE must be assembled into AN, except those which correspond to Dirichlet unknowns. These are assembled into the right-hand vector **B** at line 12. Since no finite element may have all its nodes declared to be Dirichlet nodes, one or more elements from each row of AE will have to be assembled into AN. The loop DO 30 must always be executed, and the use of parameter KK (lines 7, 15 and 19 of Section 8.7) is not necessary in the present case.

CHAPTER 9

General Purpose Algorithms

9.1. Introduction

In this chapter we present a collection of algorithms or ideas for writing algorithms for different purposes connected with sparse matrix technology. The collection does not cover any specific matter, the ideas being just those which have been dictated by our experience with programs which employ sparse matrices.

Sparse triangular matrices have already been considered in Chapter 7 in connection with the solution of systems of linear equations. Triangular matrices, however, are entitled to special consideration because of the interesting properties they have. For example, given a lower triangular matrix, it is possible to calculate the product of its inverse by another vector or matrix without calculating the inverse explicitly. Sections 9.2 to 9.6 are thus devoted to the consideration of the algorithms required for performing the most common operations with sparse triangular matrices.

The iterative solution of linear equations is discussed in several good publications, the most popular methods being those which use the Lanczos vectors. A good general account on iterative methods was published by Axelsson (1977). Another excellent review was presented more recently by Jacobs (1981). Here we present a simple Gauss–Seidel algorithm, which is discussed in Section 9.7 and given in Section 9.8.

Some ideas are presented in Section 9.9 concerning how to devise an algorithm to help debug a new program or to check input data or intermediate results.

Analysts frequently face difficulties because sparse representations were devised for computers, not for people. A simple examination of a matrix stored in sparse format may be very difficult to make. In Section 9.10 we discuss one possible solution to this difficulty.

Finally, in Sections 9.11, 9.12 and 9.13 we present three very simple yet useful algorithms. The reader who wishes to use sparse matrices is encouraged to implement the algorithms in this chapter for his convenience.

9.2. Multiplication of the inverse of a lower triangular matrix by a general matrix

In this section we consider the calculation of products of the form

$$\mathbf{X} = \mathbf{U}^{-\mathrm{T}}\mathbf{B}, \tag{9.1}$$

where $\mathbf{B}$ is a general sparse matrix, $\mathbf{U}$ is an upper triangular sparse matrix with unit diagonal, $\mathbf{U}^{\mathrm{T}}$ is its transpose and $\mathbf{U}^{-\mathrm{T}} \equiv (\mathbf{U}^{\mathrm{T}})^{-1}$. This problem reduces to forward substitution, Sections 7.27 and 7.28, when $\mathbf{B}$ and $\mathbf{X}$ are column vectors.

$\mathbf{U}^{\mathrm{T}}$ is sparse lower triangular with unit diagonal. $\mathbf{X}$ can be obtained without ever calculating the inverse of $\mathbf{U}^{\mathrm{T}}$, which would be a dense matrix. For this purpose we write (9.1) as follows:

$$\mathbf{U}^{\mathrm{T}}\mathbf{X} = \mathbf{B}, \tag{9.2}$$

which is now a system of linear equations with the elements of $\mathbf{X}$ as unknowns. The system (9.2) is solved by the usual techniques. A symbolic algorithm and a numerical algorithm are used. The multiple switch technique and the expanded real accumulator described in Sections 1.14 and 1.15 are also used in the algorithms. A simple case is illustrated in the following example and the algorithms are given in Sections 9.3 and 9.4.

Consider the following system:

$$\begin{vmatrix} 1 & 0 & 0 \\ a & 1 & 0 \\ b & c & 1 \end{vmatrix} \begin{vmatrix} x_{11} & x_{12} \\ x_{21} & x_{22} \\ x_{31} & x_{32} \end{vmatrix} = \begin{vmatrix} b_{11} & b_{12} \\ b_{21} & b_{22} \\ b_{31} & b_{32} \end{vmatrix} \tag{9.3}$$

For the first row we have:

$$(x_{11}x_{12}) = (b_{11}b_{12}) \tag{9.4}$$

where the notation means:

$$x_{11} = b_{11}$$
$$x_{12} = b_{12}$$

For the second row:

$$a(x_{11}x_{12}) + (x_{21}x_{22}) = (b_{21}b_{22})$$

Therefore:

$$(x_{21}x_{22}) = (b_{21}b_{22}) - a(x_{11}x_{12}) \tag{9.5}$$

In a similar way, for the third row we obtain:

$$(x_{31}x_{32}) = (b_{31}b_{32}) - b(x_{11}x_{12}) - c(x_{21}x_{22}) \tag{9.6}$$

Equations (9.4), (9.5) and (9.6) are solved in sequence, and the resulting matrix **X** is obtained. This algorithm is appropriate for sparse matrices in row-wise format because both $\mathbf{U}^{\mathrm{T}}$ and **B** are accessed only by rows.

9.3. Algorithm for the symbolic multiplication of the inverse of a lower triangular matrix $\mathbf{U}^{-\mathrm{T}}$ by a general matrix B

This algorithm computes the structure of $\mathbf{X} = \mathbf{U}^{-\mathrm{T}}\mathbf{B}$.

Input: IUT, JUT	structure of $\mathbf{U}^{\mathrm{T}}$ in RR(L)U, where L indicates that the lower triangle of $\mathbf{U}^{\mathrm{T}}$ is represented.
IB, JB	structure of matrix **B** in RR(C)U.
N	order of $\mathbf{U}^{\mathrm{T}}$ and number of rows of **B** and **X**.
NC	number of columns of **B** and **X**.
Output: IX, JX	structure of resulting matrix in RR(C)U.
Working space: IP	of dimension NC, multiple switch array.

```
 1.            DO 10 I=1,NC
 2.    10      IP(I)=0
 3.            JP=1
 4.            IX(1)=1
 5.            DO 70 I=1,N
 6.            IBA=IB(I)
 7.            IBB=IB(I+1)-1
 8.            IF(IBB.LT.IBA)GO TO 30
 9.            DO 20 JJ=IBA,IBB
10.            J=JB(JJ)
11.            IP(J)=I
12.            JX(JP)=J
13.    20      JP=JP+1
14.    30      IUA=IUT(I)
15.            IUB=IUT(I+1)-1
16.            IF(IUB.LT.IUA)GO TO 60
17.            DO 50 JJ=IUA,IUB
18.            J=JUT(JJ)
19.            IXA=IX(J)
20.            IXB=IX(J+1)-1
21.            IF(IXB.LT.IXA)GO TO 50
22.            DO 40 KP=IXA,IXB
23.            K=JX(KP)
24.            IF(IP(K).EQ.I)GO TO 40
25.            IP(K)=I
26.            JX(JP)=K
27.            JP=JP+1
28.    40      CONTINUE
29.    50      CONTINUE
30.    60      IX(I+1)=JP
31.    70      CONTINUE
```

In this algorithm, the multiple switch array IP is initialized to 0 at lines 1 and 2. The pointer JP to IX is initialized at line 3, is incremented at lines 13 and 27 each time a new element is added to the list JX, and is used to construct IX at line 30. The DO 70 loop scans the N rows of the matrices. The row I of **B** is loaded into JX by the DO 20 loop, at line 12, and I is stored in position J of the multiple switch IP in order to prevent any further inscription of the column index J in the description of row I in JX.

Then, the algorithm corresponding to Equations (9.4), (9.5) and (9.6) of the preceding section starts. The DO 50 loop scans row I of $\mathbf{U}^T$, and for each column index J found the DO 40 loop scans row J of **X** and inscribes in JX every column index K which was not previously inscribed. Note that position K of the multiple switch is tested at line 24, and blocked if necessary at line 25.

9.4. Algorithm for the numerical multiplication of the inverse of a lower triangular matrix $\mathbf{U}^{-T}$ by a general matrix B

This algorithm computes numerically $\mathbf{X} = \mathbf{U}^{-T}\mathbf{B}$.

Input:	IUT, JUT, UNT	given triangular matrix $\mathbf{U}^T$ in RR(L)U.
	IB, JB, BN	given general matrix **B** in RR(C)U.
	IX, JX	structure of the resulting matrix **X** in RR(C)U.
	N	order of $\mathbf{U}^T$ and number of rows of **B** and **X**.
Output:	XN	numerical values for matrix **X**, in RR(C)U.
Working space:	X	of dimension equal to the number of columns of **B** and **X**. Expanded accumulator.

```
      DO 80 I=1,N
      IH=I+1
      IXA=IX(I)
      IXB=IX(IH)-1
      IF(IXB.LT.IXA)GO TO 80
      DO 10 IP=IXA,IXB
10    X(JX(IP))=0.
      IBA=IB(I)
      IBB=IB(IH)-1
      IF(IBB.LT.IBA)GO TO 30
      DO 20 IP=IBA,IBB
20    X(JB(IP))=BN(IP)
30    IUA=IUT(I)
      IUB=IUT(IH)-1
      IF(IUB.LT.IUA)GO TO 60
      DO 50 JP=IUA,IUB
      J=JUT(JP)
      IXC=IX(J)
      IXD=IX(J+1)-1
      IF(IXD.LT.IXC)GO TO 50
```

```
21.            A=UNT(JP)
22.            DO 40 KP=IXC,IXD
23.            K=JX(KP)
24.    40      X(K)=X(K)-A*XN(KP)
25.    50      CONTINUE
26.    60      CONTINUE
27.            DO 70 IP=IXA,IXB
28.    70      XN(IP)=X(JX(IP))
29.    80      CONTINUE
```

Given a lower triangular N × N matrix with unit diagonal $\mathbf{U}^{\mathrm{T}}$ and a general matrix **B** with N rows, this algorithm determines in the array XN the numerical values of the nonzeros of the matrix $\mathbf{X} = \mathbf{U}^{-\mathrm{T}}\mathbf{B}$. The DO 80 loop scans the rows of the matrices. For each row I, those positions of the expanded accumulator X which correspond to nonzeros of row I of the matrix **X**, if any, are initialized to 0 at lines 6 and 7. The nonzeros of row I of **B**, if any, are retrieved from their compact storage in BN and stored in expanded format by the DO 20 loop in the array X. The DO 50 loop scans the nonzeros of row I of $\mathbf{U}^{\mathrm{T}}$ and performs the operations illustrated by Equations (9.4), (9.5) and (9.6) of Section 9.2. For each nonzero of row I of $\mathbf{U}^{\mathrm{T}}$ with column index J and value A, the DO 40 loop scans row J of **X** (already complete at this point since $J < I$), multiplies the nonzeros, if any, by A, and accumulates the results with the signs changed in the corresponding positions of X. Finally, the DO 70 loop retrieves the resulting values from X and stores them in XN in correspondence with the column indices JX of row I of **X**.

The technique discussed in Section 1.16 can also be used in this algorithm, instead of the accumulator X.

9.5. Algorithm for the multiplication of the inverse of an upper triangular unit diagonal matrix U by a full vector x

This algorithm computes $\mathbf{w} = \mathbf{U}^{-1}\mathbf{x}$.

Input:	IU, JU, UN	matrix **U** in RR(U)U.
	X	given vector.
	N	order of **U**, N > 1.
Output:	W	resulting vector.

```
       DO 10 I=1,N
10     W(I)=X(I)
       I=N-1
```

```
20    IUA=IU(I)
      IUB=IU(I+1)-1
      IF(IUB.LT.IUA)GO TO 40
      Z=W(I)
      DO 30 IP=IUA,IUB
30    Z=Z-UN(IP)*W(JU(IP))
      W(I)=Z
40    I=I-1
      IF(I.GT.0)GO TO 20
```

This algorithm is similar to a portion of the algorithm discussed in Section 7.28, lines 2, 3 and 14 to 23. The algorithm reduces to backward substitution, Section 7.27, when **x** and **w** are column vectors.

9.6. Algorithm for the multiplication of the transpose inverse of an upper triangular unit diagonal matrix U by a full vector

This algorithm computes $\mathbf{w} = \mathbf{U}^{-T}\mathbf{x}$.

Input:	IU, JU, UN	matrix **U** in RR(U)U.
	X	given vector.
	N	order of **U**.
Output:	W	resulting vector.

```
      NM=N-1
      DO 10 I=1,N
10    W(I)=X(I)
      DO 30 I=1,NM
      IUA=IU(I)
      IUB=IU(I+1)-1
      IF(IUB.LT.IUA)GO TO 30
      Z=W(I)
      DO 20 IP=IUA,IUB
      J=JU(IP)
20    W(J)=W(J)-Z*UN(IP)
30    CONTINUE
```

This algorithm is equivalent to the first part of the algorithm described in Section 7.28. The calculations performed are illustrated by the equations of Section 7.27.

9.7. Solution of linear equations by the Gauss–Seidel iterative method

In this section we consider the iterative solution by the Gauss–Seidel method of the system of N linear equations:

$$\mathbf{Ax} = \mathbf{b} \tag{9.7}$$

where $\mathbf{A}$ is a sparse matrix. The method is known to converge if $\mathbf{A}$ is symmetric and positive definite (Fox, 1965). The nth equation of the System (9.7) can be written:

$$\sum_{j=1}^{n-1} A_{n\,j}x_j + A_{n\,n}x_n + \sum_{j=n+1}^{N} A_{n\,j}x_j = b_n. \tag{9.8}$$

This may be arranged as follows:

$$x_n = A_{n\,n}^{-1}\left(b_n - \sum_{j=1}^{n-1} A_{nj}x_j - \sum_{j=n+1}^{N} A_{nj}x_j\right) \tag{9.9}$$

when $A_{n\,n} \neq 0$. If $\mathbf{A}$ is positive definite then $A_{n\,n} > 0$ necessarily. Equation (9.9) is solved iteratively. An initial guess x_j^0 may be available, otherwise we may take:

$$x_j^0 = A_{jj}^{-1}b_j, \qquad j = 1, 2, \ldots, N \tag{9.10}$$

Then, at the mth cycle of iteration we compute:

$$x_n^m = A_{n\,n}^{-1}\left(b_n - \sum_{j=1}^{n-1} A_{nj}x_j^m - \sum_{j=n+1}^{N} A_{nj}x_j^{m-1}\right). \tag{9.11}$$

Convergence can be improved in some cases by using over-relaxation. In this case:

$$x_n^m = x_n^{m-1} + f(x_n^{m*} - x_n^{m-1}) \tag{9.12}$$

where x_n^{m*} is the value obtained using Equation (9.11). The relaxation coefficient f usually lies between 1 and 2.

9.8. Algorithm for the iterative solution of linear equations by the Gauss–Seidel method

This algorithm solves $\mathbf{Ax} = \mathbf{b}$.

Input:	IA, JA, AN	given matrix $\mathbf{A}$ in RR(LU)U.
	AD	diagonal elements of $\mathbf{A}$, all different from zero.
	B	right-hand side vector $\mathbf{b}$.

	N	order of the system.
	F	relaxation coefficient.
	EPS	maximum permissible absolute error for any of the equations.
Output:	X	vector of unknowns **x**.

```
1.          DO 10 I=1,N
2.    10    X(I)=B(I)/AD(I)
3.          IT=0
4.    20    IT=IT+1
5.          IEND=0
6.          DO 40 I=1,N
7.          IAA=IA(I)
8.          IAB=IA(I+1)-1
9.          IF(IAB.LT.IAA)GO TO 40
10.         U=B(I)
11.         DO 30 J=IAA,IAB
12.   30    U=U-AN(J)*X(JA(J))
13.         U=U/AD(I)-X(I)
14.         IF(ABS(U).GT.EPS)IEND=1
15.         X(I)=X(I)+F*U
16.   40    CONTINUE
17.         IF(IEND.EQ.1)GO TO 20
```

The DO 10 loop at lines 1 and 2 calculates initial values for the vector of unknowns X. This loop could be by-passed if an initial approximation were available for X. IT is the iteration counter. IT is initialized at line 3 and incremented at line 4. IT is included in this algorithm because it is normally used to output partial results and to check for convergence and for maximum permissible number of iterations. The DO 40 loop scans the N equations. The DO 30 loop performs the calculations indicated by Equation (9.11) of the preceding section. At line 13, the value $x_n^{m*} - x_n^{m-1}$ is calculated and stored in U. This value is tested for convergence at line 14, where the parameter IEND, previously initialized to 0 at line 5, is set to 1 if convergence is not satisfied. At line 15, the value of x_n^m is calculated as indicated by Equation (9.12), and stored in X(I). F is the relaxation coefficient. Finally, if convergence is not satisfied, the algorithm branches from line 17 to line 4, and a new iteration is started. Note that the algorithm will terminate only when the convergence test at line 14 is satisfied for *each* of the N equations.

An improvement in efficiency can be achieved if the computer executes a multiplication faster than a division, as many computers do. The divisions in lines 2 and 13 become multiplications if the reciprocals of the diagonal elements are provided in AD.

9.9. Checking the representation of a sparse matrix

The ideas to be discussed in this section are very helpful for: debugging a new program, checking input data, checking intermediate results for a new problem under analysis, and so on. The need of an algorithm for such purposes arises from the fact that many sparse matrix routines *assume* that the representations given as input data are standard. Due to the use of features such as pointers, double addressing, etc., the routines are very sensitive to even minor errors in the input data and may give completely unexpected results. Tracing out the error is difficult in such cases, the first step being a careful verification of the input data. A sparse matrix given in row-wise format, is represented by the following information:

IA, JA, AN, AD	structure and numerical values, as described in Sections 1.8 and 1.9.
NR	number of rows.
NC	number of columns.
KS	a conventional code to indicate the representation in which the matrix is given.
KOD	a conventional code to indicate whether only the structure or both the structure and the numerical values are given.

The checking algorithm should examine at least the following properties:

(1) NR and NC must be positive, and NR = NC if the matrix is symmetric.
(2) IA must contain NR + 1 positive numbers, each larger than or equal to the preceding one. Some users also require IA(1) = 1.
(3) The integers stored in JA must be in the range 1 to NC for a RR(C)U, I + 1 to NC for a RR(U)U, I to NC for a RR(DU)U, etc., where I is the row index.
(4) There must be no repeated column indices in JA for any row.
(5) Zeros are usually allowed in AN, but a useful piece of information for the analyst is to know how many zeros there are, since too many zeros may indicate an error condition, or at least some undesirable feature.
(6) If the matrix is positive definite, only positive numbers must be stored in AD.

The Fortran algorithm will not be given here because it is strongly dependent on the conventions used by the analyst (e.g. for KS and KOD), and on the characteristics of the error messages that the algorithm is expected to issue. To write such an algorithm is a simple exercise for a Fortran programmer, following the definitions of Chapter 1.

9.10. Printing or displaying a sparse matrix

There may be many reasons why a user might wish to examine his sparse matrix. But if he gets a printout of the usual arrays IA, JA, AN, AD, he will soon realize how difficult it is for a human being to use this information for intelligent purposes. It is thus convenient to write a routine to present the printed information in some comprehensible fashion. The routine should allow the user to specify the range of rows and the range of columns he wishes to examine. The information may then be printed in either of the following ways:

(1) As a full matrix. For each row, the values of the nonzeros are fed into a full real array, in which all positions were previously initialized to zero. The array is displayed or printed in a line, and the algorithm proceeds to the next row. A very convenient feature would be to distinguish between structural zeros (zeros stored in AN or AD as a result of numerical cancellations) and nonstructural zeros (elements which are known to be exactly zero and are thus not included in JA). A non-numerical symbol, e.g. *, may be printed at the positions corresponding to nonstructural zeros. Of course, this method is restricted to cases where only a small portion of a matrix has to be examined.

(2) For each row, print the row index, and then the nonzeros of that row with their corresponding column indices in parenthesis. An improvement would be to print the nonzeros orderly. The advantage of this method is that complete rows may be printed or displayed for examination in a reduced space, but it does not provide such a clear idea as the other method of the relationships between elements in neighbouring rows.

(3) A pattern of the nonzero structure can be displayed on a high-resolution device, such as a cathode ray screen or an electrostatic or mechanical dot printer, provided the matrix is not too large or only a portion of a large matrix has to be examined. Such patterns have become very popular (see, for example, Duff, 1981a). They give only global information, concerning the distribution and number of nonzeros.

To write the corresponding program is a simple task for a programmer. A good discussion of the subject was published by Gentleman and George (1976).

9.11. Algorithm for transforming a RR(C)U of a symmetric matrix into a RR(U)U of the same matrix

Input:	IA, JA, AN	given sparse symmetric matrix in RR(C)U.
	N	order of the given matrix.
Output:	IA, JA, AN, AD	given matrix in RR(U)U.

```
 1.          JP=1
 2.          IAB=IA(1)-1
 3.          DO 40 I=1,N
 4.          AD(I)=0.
 5.          IAA=IAB+1
 6.          IAB=IA(I+1)-1
 7.          IF(IAB.LT.IAA)GO TO 40
 8.          DO 30 IP=IAA,IAB
 9.          J=JA(IP)
10.          IF(J-I)30, 10, 20
11.   10     AD(I)=AN(IP)
12.          GO TO 30
13.   20     JA(JP)=J
14.          AN(JP)=AN(IP)
15.          JP=JP+1
16.   30     CONTINUE
17.   40     IA(I+1)=JP
```

In this algorithm, the DO 40 loop scans the N rows of the given matrix. For each row I, the initial pointer IAA and the final pointer IAB to the description of row I in JA and AN are set at lines 5 and 6. Note that IAB has been initialized at line 2. The array AD is not used for input, since the given representation is complete. AD is used only for output, and it has to be initialized to 0. at line 4 because we do not know *a priori* whether a diagonal nonzero exists or not in each row I. The DO 30 loop scans the nonzeros of row I. J, at line 9, is the column index of one such nonzero. If $J < I$ (nonzero to the left of the diagonal), the algorithm branches from line 10 directly to line 16 and the nonzero is discarded. If $J = I$, the algorithm branches to line 11 and the diagonal nonzero is inscribed in AD. When $J > I$, the nonzero is inscribed in JA and AN at lines 13 and 14; JP, initialized at line 1 and incremented at line 15, acts as the pointer to both arrays, and is also used at line 17 to store in IA the initial pointer to the next row $I+1$.

9.12. Algorithm for the pre-multiplication of a sparse matrix A by a diagonal matrix D

Input:	IA, AN	given matrix **A** in RR(C)U. Note that JA is not necessary.
	D	full diagonal of the given diagonal matrix.
	N	order of **D** and number or rows of **A**.
Output:	IA, AN	resulting matrix $\mathbf{B} = \mathbf{DA}$; note that the result is overwritten in AN. The same JA is valid for B.

```
1.            DO 20 I=1,N
2.            IAA=IA(I)
3.            IAB=IA(I+1)-1
4.            IF(IAB.LT.IAA)GO TO 20
5.            DD=D(I)
6.            DO 10 J=IAA,IAB
7.      10    AN(J)=AN(J)*DD
8.      20    CONTINUE
```

The DO 20 loop scans the N rows of the sparse matrix. For each row I, the multiplier D(I) is stored in DD at line 5. Then, the DO 10 loop scans the nonzeros of row I, which are multiplied by DD at line 7. This algorithm does not change the order in which the nonzeros are given.

9.13. Algorithm for copying a sparse matrix from IA, JA, AN to IB, JB, BN

Input:	IA, JA, AN	given matrix in any row-wise representation.
	N	number of rows of the given matrix.
Output:	IB, JB, BN	given matrix copied to new arrays.

```
            NH=N+1
            DO 10 I=1,NH
      10    IB(I)=IA(I)
            IAA=IA(1)
            IAB=IA(NH)-1
            DO 20 I=IAA,IAB
            JB(I)=JA(I)
      20    BN(I)=AN(I)
```

This simple algorithm can easily be modified to serve other purposes: change of sign of a given matrix, multiplication of the given matrix by a constant, etc.

References

Aasen, J. O. (1971). On the reduction of a symmetric matrix to tridiagonal form. *BIT* **11**, 233–242.

Aho, A. V., Hopcroft, J. E. and Ullman, J. D. (1976). *The Design and Analysis of Computer Algorithms*. Addison-Wesley: Reading, MA. Third printing.

Akyuz, F. A. and Utku, S. (1968). An automatic node-relabeling scheme for bandwidth minimization of stiffness matrices. *AIAA J.* **6**, 728–730.

Alvarado, F. L. (1979). A note on sorting sparse matrices. *Proc. IEEE* **67**, 1362–1363.

Alway, G. G. and Martin, D. W. (1965). An algorithm for reducing the bandwidth of a matrix of symmetric configuration. *Comput. J.* **8**, 264–272.

Arany, I., Smyth, W. F. and Szoda, L. (1971). An improved method for reducing the bandwidth of sparse symmetric matrices. In *Proceedings of the IGFIP Conference* (Ljubljana, Yugoslavia), Booklet TA-1, pp. 6–10. North Holland: Amsterdam.

Argyris, J. H. (1960). *Energy Theorems and Structural Analysis*. Butterworths: London.

Argyris, J. H. (1964). *Recent Advances in Matrix Methods of Structural Analysis*. Pergamon Press: London.

Axelsson, O. (1977). Solution of linear systems of equations: iterative methods. In Barker (1977), pp. 1–51.

Barker, V. A. (ed.) (1977). *Sparse Matrix Techniques*, Lecture Notes in Mathematics No. 572. Springer-Verlag: Berlin.

Barker, V. A., Thomsen, P. G. and Zlatev, Z. (1976). "Logical procedure SSLEST – an ALGOLW procedure for solving sparse systems of linear equations." Report NI 76-13, Numerisk Institut, DTH, Denmark.

Barth, W., Martin, R. S. and Wilkinson, J. H. (1967). Calculation of the eigenvalues of a symmetric tridiagonal matrix by the method of bisection. *Numer. Math.* **9**, 386–393. [Reprinted in Wilkinson and Reinsch (1971), pp. 249–256.]

Berge, C. (1962). *The Theory of Graphs and its Applications*. John Wiley & Sons: New York.

Berry, R. D. (1971). An optimal ordering of electronic circuit equations for a sparse matrix solution. *IEEE Trans. Circuit Theory*. **CT-18**, 139–145.

Bettess, P. (1977). Infinite elements. *Int. J. Numer. meth. Eng.* **11**, 53–64.

Björck, Å., Plemmons, R. J. and Schneider, H. (eds) (1981). *Large Scale Matrix Problems*. North Holland: New York, Oxford.

Borland, R. E. (1981). The AQ algorithm. In Duff (1981b), pp. 309–313.

Brännström, T. (1973). "On the method of Lanczos for finding eigenvalues of unsymmetric matrices". Department of Information Processing Umeå, Sweden. Report UMINF-44.73.

Brayton, R. K., Gustavson, F. G. and Willoughby, R. A. (1970). Some results on sparse matrices. *Math. Comput.* **24**, 937–954.

Brebbia, C. A. (1978). *The Boundary Element Method for Engineers*. John Wiley: New York.

Brown, N. G. and Wait, R. (1981). A branching envelope reducing algorithm for finite element meshes. In Duff (1981b), pp. 315–324.

Bunch, J. R. (1971). Analysis of the diagonal pivoting method. *SIAM J. Numer. Anal.* **8**, 656–680.

Bunch, J. R. (1974a). Partial pivoting strategies for symmetric matrices. *SIAM J. Numer. Anal.* **11**, 521–528.

Bunch, J. R. (1974b). Analysis of sparse elimination. *SIAM J. Numer. Anal.* **11**, 847–873.

Bunch, J. R. and Hopcroft, J. E. (1974). Triangular factorization and inversion by fast matrix multiplication. *Math. Comput.* **28**, 231–236.

Bunch, J. R. and Parlett, B. N. (1971). Direct methods for solving symmetric indefinite systems of linear equations. *SIAM J. Numer. Anal.* **8**, 639–655.

Bunch, J. R. and Rose, D. J. (1974). Partitioning, tearing and modification of sparse linear systems. *J. Math. Anal. Appl.* **48**, 574–598.

Bunch, J. R. and Rose, D. J. (eds) (1976). *Sparse Matrix Computations*. Academic Press: New York.

Chang, A. (1969). Application of sparse matrix methods in electric power system analysis. In Willoughby (1969), pp. 113–122.

Chari, M. V. K. and Silvester, P. P. (eds) (1980). *Finite Elements in Electrical and Magnetic Field Problems*. John Wiley: Chichester.

Cheng, K. Y. (1973a). Note on minimizing the bandwidth of sparse symmetric matrices. *Computing* **11**, 27–30.

Cheng, K. Y. (1973b). Minimizing the bandwidth of sparse symmetric matrices. *Computing* **11**, 103–110.

Cliffe, K. A., Jackson, C. P., Rae, J. and Winters, K. H. (1978). "Finite element flow modelling using velocity and pressure variables." Report AERE-R.9202, Harwell, UKAEA.

Clint, M. and Jennings, A. (1971). A simultaneous iteration method for the unsymmetric eigenvalue problem. *J. Inst. Math. Appl.* **8**, 111–121.

Coleman, R. D. and Kushner, E. J. (1982). Sparse matrices and the FPS-164 attached processor. Sparse Matrix Symposium, Fairfield Glade, Tennessee, October 24–27, 1982.

Concus, P., Golub, G. H. and O'Leary, D. P. (1976). A generalized conjugate gradient method for the numeric solution of elliptic partial differential equations. In Bunch and Rose (1976), pp. 309–332.

Crane, H. L., Jr., Gibbs, N. E., Poole, W. G., Jr. and Stockmeyer, P. K. (1975). "Matrix bandwidth and profile minimization." Report 75-9, ICASE.

Crawford, C. R. (1973). Reduction of a band-symmetric generalized eigenvalue problem. *Comm. A.C.M.* **16**, 41–44.

Cullum, J. and Donath, W. E. (1974). A block Lanczos algorithm for computing the q algebraically largest eigenvalues and a corresponding eigenspace of large, sparse, real symmetric matrices. In *Proceedings of the IEEE Conference on Decision and Control* (Phoenix, Arizona), pp. 505–509.

Cullum, J. and Willoughby, R. A. (1977). "The equivalence of the Lanczos and the conjugate gradient algorithms." IBM Research Report RC 6903, Yorktown Heights, NY.

Cullum, J. and Willoughby, R. A. (1978). "The Lanczos tridiagonalization and the conjugate gradient algorithms with local ε-orthogonality of the Lanczos vectors." IBM Research Report RC 7152, Yorktown Heights, NY.

Cullum, J. and Willoughby, R. A. (1981). Computing eigenvalues of very large symmetric matrices. An implementation of a Lanczos algorithm with no re-orthogonalization. *J. Comp. Phys.* **44**, 329–358.

Cullum, J. and Willoughby, R. A. (1983). *Lanczos Algorithms for Large Symmetric Eigenvalue Computations*, volume in Progress in Scientific Computing Series, edited by G. Golub, H. Kreiss, S. Arbarbanel and R. Glowinski. Birkhäuser Boston Inc.: Boston.

Cullum, J., Willoughby, R. A. and Lake, M. (1981). A Lanczos algorithm for computing singular values and corresponding singular vectors of large matrices. (Submitted 1981).

Curtis, A. R. and Reid, J. K. (1971a). "Fortran subroutines for the solution of sparse sets of linear equations." Report AERE-P.6844, HMSO, London.

Curtis, A. R. and Reid, J. K. (1971b). The solution of large sparse unsymmetric systems of linear equations. *J. Inst. Math. Appl.* **8**, 344–353.

Curtis, A. R. and Reid, J. K. (1972). On the automatic scaling of matrices for Gaussian elimination. *J. Inst. Math. Appl.* **10**, 118–124.

Cuthill, E. (1972). Several strategies for reducing the bandwidth of matrices. In Rose and Willoughby (1972), pp. 157–166.

Cuthill, E. and McKee, J. (1969). Reducing the bandwidth of sparse symmetric matrices. In *Proceedings of the 24th National Conference of the ACM*, pp. 157–172. Brandon Systems Press: NJ.

Dong, S. B. (1977). A block-Stodola eigensolution technique for large algebraic systems with nonsymmetrical matrices. *Int. J. Numer. meth. Eng.* **11**, 247–267.

Duff, I. S. (1972). "Analysis of sparse systems." D.Phil. Thesis, Oxford University, UK.

Duff, I. S. (1974a). On the number of nonzeros added when Gaussian elimination is performed on sparse random matrices. *Math. Comput.* **28**, 219–230.

Duff, I. S. (1974b). Pivot selection and row ordering in Givens reduction on sparse matrices. *Computing* **13**, 239–248.

Duff, I. S. (1976). "On algorithms for obtaining a maximum transversal." Harwell Report CSS 49.

Duff, I. S. (1977). A survey of sparse matrix research. *Proc. IEEE* **65**, 500–535.

Duff, I. S. (1978). "Some current approaches to the solution of large sparse systems of linear equations." Harwell Report CSS 65.

Duff, I. S. (1979). Practical comparisons of codes for the solution of sparse linear systems. In Duff and Stewart (1979), pp. 107–134.

Duff, I. S. (1980a) (revision). "MA28 – a set of Fortran subroutines for sparse unsymmetric linear equations." Harwell Report AERE-R.8730.

Duff, I. S. (1980b). Recent developments in the solution of large sparse linear equations. In Glowinski and Lions (1980), pp. 407–426.

Duff, I. S. (1981a). A sparse future. In Duff (1981b), pp. 1–29.

Duff, I. S. (ed.) (1981b). *Sparse Matrices and their Uses*. Proceedings of the IMA Conference, University of Reading, 9–11 July 1980. Academic Press: London.

Duff, I. S. (1982). "A survey of sparse matrix software." AERE Report R-10512. Computer Science and Systems Division, AERE Harwell, Oxfordshire, UK. [To appear in *Sources and Development of Mathematical Software*, edited by W. R. Cowell. Prentice-Hall: Englewood Cliffs, NJ.]

Duff, I. S. and Reid, J. K. (1974). A comparison of sparsity orderings for obtaining a pivotal sequence in Gaussian elimination. *J. Inst. Math. Appl.* **14**, 281–291.

Duff, I. S. and Reid, J. K. (1975). On the reduction of sparse matrices to condensed forms by similarity transformations. *J. Inst. Math. Appl.* **15**, 217–224.

Duff, I. S. and Reid, J. K. (1976). A comparison of some methods for the solution of sparse overdetermined systems of linear equations. *J. Inst. Math. Appl.* **17**, 267–280.

Duff, I. S. and Reid, J. K. (1978a). An implementation of Tarjan's algorithm for the block triangularization of a matrix. *ACM Trans. Math. Software* **4**, 137–147.

Duff, I. S. and Reid, J. K. (1978b). Algorithm 529. Permutations to block triangular form. *ACM Trans. Math. Software* **4**, 189–192.

Duff, I. S. and Stewart, G. W. (eds) (1979). *Sparse Matrix Proceedings 1978.* SIAM Publications: Philadelphia.

Duff, I. S., Grimes, R. G., Lewis, J. G. and Poole, W. G., Jr. (1982). Sparse matrix test problems. Sparse Matrix Symposium, Fairfield Glade, Tennessee, October 24–27, 1982.

Duff, I. S., Munksgaard, N., Nielsen, H. B. and Reid, J. K. (1977). "Direct solution of sets of linear equations whose matrix is sparse, symmetric and indefinite." Harwell Report CSS 44.

Dulmage, A. L. and Mendelsohn, N. S. (1959). A structure theory of bipartite graphs of finite exterior dimension. *Trans. Roy. Soc. Canada* **53**, 1–13.

Dulmage, A. L. and Mendelsohn, N. S. (1967). Graphs and matrices. In Harary (1967), pp. 167–227.

Eisenstat, S. C., Schultz, M. H. and Sherman, A. H. (1975). Efficient implementation of sparse symmetric Gaussian elimination. In Vichnevetsky (1975), pp. 33–39.

Eisenstat, S. C., Schultz, M. H. and Sherman, A. H. (1976). Applications of an element model for Gaussian elimination. In Bunch and Rose (1976), pp. 85–96.

Eisenstat, S. C., George, A., Grimes, R., Kincaid, D. and Sherman, A. H. (1979). Some comparisons of software packages for large sparse linear systems. In Vichnevetsky and Stepleman (1979), pp. 98–106.

Ericsson, T. and Ruhe, A. (1980). The spectral transformation Lanczos method for the numerical solution of large sparse generalized symmetric eigenvalue problems. *Math. Comput.* **35**, 1251–1268.

Erisman, A. M. and Reid, J. K. (1974). Monitoring the stability of the triangular factorization of a sparse matrix. *Numer. Math.* **22**, 183–186.

Even, S. and Kariv, O. (1975). An $O(n^{2.5})$ algorithm for maximum matching in general graphs. In *Proceedings of the 16th. Annual Symposium on Foundations of Computer Science* (*FOCS*), Berkeley, pp. 100–112. Springer-Verlag.

Fox, L. (1965). *An Introduction to Numerical Linear Algebra.* Oxford University Press: Oxford.

Fulkerson, D. R. and Gross, O. A. (1965). Incidence matrices and interval graphs. *Pacific J. Math.* **15**, 835–855.

Fulkerson, D. R. and Wolfe, P. (1962). An algorithm for scaling matrices. *SIAM Rev.* **4**, 142–146.

Gallagher, R. H. (1975). *Finite Element Analysis Fundamentals.* Prentice-Hall: Englewood Cliffs, NJ.

Gantmacher, F. R. (1959). *The Theory of Matrices*, Vol. II. Chelsea: New York.

Garbow, B. S., Boyle, J. M., Dongarra, J. J. and Moler, C. B. (1977). *Matrix Eigensystem Routines-EISPACK Guide Extension*, Lecture Notes in Computer Science, Vol. 51. Springer-Verlag: Berlin.

Gass, S. I. (1969). *Linear Programming.* McGraw-Hill, Inc: New York.

Gear, C. W. (1975). "Round-off error in sparse linear equations", presented at Argonne Conference on Sparse Matrix Computations, Argonne National Laboratory, September 9–11, 1975.

Gentleman, W. M. and George, A. (1976). Sparse matrix software. In Bunch and Rose (1976), pp. 243–261.

George, A. (1971). "Computer implementation of the finite element method." Ph.D. Dissertation, Computer Science Department, Stanford University, Stanford, CA. Report STAN-CS-71-208.

George, A. (1973). Nested dissection of a regular finite element mesh. *SIAM J. Numer. Anal.* **10**, 345–363.

George, A. (1977). Solution of linear systems of equations: direct methods for finite element problems. In Barker (1977), pp. 52–101.

George, A. (1980). An automatic one-way dissection algorithm for irregular finite element problems. *SIAM J. Numer. Anal.* **17**, 740–751.

George, A. and Heath, M. T. (1981). Solution of sparse linear least squares problems using Givens rotations. In Björck *et al.* (1981), pp. 69–83.

George, A. and Liu, J. W. H. (1975). "An automatic partitioning and solution scheme for solving large sparse positive definite systems of linear algebraic equations." Department of Computer Science, University of Waterloo, Waterloo, Ontario, Canada. Report CS-75-17.

George, A. and Liu, J. W. H. (1976). "An automatic nested dissection algorithm for irregular finite element problems." Department of Computer Science, University of Waterloo, Waterloo, Ontario, Canada. Report CS-76-38.

George, A. and Liu, J. W. H. (1978a). An automatic nested dissection algorithm for irregular finite element problems. *SIAM J. Numer. Anal.* **15**, 1053–1069.

George, A. and Liu, J. W. H. (1978b). Algorithms for matrix partitioning and the numerical solution of finite element systems. *SIAM J. Numer. Anal.* **15**, 297–327.

George, A. and Liu, J. W. H. (1981). *Computer Solution of Large Sparse Positive Definite Systems*. Prentice-Hall: Englewood Cliffs, NJ.

George, A. and Rashwan, H. (1981). On symbolic factorization of partitioned sparse symmetric matrices. In Björck *et al.* (1981), pp. 145–157.

Geradin, M. (1971). The computational efficiency of a new minimization algorithm for eigenvalue analysis. *J. Sound and Vibration* **19**, 319–331.

Gerschgorin, S. (1931). Über die Abgrenzung der Eigenwerte einer Matrix. *Izv. Akad. Nauk SSSR, Ser. fiz. mat.* **6**, 749–754.

Gibbs, N. E., Poole, Jr., W. G. and Stockmeyer, P. K. (1976). An algorithm for reducing the bandwidth and profile of a sparse matrix. *SIAM J. Numer. Anal.* **13**, 236–250.

Gilbert, J. R. and Schreiber, R. (1982). Nested dissection with partial pivoting. Sparse Matrix Symposium, Fairfield Glade, Tennessee, October 24–27, 1982.

Gill, P. E. and Murray, W. (1976). The orthogonal factorization of a large sparse matrix. In Bunch and Rose (1976), pp. 201–212.

Gilmore, P. C. and Hoffmann, A. J. (1964). A characterization of comparability graphs and of interval graphs. *Canad. J. Math.* **16**, 539–548.

Glowinski, R. and Lions, J. L. (eds) (1980). *Computing Methods in Applied Sciences and Engineering*. North Holland: Amsterdam.

Golub, G. H. and Plemmons, R. J. (1981). Large scale geodetic least-squares adjustment by dissection and orthogonal decomposition. In Björck *et al.* (1981), pp. 3–28.

Golub, G. H. and Underwood, R. R. (1977). The block Lanczos method for computing eigenvalues. In *Mathematical Software III*, edited by J. R. Rice, pp. 361–377. Academic Press: New York.

Golub, G. H., Luk, F. T. and Overton, M. L. (1981). A block Lanczos method for computing the singular values and corresponding singular vectors of a matrix. *ACM Trans. Math. Software* **7**, 149–169.

Golub, G. H., Underwood, R. and Wilkinson, J. H. (1972). "The Lanczos algorithm for the symmetric $Ax = \lambda Bx$ problem." Computer Science Department, Stanford University, Stanford, CA. Report STAN-CS-72-270.

Grcar, J. (1981). Ph.D. Thesis, University of Illinois.

Gupta, K. K. (1976). On a numerical solution of the supersonic panel flutter eigenproblem. *Int. J. Numer. meth. Eng.* **10**, 637–645.

Gustavson, F. G. (1972). Some basic techniques for solving sparse systems of linear equations. In Rose and Willoughby (1972), pp. 41–52.

Gustavson, F. G. (1976a). Permuting matrices stored in sparse format. *IBM Tech. Discl. Bull.* **16**, 357–359. Research Report RC-6181, IBM T. J. Watson Research Center, NY.

Gustavson, F. G. (1976b). Finding the block lower triangular form of a sparse matrix. In Bunch and Rose (1976), pp. 275–289.

Gustavson, F. G. (1976c). "An efficient algorithm to perform sparse matrix multiplication," presented at Argonne Conference on Sparse Matrix Computations, Argonne National Laboratory, September 9–11, 1976. Research Report RC-6176, IBM T. J. Watson Research Center, NY.

Gustavson, F. G. (1978). Two fast algorithms for sparse matrices: multiplication and permuted transposition. *ACM Trans. Math. Software* (*TOMS*) **4**, 250–269.

Hachtel, G. D. (1976). The sparse tableau approach to finite element assembly. In Bunch and Rose (1976), pp. 349–363.

Hall, M. (1956). An algorithm for distinct representatives. *Amer. Math. Monthly* **63**, 716–717.

Hammerling, S. (1974). A note on modification to the Givens plane rotation. *J. Inst. Math. Appl.* **13**, 215–218.

Hamming, R. W. (1971). *Introduction to Applied Numerical Analysis*. McGraw-Hill: New York.

Harary, F. (1959). A graph theoretic method for the complete reduction of a matrix with a view toward finding its eigenvalues. *J. Mathematical Phys.* **38**, 104–111.

Harary, F. (ed.) (1967). *Graph Theory and Theoretical Physics*. Academic Press: New York.

Harary, F. (1969). *Graph Theory*. Addison-Wesley: Reading, MA.

Harary, F. (1971). Sparse matrices and graph theory. In Reid (1971), pp. 139–150.

Harary, F., Norman, R. Z. and Cartwright, D. (1965). *Structural Models: An Introduction to the Theory of Directed Graphs*. John Wiley: New York.

Heath, M. T. (ed.) (1982). *Sparse Matrix Software Catalog*. Prepared by Oak Ridge National Laboratory, Oak Ridge, Tennessee, USA. Operated by Union Carbide Corporation, Nuclear Division.

Heuvers, K. J. (1982). Symmetric matrices with prescribed eigenvalues and eigenvectors. *Math. Magazine* **55**, 106–111.

Hood, P. (1976). Frontal solution program for unsymmetric matrices. *Int. J. Numer. meth. Eng.* **10**, 379–399.

Hopcroft, J. E. and Karp, R. M. (1973). An $n^{5/2}$ algorithm for maximum matchings in bipartite graphs. *SIAM J. Comput.* **2**, 225–231.

Hopper, M. J. (1980). "Harwell subroutine library, a catalogue of subroutines." Report AERE-R.9185, Harwell, UKAEA.

Hotelling, H. (1943). Some new methods in matrix calculation. *Ann. Math. Stat.* **14**, 1–34.

Houbak, N. (1981). The use of records in sparse matrix programs. In Duff (1981b), pp. 343–348.

Householder, A. S. (1961). On deflating matrices. *J. SIAM* **9**, 89–93.

Irons, B. M. (1963). Eigenvalue economizers in vibration problems. *J. RAeS* **67**, 526–528.

Irons, B. M. (1970). A frontal solution program for finite element analysis. *Int. J. Numer. meth. Eng.* **2**, 5–32.

Jacobs, D. A. H. (1981). The explotation of sparsity by iterative methods. In Duff (1981b), pp. 191–222.

Jennings, A. (1966). A compact storage scheme for the solution of symmetric linear simultaneous equations. *Comput. J.* **9**, 281–285.

Jennings, A. (1981). Eigenvalue methods and the analysis of structural vibration. In Duff (1981b), pp. 109–138.

Jennings, A. and Stewart, W. J. (1975). Simultaneous iteration for partial eigensolution of real matrices. *J. Inst. Math. Appl.* **15**, 351–361.

Kahan, W. (1967). "Inclusion theorems for clusters of eigenvalues of hermitian matrices." Computer Science Department, University of Toronto, Canada. Technical Report CS42.

Key, J. E. (1973). Computer program for solution of large sparse unsymmetric systems of linear equations. *Int. J. Numer. meth. Eng.* **6**, 497–509.

King, I. P. (1970). An automatic reordering scheme for simultaneous equations derived from network systems. *Int. J. Numer. meth. Eng.* **2**, 523–533.

Knuth, D. E. (1968). *The Art of Computer Programming*, Vol. 1: Fundamental Algorithms. Addison-Wesley: Reading, MA.

Kolata, G. B. (1978). Geodesy: dealing with an enormous computer task. *Science* **200**, 421–422; 466.

König, D. (1950). *Theorie der Endlichen und Unendlichen Graphen*. Chelsea: New York.

Kung, H. T. and Leiserson, C. E. (1979). Systolic arrays (for VLSI). In Duff and Stewart (1979), pp. 256–282.

Lanczos, C. (1950). An iteration method for the solution of the eigenvalue problem of linear differential and integral operators. *J. Res. Nat. Bur. Stand.* **B45**, 225–280.

Larcombe, M. H. E. (1971). A list processing approach to the solution of large sparse sets of matrix equations and the factorization of the overall matrix. In Reid (1971a), pp. 25–40.

Levy, R. (1971). Restructuring of the structural stiffness matrix to improve computational efficiency. *Jet Propulsion Lab. Tech. Rev.* **1**, 61–70.

Lewis, J. G. (1977). "Algorithms for sparse matrix eigenvalue problems." University of California, Stanford, CA. Report STAN-CS-77-595.

Lipton, R. J. and Tarjan, R. E. (1979). A separator theorem for planar graphs. *SIAM J. Appl. Math.* **36**, 177–189.

Lipton, R. J., Rose, D. J. and Tarjan, R. E. (1977). "Generalized nested dissection." Computer Science Department, Stanford University, Stanford, CA. Technical Report STAN-CS-77-645.

Lipton, R. J., Rose, D. J. and Tarjan, R. E. (1979). Generalized nested dissection. *SIAM J. Numer. Anal.* **16**, 346–358.

Liu, W. H. and Sherman, A. H. (1975). "Comparative analysis of the Cuthill–McKee and the Reverse Cuthill–McKee ordering algorithms for sparse matrices." Department of Computer Science, Yale University, New Haven, CT. Report 28.

Longsine, D. E. and McCormick, S. F. (1981). Simultaneous Rayleigh quotient minimization methods for $Ax = \lambda Bx$. In Björck *et al.* (1981), pp. 195–234.

McDonald, B. H. and Wexler, A. (1980). Mutually constrained partial differential and integral equation field formulations. In Chari and Silvester (1980), pp. 161–190.

Markowitz, H. M. (1957). The elimination form of the inverse and its application to linear programming. *Management Sci.* **3**, 255–269.

Martelli, A. (1973). "An application of regular algebra to the enumeration of cut sets in a graph." Instituto Elaboraz. Inf., Pisa, Italy. Nota Interna B73-20.

Martin, R. S. and Wilkinson, J. H. (1965). Symmetric decomposition of positive definite band matrices. *Numer. Math.* **7**, 355–361. [Reprinted in Wilkinson and Reinsch (1971).]

Martin, R. S. and Wilkinson, J. H. (1967). Solution of symmetric and unsymmetric band equations and the calculation of eigenvectors of band matrices. *Numer. Math.* **9**, 279–301.

Martin, R. S. and Wilkinson, J. H. (1968). Similarity reduction of a general matrix to Hessenberg form. *Numer. Math.* **12**, 349–368. [Reprinted in Wilkinson and Reinsch (1971), pp. 339–358.]

Martin, R. S., Reinsch, C. and Wilkinson, J. H. (1968). Householder's tridiagonalization of a symmetric matrix. *Numer. Math.* **11**, 181–195. [Reprinted in Wilkinson and Reinsch (1971), pp. 212–226.]

Mayoh, B. H. (1965). A graph technique for inverting certain matrices. *Math. Comput.* **19**, 644–646.

Micali, S. and Vazirani, V. V. (1979). "An $O(|V|^{1/2}|E|)$ algorithm for finding maximum matching in general graphs." University of California, Berkeley. Private communication.

Munksgaard, N. (1977). "Fortran subroutines for direct solution of sets of sparse and symmetric linear equations." Report 77.05, Numerical Institute Lyngby, Denmark.

Munro, I. (1971a). Efficient determination of the transitive closure of a directed graph. *Inform. Processing Lett.* **1**, 56–58.

Munro, I. (1971b). "Some results in the study of algorithms." Ph.D. Dissertation, Department of Computer Science, University of Toronto, Toronto, Ontario, Canada. Report No. 32.

Nikolai, P. J. (1979). Algorithm 538 – Eigenvectors and eigenvalues of real generalized symmetric matrices by simultaneous iteration. *ACM Trans. Math. Software* **5**, 118–125.

Ohtsuki, T. (1976). A fast algorithm for finding an optimal ordering for vertex elimination on a graph. *SIAM J. Comput.* **5**, 133–145.

Paige, C. C. (1971). "The computation of eigenvalues and eigenvectors of very large sparse matrices." Ph.D. Thesis, University of London, London, UK.

Paige, C. C. (1972). Computational variants of the Lanczos method for the eigenproblem. *J. Inst. Math. Appl.* **10**, 373–381.

Paige, C. C. (1974). Bidiagonalisation of matrices and solution of linear equations. *SIAM J. Numer. Anal.* **11**, 197–209.

Paige, C. C. (1976). Error analysis of the Lanczos algorithm for tridiagonalizing a symmetric matrix. *J. Inst. Math. Appl.* **18**, 341–349.

Parlett, B. N. (1964). Laguerre's method applied to the matrix eigenvalue problem. *Math. Comput.* **18**, 464–485.

Parlett, B. N. (1980). *The Symmetric Eigenvalue Problem.* Prentice-Hall: Englewood Cliffs, NJ.

Parlett, B. N. (1983). "The software scene in the extraction of eigenvalues from sparse matrices." Center for Pure and Applied Mathematics, University of California, Berkeley, CA. Report PAM-132.

Parlett, B. N. and Reid, J. K. (1970). On the solution of a system of linear equations whose matrix is symmetric but not definite. *BIT* **10**, 386–397.

Parlett, B. N. and Reinsch, C. (1969). Balancing a matrix for calculation of eigenvalues and eigenvectors. *Numer. Math.* **13**, 293–304. [Reprinted in Wilkinson and Reinsch (1971), pp. 315–326.]

Parlett, B. N. and Scott, D. S. (1979). The Lanczos algorithm with selective orthogonalization. *Math. Comput.* **33**, 217–238.

Parter, S. V. (1961). The use of linear graphs in Gauss elimination. *SIAM Rev.* **3**, 119–130.

Paton, K. (1971). An algorithm for the blocks and cutnodes of a graph. *Comm. ACM* **14**, 468–475.

Peters, G. and Wilkinson, J. H. (1971). The calculation of specified eigenvectors by inverse iteration. In Wilkinson and Reinsch (1971), pp. 418–439.

Pissanetzky, S. (1979). "Gauss elimination with supersparse matrices." Brookhaven National Laboratory. Report BNL 26773.

Pissanetzky, S. (1981). KUBIK: an automatic three-dimensional finite element mesh generator. *Int. J. Numer. meth. Eng.* **17**, 255–269.

Pissanetzky, S. (1983). An infinite element and a formula for numerical quadrature over an infinite interval. *Int. J. Numer. meth. Eng.* **19**, 913–927.

Read, R. (ed.) (1972). *Graph Theory and Computing*. Academic Press: New York.

Reid, J. K. (ed.) (1971a). *Large Sparse Sets of Linear Equations*. Academic Press: London.

Reid, J. K. (1971b). A note on the stability of Gaussian elimination. *J. Inst. Math. Appl.* **8**, 374–375.

Reid, J. K. (1976). "Fortran subroutines for handling sparse linear programming bases." HMSO, London, UK. Report AERE-R.8269.

Reid, J. K. (1977). Solution of linear systems of equations: direct methods (general). In Barker (1977), pp. 102–129.

Reid, J. K. (1981). Frontal methods for solving finite element systems of linear equations. In Duff (1981b), pp. 265–281.

Reinsch, C. H. (1971). A stable rational QR algorithm for the computation of the eigenvalues of an hermitian, tridiagonal matrix. *Numer. Math.* **25**, 591–597.

Rheinboldt, W. C. and Mesztenyi, C. K. (1973). "Programs for the solution of large sparse matrix problems based on the arc-graph structure." Computer Science Center, University of Maryland, College Park, MD. Technical Report TR-262.

Rose, D. J. (1970). Triangulated graphs and the elimination process. *J. Math. Anal. Appl.* **32**, 597–609.

Rose, D. J. (1972). A graph-theoretic study of the numerical solution of sparse positive definite systems of linear equations. In Read (1972), pp. 183–217.

Rose, D. J. (1974). On simple characterizations of *k*-trees. *Discrete Math.* **7**, 317–322.

Rose, D. J. and Bunch, J. R. (1972). The role of partitioning in the numerical solution of sparse systems. In Rose and Willoughby (1972), pp. 177–187.

Rose, D. J. and Willoughby, R. A. (1972). Sparse matrices and their applications. Proceedings of Symposium at IBM Research Center, NY, September 9–10, 1971. Plenum Press: New York.

Rose, D. J., Tarjan, R. E. and Lueker, G. S. (1976). Algorithmic aspects of vertex elimination on graphs. *SIAM J. Comput.* **5**, 266–283.

Rosen, R. (1968). Matrix bandwidth minimization. In *Proceedings of the 23rd National Conference of the ACM*, pp. 585–595. Brandon Systems Press: New Jersey.

Rudolphi, I. (1973). "Orthogonalization of sparse vectors." Department of Information Processing, Umeå, Sweden. Report UMINF-38.

Ruhe, A. (1977). Computation of eigenvalues and eigenvectors. In Barker (1977), pp. 130–184.

Ruhe, A. (1979). Implementation aspects of band Lanczos algorithm for computation of eigenvalues of large sparse matrices. *Math. Comput.* **33**, 680–687.

Ruhe, A. and Wiberg, T. (1972). The method of conjugate gradients used in inverse iteration. *BIT* **12**, 543–554.

Rutishauser, H. (1970). Simultaneous iteration method for symmetric matrices. *Numer Math.* **16**, 205–223. [Reprinted in Wilkinson and Reinsch (1971), pp. 284–302.]

Saad, Y. (1980). On the rates of convergence of the Lanczos and the block-Lanczos method. *SIAM J. Numer. Anal.* **17**, 687–706.

Saad, Y. (1981). Variations on Arnoldi's method for computing eigenelements of large unsymmetric matrices. In Björck *et al.* (1981), pp. 269–295.

Saad, Y. (1982). The Lanczos biorthogonalization algorithm and other oblique projection methods for solving large unsymmetric systems. *SIAM J. Numer. Anal.* **19**, 485–506.

Sargent, R. W. H. and Westerberg, A. W. (1964). Speed-up in chemical engineering design. *Trans. Inst. Chem. Eng.* **42**, 190–197.

Schwarz, H. R. (1977). Two algorithms for treating $Ax = \lambda Bx$. *Comp. Meth. Appl. Mech. Eng.* **12**, 181–199.

Schwartz, H. R., Wilkinson, J. H. and Reinsch, C. (1971). Contribution II/8, in Wilkinson and Reinsch (1971).

Scott, D. S. (1981). The Lanczos algorithm. In Duff (1981b), pp. 139–159.

Sherman, A. H. (1975). On the efficient solution of sparse systems of linear and nonlinear equations. Ph.D. Thesis, Department of Computer Science, Yale University, New Haven, CT. Report No. 46.

Shirey, R. W. (1969). "Implementation and analysis of efficient graph planarity testing algorithms." Ph.D. Dissertation, University of Wisconsin, Madison, WI.

Silvester, P. P. (1980). Software engineering aspects of finite elements. In Chari and Silvester (1980), pp. 69–85.

Skeel, R. D. (1981). Effect of equilibration on residual size for partial pivoting. *SIAM J. Numer. Anal.* **18**, 449–454.

Smith, B. T., Boyle, J. M., Dongarra, J. J., Garbow, B. S., Ikebe, Y., Klema, V. C. and Moler, C. B. (1976). *Matrix Eigensystem Routines – EISPACK Guide*. Lecture Notes in Computer Science, Vol. 6, 2nd edn. Springer-Verlag: Berlin.

Speelpenning, B. (1978). "The generalized element method." Department of Computer Science, University of Illinois, Urbana, Champaign, Il. Report UIUCDCS-R-78.

Stewart, G. W. (1973). *Introduction to Matrix Computations*. Academic Press: New York.

Stewart, G. W. (1974). Modifying pivot elements in Gaussian elimination. *Math. Comput.* **28**, 537–542.

Stewart, G. W. (1976a). A bibliographical tour of the large sparse generalized eigenvalue problem. In Bunch and Rose (1976), pp. 113–130.

Stewart, G. W. (1976b). Simultaneous iteration for computing invariant subspaces of non-hermitian matrices. *Numer. Math.* **25**, 123–136.

Stewart, W. J. and Jennings, A. (1981). Algorithm 570.LOPSI: A simultaneous iteration algorithm for real matrices. *ACM Trans. Math. Software* **7**, 230–232.

Strassen, V. (1969). Gaussian elimination is not optimal. *Numer. Math.* **13**, 354–356.

Swift, G. (1960). A comment on matrix inversion by partitioning. *SIAM Rev.* **2**, 132–133.

Szyld, D. B. and Vishnepolsky, O. (1982). "Some operations on sparse matrices." Institute for Economic Analysis, New York University. Private communication.

Takahashi, H. and Natori, M. (1972). Eigenvalue problem of large sparse matrices. *Rep. Comput. Cent. Univ. Tokyo* **4**, 129–148.

Tarjan, R. E. (1971). "An efficient planarity algorithm." Computer Science Department, Stanford University, Stanford, CA. Technical Report 244.

Tarjan, R. E. (1972). Depth first search and linear graph algorithms. *SIAM J. Comput.* **1**, 146–160.

Tarjan, R. E. (1975). Efficiency of a good but not linear set union algorithm. *J. Assoc. Comput. Mach.* **22**, 215–225.

Tarjan, R. E. (1976). Graph theory and Gaussian elimination. In Bunch and Rose (1976), pp. 3–22.

Tewarson, R. P. (1967a). On the product form of inverses of sparse matrices and graph theory. *SIAM Rev.* **9**, 91–99.

Tewarson, R. P. (1967b). Row–column permutation of sparse matrices. *Comput. J.* **10**, 300–305.

Tewarson, R. P. (1971). Sorting and ordering sparse linear systems. In Reid (1971a), pp. 151–167.

Tewarson, R. P. (1973). *Sparse Matrices*. Academic Press: New York.

Thomsen, P. G. and Zlatev, Z. (1978). "SSLEST – a Fortran IV subroutine for solving sparse systems of linear equations." Numerisk Institut, DTH, Denmark. Report NI-78-01.

Tinney, W. F. (1969). Comments on using sparsity techniques for power systems problems. In Willoughby (1969), pp. 25–34.

Tinney, W. F. and Walker, J. W. (1967). Direct solution of sparse network equations by optimally ordered triangular factorization. *Proc. IEEE* **55**, 1801–1809.

Tomlin, J. A. (1972). Pivoting for size and sparsity in linear programming inversion routines. *J. Inst. Math. Appl.* **10**, 289–295.

Tosovic, L. B. (1973). Some experiments on sparse sets of linear equations. *SIAM J. Appl. Math.* **25**, 142–148.

Van Kats, J. M. and van der Vorst, H. A. (1977). "Automatic monitoring of Lanczos schemes for symmetric or skew-symmetric generalized eigenvalue problems." Academisch Computer Centrum, Utrecht, Netherlands. Technical Report TR-7.

Van der Sluis, A. (1970). Condition, equilibration, and pivoting in linear algebraic systems. *Numer. Math.* **15**, 74–86.

Vichnevetsky, R. (ed.) (1975). *Proceedings of the AICA International Symposium on Computer Methods for Partial Differential Equations*. Bethlehem, PA. Prentice-Hall.

Vichnevetsky, R. and Stepleman (eds) (1979). *Advances in Computer Methods for Partial Differential Equations III*. Publ. IMACE.

Von Fuchs, G., Roy, J. R. and Schrem, E. (1972). Hypermatrix solution of large sets of symmetric positive definite linear equations. *Comput. Meth. Appl. Mech. Eng.* **1**, 197–216.

Wilkinson, J. H. (1961). Error analysis of direct methods of matrix inversion. *J. ACM* **8**, 281–330.

Wilkinson, J. H. (1965). *The Algebric Eigenvalue Problem.* Oxford University Press: Oxford.

Wilkinson, J. H. and Reinsch, C. (1971). *Handbook for Automatic Computation*, Vol. II: Linear Algebra. Springer-Verlag: Berlin.

Willoughby, R. A. (ed.) (1969). "Proceedings of the symposium on sparse matrices and their applications." Yorktown Heights, NY, IBM Report RAI (No. 11707).

Willoughby, R. A. (1971). Sparse matrix algorithms and their relation to problem classes and computer architecture. In Reid (1971a), pp. 255–277.

Willoughby, R. A. (1972). "A survey of sparse matrix technology." IBM Research Report RC 3872. [An extended version of a talk given at the Conference on Computer Oriented Analysis of Shell Structures, Lockheed, Palo Alto, CA, August, 1970.]

Wisniewski, J. A. (1981). *On Solving the Large Sparse Generalized Eigenvalue Problem.* Ph.D. Thesis, Department of Computer Science, University of Illinois at Urbana-Champaign, Illinois.

Zienkiewicz, O. C. (1977). *The Finite Element Method.* McGraw-Hill: London.

Zlatev, Z. (1980). On some pivotal strategies in Gaussian elimination by sparse technique. *SIAM J. Numer. Anal.* **17**, 18–30.

Zlatev, Z. (1982). Comparison of two pivotal strategies in sparse plane rotations. *Comp. Math. Appl.* **8**, 119–135.

Subject Index

C

D

E

F

G

S